NUMERICAL ANALYSIS

An Introduction

NUMERICAL ANALYSIS
An Introduction

Based on a Symposium Organized by the
Institute of Mathematics and its Applications
Birmingham, England, 1965

EDITED BY

J. WALSH

Department of Mathematics
The University, Manchester
England

1966

ACADEMIC PRESS · LONDON AND NEW YORK

ACADEMIC PRESS INC. (LONDON) LTD.
Berkeley Square House
Berkeley Square
London, W.1

United States edition published by
THOMPSON BOOK COMPANY, INC.
National Press Building
Washington, D.C. 20004

Library of Congress Catalog Card Number: 66–29235

Printed in Great Britain by
The Whitefriars Press Ltd., London and Tonbridge

Contributors

J. CRANK, *Brunel University, London, W.3.*

A. R. CURTIS, *Atomic Energy Research Establishment, Harwell, Didcot, Berkshire.*

L. FOX, *University Computing Laboratory, Parks Road, Oxford.*

R. HETHERINGTON, *Aero Engine Division, Rolls-Royce Ltd., Derby.*

H. P. Y. HITCH, *Weybridge Division, British Aircraft Corporation (Operating) Ltd., Weybridge, Surrey.*

D. W. MARTIN, *Mathematics Division, National Physical Laboratory, Teddington, Middlesex.*

J. C. P. MILLER, *University Mathematical Laboratory, Corn Exchange Street, Cambridge.*

A. J. MOAKES, *St. Paul's School, London, W.14.*

H. H. M. PIKE, *Atomic Weapons Research Establishment, Aldermaston, Berkshire.*

M. J. D. POWELL, *Atomic Energy Research Establishment, Harwell, Didcot, Berkshire.*

H. H. ROBERTSON, *Mathematics Group, Imperial Chemical Industries Ltd., Wilton Works, Middlesbrough, Yorkshire.*

M. E. SILVESTER, *Aero Engine Division, Rolls-Royce Ltd., Derby.*

H. P. F. SWINNERTON-DYER, *University Mathematical Laboratory, Corn Exchange Street, Cambridge.*

S. VAJDA, *University of Birmingham, Edgbaston, Birmingham.*

J. WALSH, *Department of Mathematics, The University, Manchester.*

J. H. WILKINSON, *Mathematics Division, National Physical Laboratory, Teddington, Middlesex.*

Preface

An introductory book may be of two kinds; either it may give a detailed treatment of the elementary parts of a subject, or it may make a general survey of the principal topics of interest, without attempting to cover them fully. This book is of the second kind, being based on a series of lectures, arranged by the Institute of Mathematics and its Applications, which were intended to give a general picture of recent developments in Numerical Analysis for non-specialists.

The first eight chapters cover the fields of linear algebra, ordinary and partial differential equations, approximation, and function minimization. Each chapter is largely self-contained, and gives a list of references which should enable readers who want to go further to pursue the subject up to the frontiers of current research. Chapters 9 and 10 discuss two related topics, the use of computational techniques in certain problems of Pure Mathematics, and the mathematics of Operational Research, particularly Linear Programming. Chapter 11 gives some examples of the application of Numerical Analysis to major industrial problems, and the book concludes with a discussion of the effect of the increasing importance of numerical work on school and university teaching.

The editor is very grateful to the contributors for their co-operation in the detailed work of preparing the material for publication, and particularly to Professor L. Fox, who gave much valuable advice and help at all stages. Thanks are also due to Mrs. E. Connery and Miss H. Clarkson for their able assistance with the typing, and to Academic Press for their skilful handling of the text.

June 1966   JOAN WALSH

Contents

Foreword

There was a time when the total demand, from mathematics, science, engineering and industry, for numerical analysis could be largely met by specialists, in numbers that were substantial but only represented an extremely small fraction of the entire scientific population. In the past ten years a major revolution in mathematical, scientific and industrial methods has completely transformed this situation.

Today almost everybody engaged in the application of mathematics in the quantitative parts of pure and applied science, or in any branch of engineering industry, is aware that computational methods may be able to give very significant help in making his work more productive. In many cases he has already taken preliminary steps in their use.

It is to the resulting vast population of non-specialist numerical analysts, actual and potential, that this book is mainly addressed. It has been prepared in the belief that the least of their problems is the mastering of one of the relatively simple and straightforward programming languages that are available for use with the present generation of computing machines. Courses and literature on programming languages and techniques are very widely available.

The non-specialist's more pressing need is for an answer to the questions "Just what may I be able to do with numerical analysis? What kinds of problems can now be reduced to a form which can be programmed for a computing machine? What methods are used in the reduction?" Answers to these questions for readers whose main commitments, outside numerical analysis, give them time to study only a relatively slim volume, are what this book seeks to provide.

The Institute of Mathematics and its Applications, as a professional institution serving all those engaged in work of a mathematical character, recognized the widespread need for a presentation of this kind, and arranged a residential conference with the title "The State of the Art in Numerical Analysis" at Birmingham, England, in July 1965, at which specialists in different parts of the field gave lectures. The twelve chapters of which this book is comprised have been prepared on the basis of those lectures and ably edited by one of the contributors, Dr. Joan Walsh.

The resulting collection of papers, while achieving harmony between the different treatments, has succeeded in preserving the original styles of the sixteen contributors, each with his own distinctive view of numerical analysis and of its pitfalls, problems and successes. In some of the treatments it has been thought desirable to go into considerable detail, but in other areas, where finality has by no means been reached, to survey the problems more broadly. In all cases an attempt has been made to include a really valuable list of references.

I believe that a large proportion of those active in mathematical, scientific or engineering work, or operational research in industry, will wish to read this book, that their ideas of what numerical analysis and the use of computers can, and cannot, give them will, as a consequence, become far more precise than before, and that they will obtain from it guidance on where to go for such more detailed and specialized information as they may require. I believe also that an introductory survey of this kind will be valued by teachers, and for this reason a chapter on computation in school and university teaching has been included, aimed at helping them to create courses which take full account of the computational revolution.

July 1966   M. JAMES LIGHTHILL, Sec. R.S.
President, Institute of Mathematics and its Applications
Royal Society Research Professor in the Imperial College of
Science and Technology, London

Chapter 1

General Survey

L. Fox

University Computing Laboratory, Oxford

1. Introduction. Motivation

For mathematical readers who, by and large, have not specialized in numerical mathematics, this survey might best start with a brief word about motivation. Why do we, or at least some of us, study numerical methods? Computation has been practised in some form or other throughout the whole of recorded history, and of course it has always had, at least until recently, a utilitarian aspect. Practical problems demand answers in terms of numbers rather than a mathematical formulation, with existence theorems or even symbolic formulae for the solution. Mathematicians of previous centuries were clearly interested in the physical world and its practical problems. Dynamical astronomy is a particular case in point, and great mathematicians like Euler, Lagrange, Laplace, Bessel and Poincaré, and above all Newton and Gauss, made significant contributions to numerical analysis.

In modern times the growth of numerical analysis has been stimulated by the increased application of mathematics on a broad front of natural science. But simultaneously the world's mathematicians have tended to lose interest in the *complete* solution of immediate practical problems. Indeed the useful aspect of mathematics, or at least its immediately useful aspect, is played down, often quite deliberately and with "apologies". Astronomy and physical subjects have simultaneously disappeared from the university mathematical syllabus. The unfortunate fact is that this withdrawal comes at a time when practical problems are much more difficult and demanding than ever before, and when the invention of the stored-program digital computer has given scientists the impression that the speed of computation, the removal of the button-pressing and handle-turning chores, and the ease of programming have made it possible to solve even the most difficult problems with speed and accuracy.

Unfortunately the ability to communicate with the machine is not the only requirement for solving problems, that is for producing algorithms which will give good numerical results. We must know what mathematical techniques are available, and which are sound in any given context, so that our communication with the machine is not only grammatically correct but also sensible in meaning.

What techniques are available for solving difficult problems? Most scientists probably learn mathematics, or those parts of mathematics which they need, from mathematicians and books written by mathematicians. The techniques they learn are then dependent on exact arithmetic, or on the ability to linearize their problems, or they involve approximations whose quantitative significance is rarely calculated. And of course the number of such techniques is inevitably quite limited. As a result, scientists often formulate their problems in an unnecessarily approximate way, not knowing that there are computational techniques which can cope with non-linear or other difficult situations.

This is where the numerical analyst steps in. It is interesting to note that, like other mathematical disciplines, numerical analysis has also moved away from the particular to the general. Whereas in the past we invented *ad hoc* methods for particular problems, more recently we have begun to consider whole classes of problems and of methods, without particular regard for scientific context. This study has certainly been influenced and occasionally assisted by the digital computer. In particular we concentrate on those methods which are peculiarly convenient for such machines, and since these machines do their arithmetic in a consistent way (unlike the desk-machine worker who may use different numbers of figures at different stages, either by accident or by expert design) we have the possibility of conducting a satisfactory error analysis.

2. Algorithms

The job of the numerical analyst, therefore, is fundamentally to produce methods, which we call *algorithms*, for solving a large variety of problems. In scientific work, as distinct from other possible machine applications such as number theory, theorem-proving, etc., it turns out that most problems involve a combination of linear algebra (that is the solution of linear equations, inversion of matrices, and the determination of eigenvalues and vectors) and the solution of various types of ordinary differential equations, partial differential equations and integral equations. They may also involve things like finding the zeros of polynomials or of more complicated functions, finding minima or maxima of functions of many variables, and above all approximating to "difficult" functions by easily-computable forms like polynomials, rational functions, etc.

In more detail, for any given problem we have to consider the following points.

(i) *Condition.* If the data of the problem are perturbed slightly, to what extent does this affect the answer? This is clearly an important consideration in *physical* problems, in which the data are rarely exact, and in which as a consequence there is a definite limit to the number of figures worth quoting in the results. It is also important in *mathematical* problems, for which the data are exact and for which unlimited accuracy might be meaningful, because most exact numbers (numbers, for example, like e, π or 0·7 to base 10 in a binary computer) cannot be stored exactly. In any case, almost any numerical operation immediately introduces a rounding error and effectively turns the mathematical problem into a physical one. It is then difficult to solve accurately a mathematical problem corresponding to an ill-conditioned physical problem.

(ii) *Stability of algorithm.* Within the "condition" limitation (which is a function of the problem and independent of the method used to solve it), we have to enquire whether our technique, our algorithm, is *stable* in the sense that it will produce a sufficiently accurate result for the particular problem concerned.

(iii) *Convenience of programming, speed of machine computation.* We shall say virtually nothing about (iii), except to note that apparently trivial changes in mathematical technique can produce great improvements in the efficiency of an algorithm performed on a digital computer. This may happen, for example, through the separation of the machine's store into two parts, a relatively small but fast store and a relatively large backing store to and from which the transmission of information is a relatively slow process. It was noted quite recently, in a method involving similarity transformations for finding eigenvalues of matrices, that we can avoid frequent transfers of information to and from the slow-access store by carrying out in parallel certain parts of successive transformations (Rollett and Wilkinson 1961). The result was the division by 7, on the Mercury computer, of the time for finding the eigensolutions of symmetric matrices of order 96. Mathematically this is a fairly trivial advance, but to those involved in a computer service saturated with demands the advantageous effect on research is clearly very great.

(iv) *New algorithms.* Both the developments in computer design and our natural urge for perfection inspire the constant search for new efficient algorithms, satisfying the points (ii) and (iii).

We now consider some simple examples which illustrate the sense, if not the extent, of the work of numerical analysts.

3. Error Analysis. Conditioning

We examine first the problem of ill-conditioning, and for this purpose consider the solution of linear equations $A\mathbf{x} = \mathbf{b}$. For the matrix we take

$$A = \begin{bmatrix} \frac{1}{2} & \frac{1}{3} & \frac{1}{4} & \frac{1}{5} \\ \frac{1}{3} & \frac{1}{4} & \frac{1}{5} & \frac{1}{6} \\ \frac{1}{4} & \frac{1}{5} & \frac{1}{6} & \frac{1}{7} \\ \frac{1}{5} & \frac{1}{6} & \frac{1}{7} & \frac{1}{8} \end{bmatrix}, \tag{1}$$

a segment of the well-known Hilbert matrix. We suppose further that the elements of $\mathbf{b}$ are not known exactly, but have possible errors with limits $\pm\varepsilon$. Then the solution $\mathbf{x}$ has corresponding "tolerances", and the largest is in x_3 which has a tolerance of upper bound $6 \times 10^4 \varepsilon$. If $\mathbf{b}$ is such that $\mathbf{x}$ is in some measure large this may not be serious, but otherwise we may not be able to guarantee a single meaningful significant figure in the result.

The determination of $\mathbf{x}$ for this A and arbitrary $\mathbf{b}$ is here an ill-conditioned problem, but we should note that "ill-conditioned" is not just a term of abuse for this particular matrix. For example the determination of the eigensolutions for this A may be perfectly well-conditioned. Indeed even for the linear equations there are combinations $\Sigma \, \alpha_r x_r$, for some α_r, which for the same errors $\pm \varepsilon$ in $\mathbf{b}$ have much smaller "tolerances" than the individual x_r. In fact if all $\alpha_r = 1$ the tolerance in $\Sigma \, x_r$ is only about $9 \times 10^2 \varepsilon$, much smaller than that of any individual component. Our techniques should bring these facts to light.

As a second example, consider the determination of the zeros of a polynomial slightly different from $\prod_{r=1}^{20} (x-r)$, whose zeros are the integers $1, 2, \ldots, 20$. If the coefficient of x^{19} is changed from -210 to $-(210+2^{-23})$, a change which would hardly be noticed in many machines, the roots which were 16 and 17 change to the complex pair $16 \cdot 73 \ldots \pm i2 \cdot 81 \ldots$. A result such as this, which was given by Wilkinson (1959), inspires the modern numerical analyst to consider the general question of what classes of polynomials (measured perhaps by the distribution of their zeros) are seriously ill-conditioned for the determination of zeros.

4. Stability. Backward Error Analysis

This last strange and frightening result also points to the dangers of finding eigenvalues of matrices by constructing the characteristic polynomial, which is an example of an algorithm which could be unstable even for an inherently well-conditioned problem. In this section we give two more simple examples of unstable techniques.

Consider first the solution of the linear equations

$$\left. \begin{array}{l} 0 \cdot 0003 x_1 - 0 \cdot 1000 x_2 = b_1 \\ 0 \cdot 9000 x_1 + 0 \cdot 1249 x_2 = b_2 \end{array} \right\}, \qquad (2)$$

using four-decimal-digit floating-point arithmetic. In this scheme, commonly used by computers, every number, a *digital number*, is stored in the form $10^a \times b$, where a is an integer and b a four-digit number in the range $0 \cdot 1 \le |b| < 1 \cdot 0$. Then $481 \cdot 7$ is represented by $0 \cdot 4817 \times 10^3$ (and so is every number in the range $481 \cdot 65$ to $481 \cdot 75$), and $0 \cdot 0004817$ by $0 \cdot 4817 \times 10^{-3}$. To add these we write $10^3 (0 \cdot 4817 + 0 \cdot 0004817)$, round the second number to $0 \cdot 0005$ and find the result $0 \cdot 4822 \times 10^3$. To multiply them we find the product $10^{3-3} (0 \cdot 23203489)$, and round to the digital number $10^0 \times 0 \cdot 2320$.

In fact our digital numbers satisfy few of the simple axioms like

$$a + (b+c) = (a+b) + c, \qquad a(bc) = (ab)c, \qquad (3)$$

and we cannot even write $ab = c$, $a/b = c$ with exact significance.

Returning to the linear equations, the mathematical algebra books tell us to find the first non-zero element in the first column, divide that row by this element, and subtract suitable multiples from other rows to "eliminate" x_1. Repeating this process as often as necessary we produce a "row-reduced echelon form", which is equivalent to the original because we can reverse the operations and recover the original. Now in our example we can avoid the division by 0·0003, which would produce unnecessary rounding errors, and instead subtract the multiple 0·9000/0·0003 = 3000 of the first equation from the second. The new set of equations is

$$\left.\begin{aligned}0·0003x_1 - 0·1000x_2 &= \cdots \\ 0x_1 + \{0·1249 + 3000(0·1000)\}x_2 &= \cdots\end{aligned}\right\}, \tag{4}$$

and the digital number in brackets is 300·1. The same number, we note, would have been produced for any (2, 2) element in the range $0·05 \leq a_{22} \leq 0·15$.

If now we try to recover the original set by adding 3000 times the first equation of the new set to the second, we produce the set

$$\left.\begin{aligned}0·0003x_1 - 0·1000x_2 &= \cdots \\ 0·9000x_1 + 0·1000x_2 &= \cdots\end{aligned}\right\}, \tag{5}$$

which is not the original! Our solution is correspondingly quite inaccurate.

Not only does the mathematical technique fail to give a good solution, but even the existence theorems, based on exact arithmetic, cease to apply when we use digital numbers, the practical arithmetic which we have to use for all but the most trivial problems.

One method of performing the error analysis is to trace the effect of each digital error throughout the whole of the computation. This was used, for example, by von Neumann and Goldstine (1947) in a classic but very abtruse paper on the error analysis for linear equations. Their results, however, give very wide and far too pessimistic bounds for the error.

The modern method of analysis, hinted at by Turing (1948) and extended particularly by Wilkinson (see, for example, Wilkinson 1963), accepts the errors and traces them backwards, showing for our linear equations, for example, that the computed results are the exact solution of the perturbed problem $(A + \delta A)\mathbf{y} = \mathbf{b} + \delta\mathbf{b}$. This does not give the error in the solution, which clearly depends on A^{-1}, but it certainly gives a comparative evaluation of different techniques. Those for which the perturbations are small are clearly superior to those for which these are large, and many new results have been rigorously established on this basis.

For example, in the equations (2) we get a very good result by interchanging the order of the equations before starting the elimination, and in general we do even better by forgetting about elimination and finding the triangular decomposition $I_r A = LU$, where L and U are respectively lower and upper triangular matrices, and I_r is a row-permuting matrix selected so that every $|l_{rs}| \leq 1$. With some not very restrictive conditions on the size of the elements of A, and also of U, we can then show that we have the exact solution of $(A + \delta A)\mathbf{y} = \mathbf{b} + \delta\mathbf{b}$, where $|\delta a_{rs}| \leq 0·5 \times 10^{-4}$, $|\delta b_r| \leq 0·5n \times 10^{-4}$, for our four-digit computer. The perturbation of A is very small, even independent of n, and may be no greater than the original error involved in the digital storage of the matrix.

Another result obtained from this theory concerns the determination of eigensolutions of symmetric matrices by orthogonal similarity transforma-tions. These are usually performed in the iterative sequence $A_{r+1} = P_r^T A_r P_r$, $A_0 = A$, P_r orthogonal. We can transform A to a diagonal matrix in an infinite sequence of operations, though this method is now almost completely superseded by finite schemes in which A becomes "co-diagonal", or "nearly triangular", in a variety of ways.

Now the orthogonal matrix P_r is obtained from certain elements of A_r by an arithmetic process involving rounding errors, with the consequence that the final computed $\bar{A}_n$ may be quite different from the true A_n which would be obtained by exact arithmetic throughout. They may, in fact, have no figures in common. The forward error analysis would give up at this point, and class the method as useless, but in fact we can show that the computation is exactly equivalent to $\bar{A}_n = P^T(A + \delta A)P$, where an upper bound to the perturbation can often be computed quite easily and may turn out to be quite small (Wilkinson 1962). The eigenvalues of our computed $\bar{A}_n$ are then those of $A + \delta A$, and will be accurate, for sufficiently small δA, depending on the degree of conditioning of the problem. Since we have some known results for the effects on the eigenvalues of small changes in the elements of the matrix, our backward error analysis here gives some directly useful result, in addition to its advantage in evaluating different techniques.

Returning to the subject of unstable techniques, we should mention the practical use of recurrence relations or difference equations, which are ubiquitous in numerical applications. Consider the calculation, for $r = 0, 1, 2, \ldots$, of the definite integral

$$I_r = e^{-\frac{3}{4}} \int_0^1 e^{\frac{3}{4}x} x^{r+3} \, dx. \tag{6}$$

This can be done exactly by integration by parts, but for large r we have an awkward series to sum involving the cancellation of large positive and negative terms. A single integration gives the convenient recurrence formula

$$I_r = 0 \cdot 75 - 0 \cdot 75(r+3)I_{r-1}. \tag{7}$$

With one separately computed I_r, of which the easiest to compute is I_0, we can find $I_1, I_2, \ldots$ by successive use of the formula. With our four-digit machine, starting with $I_0 = 0 \cdot 1957$, which is correct to four figures, we find an I_5 of $0 \cdot 1590$, which has *no* correct figures. The reason is that the general solution of the difference equation is $p_r + A q_r$, where q_r satisfies $q_r = -0 \cdot 75(r+3)q_{r-1}$ and therefore increases rapidly in magnitude. The function p_r is a slowly varying particular solution. We want to suppress the constant A, and this would be done by using the exact I_0, followed by exact arithmetic. But the system is inherently ill-conditioned. How then do we proceed? One answer, when we can use it, as here, is to use a more stable system. This is provided by recurrence in the reverse direction, for which purpose the condition $I_n \to 0$ as $n \to \infty$, which can be produced with elementary mathematics, is perfectly adequate. Starting even with $I_5 = 0$ (the true value being about $0 \cdot 09\ldots$) we find $I_0 = 0 \cdot 1958$, a very accurate result.

5. Differential Equations

For further examples of the work of numerical mathematicians we turn to the solution of differential equations. It is probably not an overstatement to say that the use of the infinitesimal differential calculus leads to solutions in only a very limited class of problems. In numerical calculus we effectively defer the approach to the zero limit of the independent variable, thereby changing the differential problem into an approximating algebraic problem which we can usually solve. For example we may try to compute the solution at particular points $x_1, x_2, \ldots$, separated by an interval h, from a formula like

$$a_k y_{r+k} + a_{k-1} y_{r+k-1} + \cdots + a_0 y_r$$
$$= h(b_k f_{r+k} + b_{k-1} f_{r+k-1} + \cdots + b_0 f_r) + T, \quad (8)$$

relevant to the first-order equation or sets of equations $y' = f(x, y)$. Here T is the local truncation error, involving some high power of h and correspondingly high-order derivatives of y. We have to consider questions of convergence, that is does the computed y tend to the true y as $h \to 0$; and asymptotic stability, that is does the computed y have the same general behaviour as the true y for a finite h; and is there, for example, a critical h separating the boundaries of good and bad behaviour?

This formula includes almost all the main methods of this general type, and from time to time in the past particular cases have been examined in rather *ad hoc* fashion. A well-rounded rigorous mathematical theory has been produced only in the last few years (Dahlquist 1956, 1959), and similar techniques are being applied to other methods both for initial-value and also boundary-value problems in ordinary differential equations.

For partial differential equations of initial-value type, parabolic and hyperbolic, there are similar problems of convergence and stability, and again von Neumann made contributions which have been widely exploited.

The solution of elliptic equations brings up different problems, somewhat relevant to the nature of computing machines, whose solution or partial solution has extended at least our practical knowledge of matrices. The use of finite differences, say for Laplace's equation

$$\frac{\partial^2 f}{\partial x^2} + \frac{\partial^2 f}{\partial y^2} = 0, \quad (9)$$

with f given on a closed boundary, gives rise to an algebraic problem $A\mathbf{f} = \mathbf{b} + \mathbf{T}$, where $\mathbf{T}$ is the local truncation error, $\mathbf{f}$ the vector of approximate values of $f(x, y)$ at points say of a rectangular grid, and A and $\mathbf{b}$ are respectively a matrix and a vector depending on the boundary values and the finite-difference formulae. The matrix is large and sparse, and we prefer iterative methods for the solution of the approximating algebraic problem with $\mathbf{T}$ ignored. The general form of iteration is

$$\mathbf{f}^{(r+1)} = C\mathbf{f}^{(r)} + \mathbf{c}, \quad (10)$$

where $A\mathbf{f} = \mathbf{b} \Leftrightarrow \mathbf{f} = C\mathbf{f} + \mathbf{c}$, and the rate of convergence depends on the spectral radius ρ of C, the modulus of the eigenvalue of C of largest modulus. If $\rho \geqslant 1$ the process does not converge, and for a good rate of convergence we want ρ to be as small as possible.

The search for best iteration matrices C, in this sense, has been pursued with some success over the last few years, and in many cases the "art" of relaxation, effectively invented by Gauss and developed by Southwell, has been replaced by systematic computation and rigorous theory. For example, the Gauss method of iteration gives, for many of these problems, spectral radii of order $1 - O(h^2)$, where h is the finite-difference interval. By systematic point over-relaxation this can be reduced to $1 - O(h)$, and by "block iteration", and by the method of alternating directions, etc., we can get still smaller spectral radii. The classical paper on successive over-relaxation was produced by Young (1954), and has been developed by Varga (1962) in connexion with earlier work by Frobenius on p-cyclic matrices.

Another difficult problem is the determination of an upper bound, as a function of h, to the difference between the solution of the differential problem and that of the algebraic problem. Depending on the order of the local truncation error, and on other things like the smoothness of the boundary, we can in some cases prove that the difference is bounded by some power of h multiplying some higher derivatives of f. Since the latter are not known this sort of bound is rather unsatisfactory, and the search is now on for bounds depending on the data alone.

Few results are available, with virtually nothing for boundaries with sharp corners or for discontinuous boundary conditions. For example we do not know much about the difference $\lambda - \lambda(h)$ between the smallest eigenvalue of the equation

$$\nabla^2 f + \lambda f = 0, \tag{11}$$

with $f = 0$ on the boundary of an L-shaped membrane, and its finite-difference approximation. The field is wide open for new ideas.

6. Approximation

Finally, the field of approximation has had considerable recent development. We cannot use bulky mathematical tables with computing machines, and we seek to approximate complicated functions by simple functions. The Chebyshev polynomial has come back into its own, and for example we can now compute to high accuracy the Bessel function $I_0(x)$ for the whole range $0 \leq x \leq +\infty$, from two finite series of the form

$$\sum_{r=0}^{n} a_r T_r(x) \quad \text{and} \quad e^x x^{-\frac{1}{2}} \sum_{r=0}^{m} b_r T_r(8/x),$$

with the storage of a small number of coefficients, the a_r and b_r, and a simple program for the evaluation of these expressions (Clenshaw 1962).

More elaborate approximations, and rigorous analysis of the class of functions for which they can be used, are essentially practical advances on the work of Weierstrass, Bernstein, Markoff, Chebyshev, etc., under the title "the constructive theory of functions".

7. Future Developments

Details of many of these topics, and of allied problems in numerical methods, are given in subsequent chapters. They reinforce the main theme of this chapter, that numerical analysis is rapidly changing from an art to a science. Indeed the whole power of modern mathematics, with vector spaces, topology and functional analysis, is being increasingly invoked to simplify our proofs, to extend the area of our applications, and to produce new ideas. It is now difficult to find the boundary between numerical analysis and conventional mathematics. It is even more difficult to be expert in all parts of the numerical field, and modern workers concentrate, as in other parts of mathematics, on particular areas such as linear algebra, differential equations, approximation, and so on. The production of books with titles like "Numerical Analysis" will tend to decline, and we shall get books, at all levels, on each of the individual topics.

For these developments we need mathematicians trained in the modern discipline. Many of us who learnt our mathematics in a previous era, in which "space" and even "matrix" were difficult and fearful words, now spend much time in trying to administer computing services. We shall use whatever spare time we have as "middle men", explaining to those with problems to solve, and in the language which they can understand, the discoveries of modern mathematicians interested in numerical methods and their application to practical problems. For with regard to the solution of practical problems, the "useful" part of our activities, somebody must try to bridge this serious gap between mathematicians and scientists. The gap, and the present lack of very competent numerical analysts, are two problems which must interest all those concerned with mathematics and its applications.

REFERENCES

CLENSHAW, C. W. 1962. Chebyshev series for mathematical functions. *Math. Tab. Nat. Phys. Lab.* **5**. H.M. Stationery Office, London.

DAHLQUIST, G. 1956. Convergence and stability in the numerical integration of ordinary differential equations. *Math. Scand.* **4**, 33–53.

DAHLQUIST, G. 1959. Stability and error bounds in the numerical integration of ordinary differential equations. *K. Tekn. Högsk. Handl.* **130**.

VON NEUMANN, J. AND GOLDSTINE, H. H. 1947. Numerical inverting of matrices of high order. *Bull. Amer. Math. Soc.* **53**, 1021–1099.

ROLLETT, J. S. AND WILKINSON, J. H. 1961. An efficient scheme for the codiagonalization of a symmetric matrix by Givens' method in a computer with a two-level store. *Comp. J.* **4**, 177–180.

TURING, A. M. 1958. Rounding-off errors in matrix processes. *Q. J. Mech. App. Math.* **1**, 287–308.

WILKINSON, J. H. 1959. The evaluation of the zeros of ill-conditioned polynomials. *Num. Math.* **1**, 150–180.

WILKINSON, J. H. 1962. Error analysis of eigenvalue techniques based on orthogonal transformations. *J. Soc. Ind. App. Math.* **10,** 162–195.

WILKINSON, J. H. 1963. *Rounding Errors in Algebraic Processes.* Notes on Applied
Science. No. 32. H. M. Stationery Office, London.

VARGA, R. S. 1962. *Matrix Iterative Analysis.* Prentice-Hall, London.

YOUNG, D. 1954. Iterative methods for solving partial difference equations of
elliptic type. *Trans. Amer. Math. Soc.* **76,** 92–111.

Chapter 2

Linear Algebraic Equations

D. W. MARTIN

Mathematics Division, National Physical Laboratory,
Teddington, Middlesex

1. Introduction

The problem we are considering is the numerical solution of the matrix equation $Ax = b$ for the $n \times 1$ vector x when the $n \times n$ matrix A and the $n \times 1$ vector b are given. As usual a_{ij} will denote the element in the ith row and jth column of A, and x_i (b_i) will denote the element in the ith row of x (b). All quantities are assumed to be real numbers.

The ideal situation would be that we had some single method of solution which was acceptably fast and accurate regardless of the particular matrix A and of the computer available to us. The actual situation is that we have available very accurate methods for treating a general matrix, and that these methods are optimal when A is *full* (that is, when the elements of A are all non-zero): these are the direct elimination methods. However when A is *sparse* (that is, a large proportion of the elements of A are zeros), iterative methods offer certain advantages over direct methods, and for very large sparse matrices iterative methods are indispensable. Nonetheless we must bear in mind the fact that iterative methods can be guaranteed to be effective only for matrices with special properties—though these properties fortunately characterize many important practical problems. To a large extent, therefore, the choice of method depends on the proportion and disposition, as well as on the sign and size, of the non-zero elements of A.

In this survey we first indicate some connections between matrices and linear graphs. We then treat direct methods by considering Gaussian Elimination in some detail, including a sketch of the relevant error analysis, describing what should now be the standard solution routine for every program library, and indicating the merits of variants of this method. The relevance of direct methods to band matrices follows; we consider types of problem always well suited to these methods, and indicate techniques for deriving matrices of compact band form. Certain limitations of these techniques become apparent, and we consider classes of iterative methods which are widely used, together with reference to a new technique based on considerations of linear graphs for optimizing the application of Successive Block Over-Relaxation to network problems. Finally we consider some special methods which have been devised for problems involving perturbations of some given matrix.

2. Matrices and Linear Graphs

In recent years linear graphs have been found to offer a convenient device for discussing aspects of iterative methods, and this is one reason for referring to graphs in this chapter. More important, however, than those particular applications is the fact that graphs provide a viewpoint for understanding how matrices arise in practice.

Text books usually introduce matrices merely as rectangular arrays (Sylvester introduced the word "matrix" into mathematics in 1850 to denote arrays of numbers "out of which determinants can be formed"), and few students see practical applications of matrix theory except in analytical geometry: the intersection of hyperplanes, determination of centres of quadrics, rotation of co-ordinate axes. Linear graphs offer an immediate means of rectifying this situation: *the elements of a matrix define the interactions between the components of a physical assemblage.*

For, let us suppose first that A is symmetric, and that we associate with each index i and unknown x_i a vertex V_i of an *undirected linear graph*, $G(A)$, with an edge connecting the vertices V_i and V_j only if $a_{ij} = a_{ji} \neq 0$. Then the pattern of non-zero elements in A describes the interconnections between the vertices of $G(A)$. If, further, we suppose each vertex of the graph to represent a component of some physical assemblage, and the edges to represent direct connections between these components, and if we take the magnitudes of the elements a_{ij} to define the strength of the physical coupling between the components of the assemblage, then our assertion is justified. When the elements of A have only the values 0 and 1, A is called the *adjacency matrix* of the graph, and then we are concerned only with the existence or absence of connections between the corresponding components of the assemblage.

It is interesting to note that these elementary concepts are already finding a place in the new experimental mathematics syllabuses for schools (Thwaites, 1964, p. 22). At a more advanced level, the theory of electrical circuits provides a trivial application of these concepts in problems on Wheatstone's bridges, while the theory of mechanical vibrations and resonance frequencies illustrates the physical origin of eigenvalue problems.

For unsymmetric matrices we need to invoke the more complicated *directed graph* in which an edge with an arrow from vertex V_i to vertex V_j occurs if $a_{ij} \neq 0$, and another edge with an arrow from vertex V_j to vertex V_i if $a_{ji} \neq 0$. An illustration of the occurrence of the directed graph in mathematics is the fact (Varga 1962, p. 20) that a matrix A is *irreducible* (i.e. there does not exist an $n \times n$ permutation matrix P such that

$$PAP^T = \begin{bmatrix} B_{11} & B_{12} \\ 0 & B_{22} \end{bmatrix}, \tag{1}$$

where B_{11} is an $r \times r$ submatrix and B_{22} is an $(n-r) \times (n-r)$ submatrix where $1 \leq r < n$) if and only if the directed graph of A is *strongly connected* (i.e. a directed path can be found between *every* pair of vertices of $G(A)$). Again, in iterative theory, we are interested in the existence of a permutation matrix P such that, for A irreducible,

$$PAP^T = \begin{bmatrix} 0 & 0 & & 0 & B_{1,p} \\ B_{21} & 0 & & 0 & 0 \\ 0 & B_{32} & 0 & 0 & 0 \\ & & 0 & & \cdots \\ 0 & 0 & & 0 & B_{p,p-1} & 0 \end{bmatrix}, \tag{2}$$

where the null diagonal submatrices are square.

If such a permutation matrix exists, A is said to be *cyclic of index p*. Equivalently, we can consider for each vertex V_i of $G(A)$ all closed paths connecting V_i to itself. If m_i is the length of any such path, and p_i is the greatest common divisor of all the m_i associated with V_i, then $p_1 = p_2 = p_3 = \ldots = p_n = p > 1$ when A is cyclic of index p (Varga 1962, p. 49).

A form of linear graph which is particularly important in some methods of solving linear equations is the *tree*: this is a graph containing no closed loops. Its significance will be discussed later.

3. Gaussian Elimination

As is well known, the essence of this method is to reduce the given set of equations to a set with a matrix of upper triangular form, by stages in each of which all the subdiagonal elements in a single column are replaced by zeros. If we write our given matrix A in the form

$$A = A^{(1)} = \begin{bmatrix} a_{11}^{(1)} & a_{12}^{(1)} & \cdots & a_{1n}^{(1)} \\ a_{21}^{(1)} & a_{22}^{(1)} & \cdots & a_{2n}^{(1)} \\ \cdots & \cdots & \cdots & \cdots \\ a_{n1}^{(1)} & a_{n2}^{(1)} & \cdots & a_{nn}^{(1)} \end{bmatrix}, \tag{3}$$

we introduce these zeros by subtracting

$m_{21} = \dfrac{a_{21}^{(1)}}{a_{11}^{(1)}}$ times the first row from the second,

$m_{31} = \dfrac{a_{31}^{(1)}}{a_{11}^{(1)}}$ times the first row from the third,

and so on.

If we write

$$M_1 = \begin{bmatrix} 1 & & & \\ -m_{21} & 1 & & \\ -m_{31} & 0 & 1 & \\ \cdots & & & \\ -m_{n1} & 0 & \cdots & 0 & 1 \end{bmatrix}, \tag{4}$$

we have

$$M_1 A^{(1)} = A^{(2)} = \begin{bmatrix} a_{11}^{(1)} & a_{12}^{(1)} & \cdots & a_{1n}^{(1)} \\ 0 & a_{22}^{(2)} & \cdots & a_{2n}^{(2)} \\ \cdot & & \cdots & \\ 0 & a_{n2}^{(2)} & \cdots & a_{nn}^{(2)} \end{bmatrix}. \tag{5}$$

The amount of work involved in this reduction is $(n-1)^2$ multiplications, essentially. Proceeding in similar fashion with matrices $M_2, M_3, \ldots, M_{n-1}$, where

$$
M_2 = \begin{bmatrix}
1 & & & & & \\
0 & 1 & & & & \\
0 & -m_{32} & 1 & & & \\
0 & -m_{42} & 0 & & & \\
& \cdots & & & & \\
0 & -m_{n2} & 0 & \cdots & 0 & 1
\end{bmatrix}
\tag{6}
$$

and

$$
m_{32} = \frac{a_{32}^{(2)}}{a_{22}^{(2)}}, \quad \text{etc.,}
$$

we obtain

$$
M_{n-1} M_{n-2} \ldots M_2 M_1 A^{(1)} = U = \begin{bmatrix}
a_{11}^{(1)} & a_{12}^{(1)} & & \cdots & a_{1n}^{(1)} \\
0 & a_{22}^{(2)} & & \cdots & a_{2n}^{(2)} \\
& & a_{33}^{(3)} & \cdots & a_{3n}^{(3)} \\
& \cdot & \cdot & \cdot & \cdot \\
& & & & a_{nn}^{(n)}
\end{bmatrix}.
\tag{7}
$$

Equivalently, $A^{(1)} = LU$, where

$$
L = M_1^{-1} M_2^{-1} \ldots M_{n-1}^{-1} = \begin{bmatrix}
1 & & & & \\
m_{21} & 1 & & & \\
m_{31} & m_{32} & 1 & & \\
\cdots & \cdots & \cdots & \cdots & \cdots \\
& & & 1 & \\
m_{n1} & \cdots & & m_{n,n-1} & 1
\end{bmatrix},
\tag{8}
$$

and the solution of our given problem is achieved by undertaking the forward and back substitutions required to solve

$$
L\mathbf{y} = \mathbf{b}, \qquad U\mathbf{x} = \mathbf{y}.
\tag{9}
$$

The total amount of work involved is essentially

$$
\sum_{r=1}^{n} (r-1)^2 \sim \tfrac{1}{3} n^3 \quad \text{multiplications.}
$$

4. Results from Error Analysis

The above description of the process ignores the rounding errors which are inevitable when we perform arithmetic to a finite number of figures. For example, the equation

$$
a_{22}^{(2)} = a_{22}^{(1)} - m_{21} a_{12}^{(1)}
\tag{10}
$$

ignores two errors: one arises because m_{21} is really equal to $\dfrac{a_{21}^{(1)}}{a_{11}^{(1)}} + \varepsilon$, and a second because $m_{21} a_{12}^{(1)}$ cannot in general be represented by a single-length number, and because in addition and subtraction rounding may also be necessary to provide a single-length result. These errors are discussed in detail by Wilkinson (1963), who shows that the triangular factors L and U obtained by the elimination process correspond *exactly* to some perturbation of our given matrix A:

$$LU = A^{(1)} + E \tag{11}$$

where the elements of E incorporate all the rounding errors which are made in the reduction.

An additional point is that if the computation is carried out exactly as described, the quantities m_{ij} may become arbitrarily large. At the jth stage of the reduction, therefore, we select the pivotal row to ensure that all $|m_{ij}| \leq 1$, usually by interchanging the jth row with that row for which $|a_{ij}^{(j)}|$, $i \geq j$, is largest. This does not affect the validity of our result (11), provided we assume that $A^{(1)}$ denotes our given matrix with its rows suitably permuted.

If we now assume that we are working in t-digit floating-point binary arithmetic with a double-precision accumulator, and if we denote the maximum element in any $A^{(r)}$ by g, then Wilkinson (1963) shows that the elements of the error matrix E are bounded by

$$|E| \leq 2 \cdot 01 . g . 2^{-t} \begin{bmatrix} 0 & 0 & 0 \cdots & 0 & 0 \\ 1 & 1 & 1 \cdots & 1 & 1 \\ 1 & 2 & 2 \cdots & 2 & 2 \\ 1 & 2 & 3 \cdots & 3 & 3 \\ \cdots\cdots\cdots\cdots \\ 1 & 2 & 3 \cdots & n-1 & n-1 \end{bmatrix}. \tag{12}$$

Similarly we can show that in place of the first of (9), we solve exactly

$$(L + \delta L)\mathbf{y} = \mathbf{b}, \tag{13}$$

where

$$|\delta L| \leq 2^{-t} \begin{bmatrix} |\ell_{11}| \\ 2|\ell_{21}| & 2|\ell_{22}| \\ 3|\ell_{31}| & 2|\ell_{32}| & 2|\ell_{33}| \\ \cdots & & & 2|\ell_{n-1,n-1}| \\ n|\ell_{n1}| & (n-1)|\ell_{n2}| & \cdots & 2|\ell_{n,n-1}| & 2|\ell_{nn}| \end{bmatrix}. \tag{14}$$

An analogous result holds for the back substitution

$$(U + \delta U)\mathbf{x} = \mathbf{y}. \tag{15}$$

Thus we see that the problem to which we produce the exact solution is

$$(A + E + L\delta U + \delta LU + \delta L \delta U)\mathbf{x} = \mathbf{b}, \tag{16}$$

and we wish to know the extent to which this solution differs from that of $A\mathbf{x} = \mathbf{b}$. To do this we cease to follow the magnitudes of individual elements in any matrix, and we use instead a single number as a measure of the size of an entire matrix or vector. This number is called a *norm*, and the norm of a matrix is denoted by $\|A\|$, and of a vector by $\|\mathbf{x}\|$.

For a vector $\mathbf{x}$, convenient norms are

$\|\mathbf{x}\|_\infty = \max_i |x_i|$, the modulus of the largest element,

$\|\mathbf{x}\|_1 = |x_1| + |x_2| + \cdots + |x_n|$,

$\|\mathbf{x}\|_2 = [x_1^2 + x_2^2 + \cdots + x_n^2]^{\frac{1}{2}}$, the length of the vector in Euclidean n-space.

For a matrix A, the corresponding norms are

$\|A\|_\infty = \max_i \sum_j |a_{ij}|$, the maximum absolute row sum,

$\|A\|_1 = \max_j \sum_i |a_{ij}|$, the maximum absolute column sum,

$\|A\|_2 = (\text{max. eigenvalue of } A^T A)^{\frac{1}{2}}$

$ = \rho(A)$, the spectral radius of A, when A is symmetric.

Now if instead of solving $A\mathbf{x} = \mathbf{b}$, we solve $(A+E)(\mathbf{x}+\mathbf{h}) = \mathbf{b}$, it is a simple matter to show (Wilkinson 1963) that

$$\frac{\|\mathbf{h}\|}{\|\mathbf{x}\|} \leq \frac{\|A^{-1}\| \, \|E\|}{1 - \|A^{-1}\| \, \|E\|} = \frac{\|A\| \, \|A^{-1}\| \dfrac{\|E\|}{\|A\|}}{1 - \|A\| \, \|A^{-1}\| \dfrac{\|E\|}{\|A\|}}, \tag{17}$$

provided

$$\|A^{-1}\| \, \|E\| < 1. \tag{18}$$

Thus we see that if $\|A\| \, \|A^{-1}\|$ is large, small relative changes in our data are liable to induce large relative changes in the solution. This is one way of defining ill-conditioning in a problem, and the number $\|A\| \, \|A^{-1}\|$ is often referred to as *the spectral condition number of A with respect to inversion*.

It can be shown for several norms that $\|\delta L\| \leq n.2^{-t}\|L\|$, and equation (13) then provides the estimate

$$\frac{\|\mathbf{y} - L^{-1}\mathbf{b}\|}{\|L^{-1}\mathbf{b}\|} \leq \frac{n.2^{-t}\|L\| \, \|L^{-1}\|}{1 - n.2^{-t}\|L\| \, \|L^{-1}\|}. \tag{19}$$

This would lead us to expect large relative errors when $\|L^{-1}\|$ is large. However, *in practice, large errors do not materialize in the solution of triangular sets of equations*, and in place of (19) Wilkinson (1963) has found that a realistic estimate is

$$\frac{\|\mathbf{y} - L^{-1}\mathbf{b}\|}{\|L^{-1}\mathbf{b}\|} \leq f(n).2^{-t}, \tag{20}$$

where $f(n)$ is some simple function of n which depends on the particular mode of arithmetic employed, but which does not depend on the condition of L. Although this result can be derived analytically only for special classes of matrices, the classes embrace most matrices which arise in practice, and *the result* (20) *is observed to hold almost universally*.

If we assume the validity of (20), we obtain

$$\mathbf{y} - L^{-1}\mathbf{b} = \mathbf{e}, \qquad \|\mathbf{e}\| \leq f(n).2^{-t}\|L^{-1}\mathbf{b}\|, \tag{21}$$

$$\mathbf{x} - U^{-1}\mathbf{y} = \mathbf{e}', \qquad \|\mathbf{e}'\| \leq f(n).2^{-t}\|U^{-1}\mathbf{y}\|, \tag{22}$$

$$\mathbf{x} = U^{-1}L^{-1}\mathbf{b} + U^{-1}\mathbf{e} + \mathbf{e}', \tag{23}$$

and hence

$$\left\|\mathbf{x}-(LU)^{-1}\mathbf{b}\right\| \le f(n).2^{-t}(2+f(n).2^{-t})\left\|U^{-1}\right\|\left\|L^{-1}\mathbf{b}\right\|. \qquad (24)$$

If

$$\left\|(LU)^{-1}\mathbf{b}\right\| \sim \left\|U^{-1}\right\|\left\|L^{-1}\mathbf{b}\right\|, \qquad (25)$$

then we can show that

$$\frac{\left\|\mathbf{x}-(LU)^{-1}\mathbf{b}\right\|}{\left\|(LU)^{-1}\mathbf{b}\right\|} \sim g(n).2^{-t}, \qquad (26)$$

where $g(n)$, like $f(n)$, is some simple function of n. Now (25) will be true except for special $\mathbf{b}$ of the form $\mathbf{b} = LU\mathbf{d}$, say, where $\|\mathbf{d}\| \sim 1$. In these special cases, $\|(LU)^{-1}\mathbf{b}\| = \|\mathbf{d}\| \sim 1$, while $\|U^{-1}\|$ can be very large—for example when cancellation occurs in the determination of U, giving a small pivot in the elimination process.

The practical consequence of the result (26) is very important: it means that where $\mathbf{b}$ is such that the corresponding solution reveals the ill-conditioning of LU, *it is the errors E incurred in the decomposition* (11) *which limit the accuracy of the computed solution as a solution of $A\mathbf{x} = \mathbf{b}$.*

5. Recommended Standard Procedure for Elimination

We have seen that if A is ill-conditioned our computed solution may be insufficiently accurate, and we must therefore consider how to assess the inaccuracy, and perhaps to improve our solution. One symptom of ill-conditioning is a small last pivot in U, and another is the size of $\mathbf{x}$ relative to $\mathbf{b}$, though this may not manifest itself for a single right-hand side. Certainly by solving for n orthogonal right-hand sides, e.g. by taking $\mathbf{b}$ equal to the columns of I in turn, so that we actually compute A^{-1}, we could not fail to detect the ill-conditioning of A; but a quicker method which simultaneously improves the solution is available from the following considerations.

From our solution $\mathbf{x} = \mathbf{x}^{(1)}$, say, we can compute the residual,

$$\mathbf{r}^{(1)} = \mathbf{b} - A\mathbf{x}^{(1)}. \qquad (27)$$

Now

$$\mathbf{b} - A\mathbf{x} = (E + L\delta U + \delta LU + \delta L\delta U)\mathbf{x}, \qquad (28)$$

and we can show that E, δL, δU have elements no larger than $n.2^{-t}$, essentially. Hence

$$\left\|\mathbf{b} - A\mathbf{x}\right\|_{\infty} \le f(n).g.2^{-t}\|\mathbf{x}\|_{\infty}, \qquad (29)$$

where $g \ge |u_{ij}|$ and $f(n)$ is O(n) in practice. Thus $\mathbf{r}^{(1)}$ is bound to be small relative to $\mathbf{x}^{(1)}$, regardless of the accuracy of $\mathbf{x}^{(1)}$; and the expression

$$\mathbf{x} - \mathbf{x}^{(1)} = A^{-1}\mathbf{b} - \mathbf{x}^{(1)} = A^{-1}\mathbf{r}^{(1)} \qquad (30)$$

shows immediately that large errors can accompany small residuals when A^{-1} contains large elements.

If we define a sequence of back-substitutions using the computed L, U by

$$\left.\begin{array}{l} \mathbf{r}^{(s)} = \mathbf{b} - A\mathbf{x}^{(s)} \\ \mathbf{x}^{(s+1)} = \mathbf{x}^{(s)} + (LU)^{-1}\mathbf{r}^{(s)} \end{array}\right\}, \tag{31}$$

we can show (Wilkinson 1963) that if

$$\|A^{-1}\| \, \|E\| < 2^{-p}, \qquad p > 1, \tag{32}$$

then

$$\|\mathbf{x}^{(s+1)} - \mathbf{x}\| \leq \frac{2^{-p}}{1 - 2^{-p}} \, \|\mathbf{x}^{(s)} - \mathbf{x}\|. \tag{33}$$

Thus the error in our solution $\mathbf{x}^{(s)}$ decreases by the factor $2^{-p}/(1 - 2^{-p})^{-1}$ (at least) with each iteration. For $p \geq 2$, we gain p binary figures per iteration.

The benefits of this result can be obtained in practice without working to more than single-length precision *except in the accumulation of the scalar product* $\mathbf{r}^{(s)}$, where double-length working is essential. (This is because we know that extensive cancellation is bound to occur in computing $\mathbf{r}^{(s)}$, and rounding errors of order 2^{-t} in each term in the scalar product will make (33) invalid.) Since the work of calculating the quantities in (31) is only $O(1/n)$ times that involved in the original determination of L and U, the cost of the improved accuracy is negligible. On a modern digital computer, a single refinement of $\mathbf{x}^{(1)}$ should suffice for most practical problems. Output of the quantity $\|\mathbf{x}^{(2)} - \mathbf{x}^{(1)}\|_\infty / \|\mathbf{x}^{(2)}\|_\infty$ together with $\mathbf{x}^{(2)}$ then provides an index of the accuracy of this solution.

We note that if the behaviour predicted by (33) is not obtained in practice, we must assume that A is so ill-conditioned that $\|A^{-1}\| \, \|E\| \not< 2^{-p}$, $p > 1$. In this case, double-length working throughout is unavoidable.

6. Variants of Gaussian Elimination

We have seen that Gaussian Elimination produces triangular matrices which satisfy $LU = A$, ignoring rounding errors. This matrix relation can also be used directly to provide an alternative and more accurate derivation of the elements of L and U. For, if we equate corresponding elements in the relation, we obtain

$$\left.\begin{array}{ll} \ell_{i1}u_{1j} + \ell_{i2}u_{2j} + \ldots + \ell_{i,i-1}u_{i-1,j} + u_{ij} = a_{ij}, & j \geq i \\ \ell_{i1}u_{1j} + \ldots + \ell_{ij}u_{jj} \qquad\qquad\quad = a_{ij}, & i > j \end{array}\right\}. \tag{34}$$

Rewriting these equations in the form

$$\left.\begin{array}{ll} u_{ij} = a_{ij} - \ell_{i1}u_{1j} - \ldots - \ell_{i,i-1}u_{i-1,j}, & j \geq i \\ \ell_{ij} = (a_{ij} - \ell_{i1}u_{1j} - \ldots - \ell_{i,j-1}u_{j-1,j})/u_{jj}, & i > j \end{array}\right\}, \tag{35}$$

we see that the rows of U and L alternately can be determined in their natural order. If we accumulate inner-products double-length and divide into the double-length result, only one rounding error is made in the determination of each element, and Wilkinson (1963) shows that when this is done, (11) is satisfied with

$$|E| < \tfrac{1}{2}g2^{-t} \begin{bmatrix} 0 & 0 & 0 & \cdots & 0 \\ |u_{11}| & 1 & 1 & & 1 \\ |u_{11}| & |u_{22}| & 1 & & 1 \\ & & |u_{33}| & & \\ & & \cdots & & \\ |u_{11}| & |u_{22}| & & & 1 \end{bmatrix} \tag{36}$$

in place of (12), where g still relates to the Gaussian Elimination.

When A is symmetric and positive definite, the Cholesky decomposition $A = LL^T$ can be used. In this case separate storage of $U (=L^T)$ is unnecessary, and interchanges are not required.

For a general matrix, an alternative way of arranging the elimination is sometimes useful. In this procedure (Nat. Phys. Lab. 1961, p. 17), x_1 is eliminated from the second equation using only the first two rows of the matrix; x_1 and x_2 are eliminated from the third equation using only the first three rows; and so on. An important advantage of this variant is that the values of the principal minors of A are equal to those of the principal minors of the partial upper triangles associated with each stage of the reduction.

7. Band Matrices

In some sparse matrices, the non-zero elements are located in a well-defined band centred along the principal diagonal. If we work outwards in either direction from the principal diagonal labelling $1, 2, \ldots, k$, the parallel diagonals which we traverse in any row, until only zero elements lie in the remaining diagonals, the number $2k+1$ is called the *bandwidth* of the matrix. In the following discussion we assume that there are k diagonals on each side of the principal diagonal.

Equations associated with a band matrix are particularly well suited for solution by Gaussian Elimination for, if we ignore the possibility of row interchanges, (34) shows that zeros in A which lie outside the band are preserved in the triangular factors L and U. These elements may therefore be excluded from the elimination procedure. When row interchanges are admitted, the bandwidth of L is unaltered, but that of U will be doubled if the bottom row with a non-zero element in the column under consideration is interchanged with the top row. To cover this contingency in a general program, we must assume that the original matrix with $(2k+1)n$ non-zero elements (ignoring the special appearance of the first and last k rows), will be replaced by kn elements in L and $(2k+1)n$ in U, or $(3k+1)n$ elements in all, in contrast to n^2 for a general matrix. The amount of work involved in the reduction is of order $2k^2n$ multiplications, in contrast to $\tfrac{1}{3}n^3$ for a general matrix. For a matrix with $n = 500$ and $k = 20$, it follows that attention to the band form reduces the work of solution to one-hundredth.

In some practical problems, like those involving finite-difference equations on a linear or rectangular lattice, the band form of the matrix is compact;

but in other problems, particularly those arising from electrical and hydraulic networks, the non-zero elements in the sparse matrix are distributed in a haphazard fashion. It is therefore important to realize that the bandwidth of a matrix A depends on the particular sequence in which the vertices V_i of the linear graph $G(A)$ are labelled. For example, if the linear graph is a polygon, and we number the vertices sequentially $1, 2, 3, \ldots$ in a clockwise direction around the perimeter, the adjacency matrix of the graph has the form

$$\begin{bmatrix} 1 & 1 & & & & & 1 \\ 1 & 1 & 1 & & & & \\ & 1 & 1 & 1 & & & \\ & & & \cdots & & & \\ & & & & 1 & 1 & 1 \\ 1 & & & & & 1 & 1 \end{bmatrix}.$$

Such a matrix cannot usefully be considered as a band matrix at all. However if starting from vertex 1 we renumber the other vertices $2, 4, 6, \ldots$ in a clockwise direction, and $3, 5, 7, \ldots$ in an anticlockwise direction, the corresponding adjacency matrix has the form

$$\begin{bmatrix} 1 & 1 & 1 & & & & \\ 1 & 1 & 0 & 1 & & & \\ 1 & 0 & 1 & 0 & 1 & & \\ & & & \cdots & & & \\ & & 1 & 0 & 1 & 0 & 1 \\ & & & 1 & 0 & 1 & 1 \\ & & & & 1 & 1 & 1 \end{bmatrix},$$

for which k is 2.

Techniques for renumbering the vertices of $G(A)$ to provide a matrix with the smallest possible bandwidth are therefore of considerable interest. In special cases, like the nearest-neighbour interactions in a linear chain (e.g. the polygon) or on a rectangular lattice, the optimum orderings are well known, but in general it is not a simple matter to determine the optimum ordering. An algorithm has been constructed for use on a computer when A is symmetric (Alway and Martin 1965), and this has proved effective for matrices of order 200 or so; but further developments of these ideas would be valuable.

Despite the benefits which come from adapting Gaussian Elimination to the band form of many matrices, serious limitations are sometimes imposed by the fact that the method does not preserve sparseness *within* the band. In general, nearly all the $(3k+1)n$ elements of L and U will be non-zero, regardless of the form of A. When the band is already filled with non-zero elements (the simplest example is the tridiagonal matrix associated with ordinary differential equations and other one-dimensional problems), or when k is appreciably less than $\sqrt{n}$ (as with finite-difference equations on a uniform mesh in a long thin rectangle), little or no hardship is caused by this fact; but when A has very few non-zero elements within a wide band, the amount of work and storage involved in the direct method may be unacceptable. For example, nearest-neighbour interactions on a $10 \times 10 \times 10$ cubic lattice lead to a matrix with $n = 1000$ and $k = 100$, but with only 7 non-zero elements in any row. Even when A is symmetric and positive definite, so that Cholesky decomposition may be used, the storage of 100,000 non-zero elements is required. For such problems we are bound to seek some radically different approach to the solution, and this is found in the iterative methods which are based on successive approximation.

8. General Remarks on Iterative Methods

An iterative method starts from an approximation to the true solution, and if successful derives a convergent sequence of closer approximations from a computational cycle which is repeated as often as necessary. For example, given $x_1^{(1)}, x_2^{(1)}, \ldots, x_n^{(1)}$ we might compute

$$
\left.
\begin{aligned}
x_1^{(2)} &= (b_1 - a_{12}x_2^{(1)} - \ldots - a_{1n}x_n^{(1)})/a_{11} \\
x_2^{(2)} &= (b_2 - a_{21}x_1^{(2)} - a_{23}x_3^{(1)} - \ldots - a_{2n}x_n^{(1)})/a_{22} \\
&\cdot \quad \cdot \quad \cdot \quad \cdot \quad \cdot \quad \cdot \quad \cdot \quad \cdot \quad \cdot \quad \cdot \\
x_n^{(2)} &= (b_n - a_{n1}x_1^{(2)} - a_{n2}x_2^{(2)} - \ldots - a_{n,n-1}x_{n-1}^{(2)})/a_{nn}
\end{aligned}
\right\}, \tag{37}
$$

and so on.

A popular feature of methods such as the above is that the elements of the given matrix A are used throughout in unmodified form. We must note at once, therefore, that we are still bound to make errors in determining the quantities on the left of (37), because we use finite-precision arithmetic. In place of (37), we actually obtain (Wilkinson 1961)

$$
x_1^{(2)} = [b_1(1+\varepsilon_1) - a_{12}x_2^{(1)}(1+\varepsilon_2) - \ldots - a_{1n}x_n^{(1)}(1+\varepsilon_n)]/a_{11} \tag{38}
$$

and so on, where the ε_i are errors depending on the particular form of arithmetic employed. Thus we are again working with $A + E$ rather than A, and the effects of ill-conditioning are not avoided merely because we do not modify the elements of A explicitly. In an extreme case convergence of the iterations can be inhibited completely by the rounding errors (Wilkinson 1961).

9. Stationary Methods

The process described in (37) is commonly known as the Gauss-Seidel iteration, and it represents merely one way of splitting the matrix A into $B - C$, so that $Ax = b$ becomes $Bx = Cx + b$, whence we derive the iteration

$$
Bx^{(k+1)} = Cx^{(k)} + b. \tag{39}
$$

The iteration defined by (39) is called *stationary* because no variation of the process occurs from one cycle to another.

If we represent A as the sum $D - L - U$, where D is a diagonal matrix, and L and U are respectively lower and upper triangular matrices with zero diagonal elements, then (37) corresponds to the choice $B = D - L$, $C = U$. If we choose $B = D$, $C = L + U$, (39) defines the Jacobi iteration, and if

$$B = \frac{1}{\omega} D - L, \qquad C = U + \frac{1 - \omega}{\omega} D, \qquad \omega > 0, \qquad (40)$$

we have Successive Over-Relaxation (SOR).

It follows from (39) that

$$B(\mathbf{x}^{(k+1)} - \mathbf{x}) = C(\mathbf{x}^{(k)} - \mathbf{x}), \qquad (41)$$

and hence that

$$\mathbf{x}^{(k+1)} - \mathbf{x} = B^{-1}C(\mathbf{x}^{(k)} - \mathbf{x}) = (B^{-1}C)^{k+1}(\mathbf{x}^{(0)} - \mathbf{x}). \qquad (42)$$

If we expand $\mathbf{x}^{(0)} - \mathbf{x}$ in the form $\alpha_1 \mathbf{u}_1 + \alpha_2 \mathbf{u}_2 + \ldots + \alpha_n \mathbf{u}_n$, where $\mathbf{u}_1$, $\mathbf{u}_2, \ldots, \mathbf{u}_n$ are the eigenvectors and principal vectors of $B^{-1}C$, corresponding to eigenvalues $\lambda_1, \lambda_2, \ldots, \lambda_n$, then

$$\mathbf{x}^{(k)} - \mathbf{x} = \alpha_1 \lambda_1^k \mathbf{u}_1 + \alpha_2 \lambda_2^k \mathbf{u}_2 + \ldots + \alpha_n \lambda_n^k \mathbf{u}_n. \qquad (43)$$

Thus the progress of the iteration (39) depends on $\rho(B^{-1}C)$, the spectral radius (i.e. the modulus of the largest eigenvalue) of $B^{-1}C$. For convergence we require $\rho < 1$, and for practical utility we need ρ significantly less than 1.

Thus our problem of solving $A\mathbf{x} = \mathbf{b}$ has been replaced by that of finding a splitting of A which provides rapid convergence. For a general matrix A this second problem is as substantial as the first, but for certain classes of matrices which occur frequently in practice, theoretical results have been established which provide a basis for practical computations. Classes of matrices which have been treated cover

(i) symmetric positive definite matrices;
(ii) diagonally dominant matrices, where $|a_{ii}| > \sum_{j \neq i} |a_{ij}|$;
(iii) matrices for which $D > 0$, $L + U \geq 0$;
(iv) matrices which are cyclic of index p.

By permitting D to denote a block diagonal matrix, we can include the *block iterative* methods in our considerations.

As illustration of the body of knowledge which has been constructed (see Varga 1962), we have the following theorems

1. *The Stein-Rosenberg theorems.* If $D = I$, and $L + U \geq 0$, then the Jacobi and Gauss-Seidel processes both converge or both diverge, and when they converge

$$\rho((I - L)^{-1} U) < \rho(L + U). \qquad (44)$$

2. *The Ostrowski-Reich theorem.* If $A = D - E - E^T$, where D is symmetric and positive definite, and $D - \omega E$ is non-singular, $0 \leq \omega \leq 2$, then

$$\rho[(D - \omega E)^{-1}(\omega E^T + (1 - \omega)D)] < 1 \qquad (45)$$

if and only if A is symmetric and positive definite and $0 < \omega < 2$. Thus by supposing D to be block diagonal, we are assured of the convergence of Successive Block Over-Relaxation (SBOR) for symmetric positive definite matrices.

3. If A is *consistently ordered* (see Varga 1962) and its Block Jacobi matrix B is cyclic of index p with eigenvalues μ for which $0 \leq |\mu| < 1$, and μ^p is real and non-negative, then the value of ω given by

$$(\omega\rho(B))^p = [p^p(p-1)^{1-p}](\omega-1) \tag{46}$$

provides the smallest attainable value $(\omega-1)(p-1)$ for

$$\rho[(I-\omega L)^{-1}(\omega U+(1-\omega)I)].$$

Here $\rho(B)$ is assumed known, though its determination in practice may not be a trivial undertaking. Nonetheless (46) is an extremely useful result for practical problems. An algorithm for determining the optimum ω as the iterations proceed has been formulated by Carré (1961), who recently added to this an algorithm which divides an undirected graph (such as arises in electrical network equations) into mutually exclusive trees (Carré 1966). These trees define diagonal blocks for SBOR which are only weakly coupled through the elements of $L+U$, and which are particularly well-suited to Gaussian Elimination (see Parter 1961).

10. Linearly Accelerated Methods

It is clear from (43) that, by means of a fixed iterative cycle, a stationary method reduces $\mathbf{x}^{(k)}-\mathbf{x}$ towards zero by weighting each component $\alpha_i\mathbf{u}_i$ of the initial error $\mathbf{x}^{(0)}-\mathbf{x}$ with λ_i^k, the value of the polynomial z^k for the particular argument λ_i. Once this strategy is recognized as the essence of stationary methods the question arises whether the fastest possible convergence is achieved by using the polynomial z^k, or whether some other function of the eigenvalues should be used instead. Polynomials which can be generated recursively by means of linear combinations of the vectors $\mathbf{x}^{(k)}$ are most convenient for the purpose, and for this class of function the answer to our question is straightforward. If the eigenvalues of $B^{-1}C$ are complex, then a linear combination of $\mathbf{x}^{(k)}, \mathbf{x}^{(k-1)}, \ldots, \mathbf{x}^{(0)}$ will not in general be a better approximation than $\mathbf{x}^{(k)}$ to $\mathbf{x}$. However if the λ_i are all real, and upper and lower bounds for the set of the λ_i are available, then we can improve the stationary process by generating Chebyshev polynomials. Suppose that $-1 < -\ell \leq |\lambda| \leq \ell < 1$, then we generate the polynomial $T_k(x/\ell)$ by the process

$$\mathbf{X}^{(k+1)} = \mathbf{x}^{(k+1)} + \frac{T_{k-1}(1/\ell)}{T_{k+1}(1/\ell)}[\mathbf{x}^{(k+1)}-\mathbf{X}^{(k-1)}], \tag{47}$$

where

$$B\mathbf{x}^{(k+1)} = C\mathbf{X}^{(k)} + \mathbf{b}.$$

Such a process is said to be a *linear acceleration* of the stationary process, or to be a *semi-iterative* process.

11. Gradient Methods

When A is symmetric and positive definite the equation $f(\mathbf{x}) = c$, where

$$f(\mathbf{x}) = \mathbf{x}^T A\mathbf{x} - 2\mathbf{x}^T\mathbf{b} + \mathbf{b}^T A^{-1}\mathbf{b}, \tag{48}$$

defines for various c a family of similar and similarly situated ellipsoids in Euclidean n-space, whose common centre is $A^{-1}\mathbf{b}$, the point at which $f(\mathbf{x})$ takes its minimum value of zero.

Any estimate $\mathbf{x}^{(k)}$ of $A^{-1}\mathbf{b}$ defines a point in the space and the ellipsoid through this point. Approach to the centre can be represented by a sequence of vector displacements

$$\mathbf{x}^{(k+1)} - \mathbf{x}^{(k)} = \sigma_k\,\mathbf{p}^{(k)}, \tag{49}$$

where σ_k is a scalar and $\mathbf{p}^{(k)}$ is a vector.

The residual vector $\mathbf{r}^{(k)}$ is the inward normal at $\mathbf{x}^{(k)}$ to the ellipsoid through $\mathbf{x}^{(k)}$, since

$$\mathbf{r}^{(k)} = \mathbf{b} - A\mathbf{x}^{(k)} = -\tfrac{1}{2}[\operatorname{grad} f(\mathbf{x})]_{x^{(k)}}. \tag{50}$$

Accordingly a *gradient method* is an iteration which is defined by a recursion of the form

$$\mathbf{x}^{(k+1)} = \mathbf{x}^{(k)} + \sum_{i=0}^{k} c_{ki}\mathbf{r}^{(i)}. \tag{51}$$

The magnitude of the displacement from $\mathbf{x}^{(k)}$ in the direction $\mathbf{p}^{(k)}$ can be calculated so that $\mathbf{x}^{(k+1)}$ lies on the smallest ellipsoid which can be reached in that direction from $\mathbf{x}^{(k)}$. For, if we consider the function

$$f(\mathbf{x}^{(k)} + \sigma_k\mathbf{p}^{(k)}) = \sigma_k^2\mathbf{p}^{(k)T}A\mathbf{p}^{(k)} - 2\sigma_k\mathbf{p}^{(k)T}\mathbf{r}^{(k)} + f(\mathbf{x}^{(k)}), \tag{52}$$

differentiation shows that the minimum value is given by

$$\sigma_k^* = \mathbf{p}^{(k)T}\mathbf{r}^{(k)}/\mathbf{p}^{(k)T}A\mathbf{p}^{(k)}. \tag{53}$$

If $\mathbf{p}^{(k)}$ is in the direction of $\mathbf{r}^{(k)}$, we have the *method of steepest descents*. Unfortunately its convergence is usually too slow for the method to be of practical value: when A is ill-conditioned, the ellipsoids are long and thin, and along the surface the normals are nearly coplanar.

A superior strategy is based on the knowledge that the centre of an ellipsoid lies in the plane conjugate to a given chord. In three dimensions, the centre can be reached from an arbitrary first guess, $\mathbf{x}^{(0)}$, as follows. The first move is an optimum gradient step to $\mathbf{x}^{(1)}$ along the normal $\mathbf{r}^{(0)}$ to the ellipsoid through $\mathbf{x}^{(0)}$. The second step is the optimum displacement with respect to the ellipse which lies in the plane conjugate to $\mathbf{r}^{(0)}$ and which passes through $\mathbf{x}^{(1)}$. The third and final step is the optimum displacement along the diameter of the ellipse which is conjugate to the chord defined by the previous step.

This *conjugate gradient* method is generalized readily to n dimensions, and is represented by the algorithm:

$$\mathbf{p}^{(0)} = \mathbf{r}^{(0)} = \mathbf{b} - A\mathbf{x}^{(0)}, \qquad \mathbf{x}^{(0)} \text{ arbitrary}, \tag{54}$$

$$\left.\begin{aligned} \mathbf{x}^{(k+1)} &= \mathbf{x}^{(k)} + \sigma_k\mathbf{p}^{(k)} \\ \mathbf{r}^{(k+1)} &= \mathbf{r}^{(k)} - \sigma_k A\mathbf{p}^{(k)} \\ \mathbf{p}^{(k+1)} &= \mathbf{r}^{(k+1)} + \tau_k\mathbf{p}^{(k)} \end{aligned}\right\}, \tag{55}$$

where

$$\left.\begin{aligned} \sigma_k &= \mathbf{r}^{(k)T}\mathbf{p}^{(k)}/\mathbf{p}^{(k)T}A\mathbf{p}^{(k)} \\ \tau_k &= -\mathbf{r}^{(k+1)T}A\mathbf{p}^{(k)}/\mathbf{p}^{(k)T}A\mathbf{p}^{(k)} \end{aligned}\right\}. \tag{56}$$

The relation $\mathbf{p}^{(k+1)T}A\mathbf{p}^{(k)} = 0$ holds for all k, and so the directions $\mathbf{p}^{(k)}$ are conjugate to each other with respect to A.

In theory the process terminates after exactly n steps, but rounding errors perturb the strategy in practice, and cycles of n steps are therefore undertaken. Variants of this algorithm are described by Hestenes and Stiefel (1952).

12. Comparison of Methods

Engeli *et al.* (1959) undertook an extensive comparison of direct and iterative methods, applied to the comparatively ill-conditioned problem of the biharmonic equation for a flat plate, and, as their conclusions seem to be not widely known, we summarize them here.

(i) "As long as the matrix can be stored, elimination is the best method. For full matrices we would recommend elimination only, since for those the storage problem is the same for iteration and elimination."

(ii) "For matrices of moderate condition, and certainly for all problems of Dirichlet and Poisson type, the over-relaxation methods are superior to all gradient methods, provided the over-relaxation factor ω is chosen properly."

(iii) "For matrices of very bad condition the conjugate gradient methods are superior by far to all other methods except probably elimination."

(iv) "It is an additional point in favour of the conjugate gradient method that it requires *absolutely no information* about the eigenvalues of the matrix for starting the computation, whereas for the Tchebycheff method" (they refer to linear acceleration of the Jacobi method) "lower and upper bounds of the spectrum must be known, and for the over-relaxation methods the over-relaxation factor must be estimated."

13. Problems Involving Modified Matrices

A problem of interest to electrical and water engineers is to determine the effect on a power or hydraulic network of removing various connections—for example, to simulate the breakdown of one or more transmission lines in an electricity supply grid. An analogous problem in structural engineering concerns the development of plastic hinges in a rigidly jointed framework. Mathematically, these problems involve the solution of linear equations with matrices which differ only in a few elements from a matrix whose triangular factors, L and U, have already been determined. If L and U could be modified directly, so that the factors of the modified matrices could be obtained without repetition of substantial portions of work undertaken in determining the original L and U, then a useful saving of computer time would result.

An algorithm for this purpose has been devised by Bennett (1965), who shows that the triangular factors of $A + XCY^T$, where X and Y are $m \times n$ matrices and C is an $m \times m$ matrix ($m \ll n$), can be obtained in about $2mn^2$ arithmetic operations when A is full. Additional economies are available automatically when A is of band form.

The advent of such an algorithm is important because hitherto the formula

$$(A+XCY^T)^{-1} = A^{-1}+A^{-1}X(C^{-1}+Y^TA^{-1}X)^{-1}Y^TA^{-1} \qquad (57)$$

has commonly been used to derive the inverse of a modified matrix from A^{-1}, and about $3mn^2$ operations are required for this process. The solution to the modified equations is then obtained by multiplying the right-hand side by this inverse. Since the determination of A^{-1} involves about three times as much work as merely to determine L and U, this technique for solving linear equations is to be avoided whenever possible. In the case of band equations it is particularly inconvenient because A^{-1} is full in general, whereas we have seen in §4 that L and U have only $(3k+1)n$ non-zero elements.

REFERENCES

ALWAY, G. G. AND MARTIN, D. W. 1965. An algorithm for reducing the bandwidth of a matrix of symmetrical configuration. *Comp. J.* **8**, 264–272. ●

BENNETT, J. M. 1965. Triangular factors of modified matrices. *Num. Math.* **7**, 217–221.

CARRÉ, B. A. 1961. The determination of the optimum accelerating factor for successive over-relaxation. *Comp. J.* **4**, 73–78.

CARRÉ, B. A. 1966. The partitioning of network equations for block iteration. *Comp. J.* **9**, 84–97.

ENGELI, M., GINSBURG, T., RUTISHAUSER, H. AND STIEFEL, E. 1959. *Refined Iterative Methods for Computation of the Solution and the Eigenvalues of Self-Adjoint Boundary Value Problems*. Birkhäuser, Basel.

HESTENES, M. R. AND STIEFEL, E. 1952. Methods of conjugate gradients for solving linear systems. *J. Res. Nat. Bur. Stand.* **49**, 409–436.

NATIONAL PHYSICAL LABORATORY. 1961. Notes on Applied Science, **16**. *Modern Computing Methods*. H.M. Stationery Office, London.

PARTER, S. 1961. The use of linear graphs in Gauss elimination. *Soc. Ind. App. Math. Rev.* **3**, 119–130.

THWAITES, B. 1964. *The School Mathematics Project. Director's Report 1962/63*. The University, Southampton.

VARGA, R. S. 1962. *Matrix Iterative Analysis*. Prentice-Hall, London.

WILKINSON, J. H. 1961. Error analysis of direct methods of matrix inversion. *J. Assoc. Comp. Mach.* **8**, 281–330.

WILKINSON, J. H. 1963. *Rounding Errors in Algebraic Processes*. H.M. Stationery Office, London. (N.P.L. Notes on Applied Science, **32**.)

Chapter 3

Calculation of Eigensystems of Matrices

J. H. WILKINSON

Mathematics Division, National Physical Laboratory,
Teddington, Middlesex

1. Introduction

The algebraic eigenvalue problem admits of a deceptively simple formulation. For a given $n \times n$ matrix A the values of λ are required for which the system of equations

$$A\mathbf{x} = \lambda\mathbf{x} \tag{1}$$

has a non-trivial solution. Each such λ is called an *eigenvalue* (*characteristic* value or *proper* value) of A and the associated vector is called an *eigenvector* (*characteristic* vector or *proper* vector) corresponding to λ.

From the theory of linear equations the eigenvalues satisfy the equation $\det(\lambda I - A) = 0$. By direct expansion we have

$$\det(\lambda I - A) = \lambda^n - p_{n-1}\lambda^{n-1} - p_{n-2}\lambda^{n-2} - \ldots - p_0, \tag{2}$$

so that we are concerned with the zeros of a polynomial of degree n. The polynomial is referred to as the *characteristic polynomial* of A and the corresponding equation is called the *characteristic equation*. Since the latter is of degree n there are always n eigenvalues provided we take full account of multiple roots; the eigenvalues may be complex even when A is real.

Although the background theory, that of canonical forms, has been well known for many years, the determination of an accurate eigensystem, even for a matrix of modest order, remained a formidable problem until quite recently. Indeed, before the advent of electronic computers surprisingly few eigenvalue problems had been solved. Now the determination of the complete eigensystem of a matrix of order 50 (say) and the calculation of the *residual vectors*, that is of $A\mathbf{x} - \lambda\mathbf{x}$ for each λ and $\mathbf{x}$, takes of the order of one minute on a computer such as KDF9.

This tremendous advance is not entirely the result of the speed of modern computers. Since 1950 a remarkable number of algorithms have been developed and the best of them are far superior to those which were previously known. Only two algorithms which were known before 1950 are still in common use and although a very large number of eigenvalue problems have been solved at the National Physical Laboratory in the last two years, all of them have been treated using modern algorithms.

2*

2. A Typical Unstable Method

Before discussing the more satisfactory algorithms it will be instructive to consider a typical unsatisfactory algorithm and to expose the nature of its shortcomings. Since we are concerned with the zeros of a polynomial it is at first sight attractive to compute the characteristic polynomial explicitly. Although we know that the coefficient of λ^n in $\det(\lambda I - A)$ is unity we may write

$$\det(\lambda I - A) = \sum_{j=0}^{n} \lambda^j c_j \tag{3}$$

and we then have the relation $c_n = 1$ as a check.

If we evaluate $\det(\lambda I - A) = f(\lambda)$ for $n+1$ different values x_i of λ we have

$$\sum_{j=0}^{n} x_i^j c_j = f(x_i) \qquad (i = 1, \ldots, n+1). \tag{4}$$

This is a system of $n+1$ simultaneous linear equations for the coefficients c_j and, in theory, it enables us to calculate the characteristic polynomial. We may write the equations in the form

$$X\mathbf{c} = \mathbf{f} \quad \text{or} \quad \mathbf{c} = X^{-1}\mathbf{f}. \tag{5}$$

Now X is a Vandermonde matrix and the explicit form of its inverse is well known. Further, if we have an upper bound a for the moduli of the eigenvalues of A we can take as our x_i the $n+1$ equidistant points in the interval $(-a, a)$. Apart from column scaling factors the matrix X is then dependent only upon n, and X^{-1} can be computed accurately once and for all.

In order to assess the method an error analysis is required. There are two main stages in the analysis:

(i) Estimation of the errors in the computed coefficients c_i.

(ii) An analysis of the effect of the errors in c_i on the zeros of the polynomial.

A complete analysis of (i) is very difficult, but in fact this algorithm is so unstable that quite a superficial examination suffices to expose its limitations. Suppose we make the following extremely favourable assumptions:

(a) Each of the values $f(x_i)$ has been determined very accurately and is correct apart from the inevitable rounding error in its last figure. (In fact determinant evaluation *is* very accurate, although until comparatively recently it would probably have been thought that this would be the weakest link in the algorithm.)

(b) The elements of X^{-1} are known exactly as rational fractions.

If we denote the computed values of $f(x_i)$ by $\bar{f}_i$ and their true values by f_i, the computed coefficients $\bar{c}_i$ are given by

$$\bar{c}_i = \sum_j (X^{-1})_{ij} \bar{f}_j \quad \text{while} \quad c_i = \sum_j (X^{-1})_{ij} f_j. \tag{6}$$

In spite of these very favourable assumptions we find that for many quite innocuous looking distributions of eigenvalues the computed $\bar{c}_i$ have very high relative errors. This is because the individual $(X^{-1})_{ij} \bar{f}_j$ are often of much greater magnitudes than the sum; very extensive cancellation takes place when the $\bar{c}_i$ are computed so that the values obtained are determined almost entirely by the rounding errors in the $\bar{f}_j$.

We turn now to an analysis of (ii). This is important in a much wider context because a number of algorithms are designed to compute the characteristic polynomial explicitly. If λ_i is a simple zero of the characteristic polynomial it is easy to show that the effect of a perturbation δc_r in c_r is to give a perturbation $\delta\lambda_i$ such that

$$\delta\lambda_i \sim \delta c_r(\lambda_i)^r \Big/ \Big\{ c_n \prod_{j \neq i} (\lambda_i - \lambda_j) \Big\}. \tag{7}$$

Again we find that for many quite ordinary distributions of the λ_i the ratio $\delta\lambda_i/\delta c_r$ can be very large for some values of i and r. For example if $n = 20$ and $\lambda_i = i$

$$\delta\lambda_{16} \sim (0{\cdot}38)10^{15}\delta c_{15}/c_{15}, \tag{8}$$

so that an error of one part in 10^{10} in c_{15} changes λ_{16} completely.

Clearly any algorithm which depends on the calculation of the characteristic polynomial is likely to be unsatisfactory.

3. Condition of the Eigenvalue Problem

The discussion of the last section naturally leads to a consideration of the sensitivity of the eigenvalues of a matrix with respect to perturbations in its elements. This is obviously of fundamental practical importance since if the elements of A are derived experimentally they will be subject to errors of observation. Even if they are defined mathematically they may not be expressible exactly by numbers of the word length used by the computer, or we may find it difficult to evaluate them accurately.

We consider first the case when A is Hermitian, that is, $A = A^H$, where A^H is the complex conjugate transpose of A. The eigenvalues of a Hermitian matrix are always real. The most important case is when A is real in which case $A = A^T$, so that A is symmetric. In general we shall be interested in perturbation matrices which are also Hermitian and in this case the following theorems give us the required information.

If $C = A + B$ and A, B, C are Hermitian with eigenvalues $\alpha_i, \beta_i, \gamma_i$ respectively arranged in non-increasing order then

$$\alpha_i + \beta_n \leq \gamma_i \leq \alpha_i + \beta_1 \tag{9}$$

and

$$\sum_i (\gamma_i - \alpha_i)^2 \leq \sum_i \beta_i^2 = \sum_i \sum_j |b_{ij}|^2 = \|B\|_F^2, \tag{10}$$

where $\|B\|_F$ denotes the Frobenius norm of B.

The first theorem shows that when B is added to A all the eigenvalues of A are shifted by an amount which lies between the largest and smallest eigenvalue of B. This is a fairly simple consequence of the Courant-Fischer characterisation of the eigenvalues of Hermitian matrices. (See, for example, Courant and Hilbert 1953.) The second result, which is due to Hoffman and Wielandt (1953), may be expressed in the form

$$\Big(\sum (\gamma_i - \alpha_i)^2 / \sum \alpha_i^2 \Big)^{\frac{1}{2}} \leq \|B\|_F / \|A\|_F. \tag{11}$$

Both of these results are true whether B is small or not and independent of any multiplicities in the eigenvalues of A, B and C.

In practical applications B is the matrix of perturbations of A and if $|b_{ij}| \leq \varepsilon$ we have

$$-n\varepsilon \leq \beta_n \leq \beta_1 \leq n\varepsilon, \qquad (12)$$

giving $-n\varepsilon \leq \delta\lambda_i \leq n\varepsilon$.

With the same assumption the second theorem gives the stronger result

$$\left(\sum \delta\lambda_i^2\right)^{\frac{1}{2}} \leq n\varepsilon. \qquad (13)$$

These results imply that *the eigenvalue problem for a Hermitian matrix is always well-conditioned*, even when there are some multiple eigenvalues. If then we start with a Hermitian matrix having the eigenvalues $1, 2, \ldots, 20$ and derive its characteristic polynomial we are transforming a *well-conditioned* problem into an *ill-conditioned* problem.

For non-Hermitian matrices the effect of perturbations is far more complex. A detailed account is given by Wilkinson (1965). We give here the simplest and perhaps the most useful result.

It involves the eigensystem of A^T as well as that of A. Since $\det(\lambda I - A) = \det(\lambda I - A^T)$ the eigenvalues of A and A^T are the same, but the eigenvectors are in general different. If $A^T \mathbf{y} = \lambda \mathbf{y}$ we have $\mathbf{y}^T A = \lambda \mathbf{y}^T$ and for this reason the eigenvectors of A^T are usually called the *left-hand* eigenvectors of A while the usual vectors are called the *right-hand* eigenvectors.

Suppose λ_i is a simple eigenvalue of A and $\mathbf{x}_i$ and $\mathbf{y}_i$ are the corresponding right-hand and left-hand eigenvectors normalized so that their Euclidean lengths are unity. Then as B tends to the null matrix, $A+B$ has an eigenvalue $\lambda_i + \delta\lambda_i$ such that

$$\delta\lambda_i \sim \mathbf{y}_i^T B \mathbf{x}_i / \mathbf{y}_i^T \mathbf{x}_i. \qquad (14)$$

Notice that in contrast to the result for Hermitian matrices the relation (14) comes into evidence only when B is "small". From (14) we have

$$|\delta\lambda_i| \leq \|B\|_2 / |\mathbf{y}_i^T \mathbf{x}_i|. \qquad (15)$$

and $\mathbf{y}_i^T \mathbf{x}_i$ is the cosine of the angle θ_i between $\mathbf{y}_i$ and $\mathbf{x}_i$.

Unfortunately matrices can be constructed having simple eigenvalues for which the $\cos\theta_i$ are arbitrarily small and any such eigenvalue is very sensitive to perturbations in the elements. If A is Hermitian $\mathbf{y}_i = \bar{\mathbf{x}}_i$ so that $\mathbf{y}_i^T \mathbf{x}_i = \mathbf{x}_i^H \mathbf{x}_i = 1$, showing once again that the eigenvalues of a Hermitian matrix are well-conditioned. Notice though that if $\|B\|_2 = \varepsilon$ we have

$$|\delta\lambda_i| \leq \varepsilon / \cos\theta_i \qquad (16)$$

and the right-hand side is linear in ε. If λ_i is not a simple root the situation may be worse than this. For example, the matrix

$$\begin{bmatrix} a & 0 \\ 1 & a \end{bmatrix} \qquad (17)$$

has the repeated eigenvalue $\lambda = a$ while the matrix

$$\begin{bmatrix} a & \varepsilon \\ 1 & a \end{bmatrix} \qquad (18)$$

has the eigenvalues $a \pm \varepsilon^{\frac{1}{2}}$. The matrix (17) has a *non-linear elementary divisor* and is said to be *defective*. The multiple eigenvalues of defective matrices are always very sensitive.

If a given matrix A has a sensitive eigenvalue then it is unlikely that the latter can be determined accurately without working to high precision. On the other hand if an eigenvalue λ_i of A is well-conditioned, that is if $\cos \theta_i$ is not small, λ_i is well-determined and a *good algorithm should give accurate results*.

4. Condition of the Eigenvector Problem

The sensitivity of the eigenvectors of a matrix with respect to perturbations in its elements is a more complex problem than that of the eigenvalues. Even in the Hermitian case eigenvectors corresponding to close eigenvalues are very sensitive. This is not surprising because if a Hermitian matrix has a double eigenvalue it has two orthogonal corresponding eigenvectors. If $A\mathbf{x}_1 = \lambda\mathbf{x}_1$ and $A\mathbf{x}_2 = \lambda\mathbf{x}_2$ we have

$$A(\alpha\mathbf{x}_1 + \beta\mathbf{x}_2) = \lambda(\alpha\mathbf{x}_1 + \beta\mathbf{x}_2). \tag{19}$$

In this case the eigenvectors are not unique and any two orthogonal vectors in the subspace spanned by $\mathbf{x}_1$ and $\mathbf{x}_2$ serve equally well.

For a general matrix with distinct eigenvalues λ_i and normalized left-hand and right-hand vectors $\mathbf{x}_i$ and $\mathbf{y}_i$, the eigenvector $\mathbf{x}_i'$ of $A+B$ corresponding to $\mathbf{x}_i$ is such that as $\|B\| \to 0$

$$\mathbf{x}_i' - \mathbf{x}_i \sim \sum_{k \neq i} (\mathbf{y}_k^T B \mathbf{x}_i)\mathbf{x}_k / \{\mathbf{y}_k^T \mathbf{x}_k (\lambda_i - \lambda_k)\} = \sum_{k \neq i} (\mathbf{y}_k^T B \mathbf{x}_i)\mathbf{x}_k / \{(\lambda_i - \lambda_k)\cos\theta_k\}. \tag{20}$$

Again we see that the quantities $\cos \theta_k$ are important.

In the Hermitian case $\mathbf{y}_k = \bar{\mathbf{x}}_k$ and all the $\cos \theta_k$ are unity; the sensitivity of the eigenvector $\mathbf{x}_i$ is therefore dependent only on the proximity of λ_i to other eigenvalues. Notice that if λ_i is close to λ_{i+1} but well separated from the other eigenvalues, perturbations in A introduce an error in $\mathbf{x}_i$ which is mainly in the direction of $\mathbf{x}_{i+1}$. This means that if, for example, A has the eigenvalues 1, $1-10^{-10}$, 0·8, 0·6, 0·4 and we work to ten decimal places we can scarcely expect to find $\mathbf{x}_1$ and $\mathbf{x}_2$ at all accurately. We should, however, obtain two orthogonal vectors lying almost exactly in the space spanned by $\mathbf{x}_1$ and $\mathbf{x}_2$ and having only very small components in the direction of $\mathbf{x}_3, \mathbf{x}_4, \mathbf{x}_5$. The last three vectors should be determined accurately.

In the non-Hermitian case the factors $\cos \theta_k$ give an additional complication but if none of the $\cos \theta_k$ is small the behaviour is much the same as that of Hermitian matrices.

5. Similarity Transformations

If H is any non-singular matrix the eigenvalues of HAH^{-1} are the same as those of A since we have

$$\det(\lambda I - HAH^{-1}) = \det[H(\lambda I - A)H^{-1}] = \det(\lambda I - A). \tag{21}$$

Further if $A\mathbf{x} = \lambda\mathbf{x}$ we have $(HAH^{-1})H\mathbf{x} = \lambda H\mathbf{x}$ showing that $H\mathbf{x}$ is an eigenvector of HAH^{-1}. The matrix HAH^{-1} is called a *similarity transform* of A and HAH^{-1} is said to be *similar to A*.

The theory of canonical forms is concerned, among other things, with the reduction of A to a matrix of "simple form" by means of similarity transformations. These matrices of simple form are generally such that their eigensystems can be determined very simply. Hence the background theory is a useful source of algorithms for the solution of the eigenvalue problem.

Generally the reduction to the simplified form takes place progressively in a number of stages, each of which involves a similarity transformation. Thus renaming the original matrix $A^{(0)}$, a sequence of matrices $A^{(r)}$ is determined such that

$$A^{(r+1)} = H^{(r)} A^{(r)} (H^{(r)})^{-1}. \tag{22}$$

Usually zeros are introduced progressively at each stage until the final matrix $A^{(s)}$ is of the simplified form. The matrices $H^{(r)}$ of the transformations are themselves specialized and are usually referred to as "elementary" matrices. They are of two main classes, "unitary" and "non-unitary".

In the theoretical treatment we are not concerned with problems of numerical stability, but for practical algorithms this is of paramount importance. It is vital that the condition of the successive $A^{(r)}$ should not suffer a progressive deterioration. Now if x_i and y_i are right-hand and left-hand eigenvectors of A, the corresponding vectors for HAH^{-1} are Hx_i and $(H^{-1})^T y_i$, and if H is a unitary matrix these have the same Euclidean lengths as x_i and y_i. In any case we have

$$[(H^{-1})^T y_i]^T H x_i = y_i^T x_i. \tag{23}$$

We see therefore that the quantity $\cos \theta_i$ is preserved by unitary transformations so that the condition of the eigenvalues cannot deteriorate. When H is non-unitary Hx_i and $(H^{-1})^T y_i$ may be much larger than x_i and y_i respectively and there can be a serious deterioration in the condition.

When $A^{(0)}$ is Hermitian the incentive to use unitary transformations is even greater since this preserves the Hermitian property. Not only does this ensure numerical stability but we may work with the upper triangle only of $A^{(r)}$ at each stage, thereby halving the computation.

6. Elementary Unitary Matrices

Two main types of elementary unitary matrices are used in practice. The first type is called a *plane rotation*. For a rotation in the (p, q) plane the relevant matrix $R(p, q)$ is defined by the relations

$$\left. \begin{array}{ll} r_{pp} = e^{i\alpha} \cos \theta, & r_{pq} = e^{i\beta} \sin \theta \\ r_{qp} = -e^{-i\beta} \sin \theta, & r_{qq} = e^{-i\alpha} \cos \theta \\ r_{ij} = \delta_{ij} \quad \text{otherwise} \end{array} \right\} \tag{24}$$

Here δ_{ij} is the Kronecker symbol and α, β, θ are real. When α and β are zero the corresponding transformation is equivalent to a rotation through the angle θ in the (p, q) plane. We observe that the four critical elements may be expressed in the form

$$r_{pp} = \bar{x}/r, \quad r_{qq} = x/r, \quad r_{pq} = \bar{y}/r, \quad r_{qp} = -y/r, \quad \text{where } r = (|x|^2 + |y|^2)^{\frac{1}{2}}. \quad (25)$$

Pre-multiplication by $R(p, q)$ affects only rows p and q and post-multiplication affects columns p and q. In the pre-multiplication of a matrix A each column of A is treated independently; similarly in a post-multiplication each row is treated independently. In the pre-multiplication of a vector $\mathbf{x}$ by $R(p, q)$ only elements x_p and x_q are changed. If we take

$$r_{pp} = \bar{x}_p/r, \qquad r_{qq} = x_p/r, \qquad r_{pq} = \bar{x}_q/r, \qquad r_{qp} = -x_q/r \qquad (26)$$

where
$$r = (|x_p|^2 + |x_q|^2)^{\frac{1}{2}} \qquad (27)$$

and write $\mathbf{y} = R(p, q)\mathbf{x}$ we have

$$y_p = r, \qquad y_q = 0, \qquad y_i = x_i \quad \text{otherwise.} \qquad (28)$$

If $x_q = 0$ we can take $R(p, q)$ to be the identity matrix. Hence by means of a rotation in the (p, q) plane we can reduce the qth component of a vector to zero. Since each column of a matrix is treated independently we can choose $R(p, q)$ so that $B = R(p, q)A$ has its (q, k) element equal to zero. This is the basis of a considerable number of important algorithms.

The second type of elementary unitary matrix in general use is called an *elementary Hermitian matrix*. These matrices are of the form $P^{(r)}$ defined by

$$P^{(r)} = I - 2\mathbf{w}^{(r)}(\mathbf{w}^{(r)})^H, \qquad \text{where } \|\mathbf{w}^{(r)}\|_2 = 1 \qquad (29)$$

and
$$(\mathbf{w}^{(r)})^T = (0, \ldots, 0, w_{r+1}^{(r)}, \ldots, w_n^{(r)}). \qquad (30)$$

The matrix $P^{(r)}$ is Hermitian as well as unitary. When $\mathbf{w}^{(r)}$ is real $P^{(r)}$ is real, symmetric and orthogonal. Since

$$P^{(r)}A = A - 2\mathbf{w}^{(r)}(\mathbf{w}^{(r)})^H A \qquad (31)$$

we see that pre-multiplication by $P^{(r)}$ affects only rows $r+1$ to n and treats each column of A independently. Similar remarks apply to post-multiplication.

Given a vector $\mathbf{x}$ we can choose the elements $w_i^{(r)}$ in $\mathbf{w}^{(r)}$ in such a way that $P^{(r)}\mathbf{x}$ has zero components in positions $r+2, \ldots, n$. For this $P^{(r)}$ is best expressed in the form

$$P^{(r)} = I - \mathbf{u}^{(r)}(\mathbf{u}^{(r)})^H/H, \qquad (32)$$

where $\mathbf{u}^{(r)}$ is parallel to the appropriate $\mathbf{w}^{(r)}$ and

$$S^2 = |x_{r+1}^2| + \ldots + |x_n|^2, \qquad (33)$$

$$T = (|x_{r+1}|^2 S^2)^{\frac{1}{2}}, \qquad H = S^2 + T, \qquad (34)$$

$$(\mathbf{u}^{(r)})^T = (0, \ldots, 0, x_{r+1}(1 + S^2/T), x_{r+2}, \ldots, x_n). \qquad (35)$$

Notice that only one square root is involved. When $\mathbf{x}$ is real $\mathbf{u}^{(r)}$ is real and the relations are best expressed in the form

$$S^2 = x_{r+1}^2 + \ldots + x_n^2, \qquad H = S^2 + |x_{r+1}|S, \qquad (36)$$

$$(\mathbf{u}^{(r)})^T = (0, \ldots, 0, x_{r+1} \pm S, x_{r+2}, \ldots, x_n), \qquad (37)$$

where $\pm S$ is chosen to have the same sign as x_{r+1}. Notice that element $r+1$ of $P^{(r)}\mathbf{x}$ is given by $\mp S$.

Observe that we can achieve the same effect with $P^{(r)}$ as can be achieved by multiplying with $R(r+1, r+2)$, $R(r+1, r+3), \ldots, R(r+1, n)$ in succession. Since each column of A is treated independently in forming $P^{(r)}A$ we can choose $P^{(r)}$ so as to reduce elements $r+2, \ldots, n$ of any column of A to zero while leaving its first r elements unchanged. Again this is the basis of several important algorithms.

7. Elementary Non-Unitary Transformations

In the classical theory of canonical forms transformations involving non-unitary matrices are frequently used. We shall discuss only one elementary non-unitary matrix here and we shall denote it by $M^{(r)}$. This is defined by the relation

$$(M^{(r)})_{ir} = -m_{ir} \quad (i > r), \qquad (M^{(r)})_{ij} = \delta_{ij} \quad \text{otherwise.} \qquad (38)$$

Pre-multiplication of A with $M^{(r)}$ leaves the first r rows of A unaltered. For $i > r$ we replace row i by (row $i - m_{ir} \times$ row r). Post-multiplication by $M^{(r)}$ changes column r only, replacing it by (column $r - \sum\limits_{i=r+1}^{n} m_{ij} \times$ column i). The inverse of $M^{(r)}$ is a matrix of the same form but with the signs of the (i, r) elements $(i > r)$ changed.

The main weakness of transformations using this matrix is exposed if we consider the determination of an $M^{(r)}$ such that $M^{(r)}\mathbf{x}$ has zero components in positions $r+1, \ldots, n$. Clearly we have, in general,

$$m_{ir} = x_i/x_r \quad (i > r). \qquad (39)$$

This transformation breaks down if $x_r = 0$ and $x_i \neq 0$ for some i greater than r. We find that wherever an algorithm in the classical theory can break down as the result of the emergence of a transformation matrix with infinite elements there is a severe danger of the algorithm being numerically unstable in general.

In fact wherever x_r is small compared with any of the x_i the corresponding (m_{ir}) is very large. When a similarity transformation is performed using such an $M^{(r)}$ the rounding errors are very large and we find that the computed transformed matrix is not exactly similar to any matrix "close" to the original.

The danger of numerical instability may be very greatly reduced by a simple device usually referred to as *pivoting*. To describe this we introduce a simple orthogonal matrix denoted by $I^{(p,q)}$ and defined by the relations

$$I_{pp}^{(p,q)} = I_{qq}^{(p,q)} = 0, \qquad I_{pq}^{(p,q)} = I_{qp}^{(p,q)} = 1, \qquad I_{ij}^{(p,q)} = \delta_{ij} \quad \text{otherwise.} \qquad (40)$$

Pre-multiplication by $I^{(p,q)}$ interchanges rows p and q and post-multiplication interchanges columns p and q. Obviously we have

$$(I^{(p,q)})^{-1} = I^{(p,q)} = (I^{(p,q)})^T. \qquad (41)$$

We now reconsider the transformation of a vector $\mathbf{x}$ discussed above. Let r' be the smallest integer such that

$$|x_{r'}| = \max_{i \geq r} |x_i|. \tag{42}$$

If we define $\mathbf{z}$ by the relation $\mathbf{z} = I^{(r,r')}\mathbf{x}$ and choose $M^{(r)}$ so that $M^{(r)}\mathbf{z}$ has zero components in positions $r+1, \ldots, n$ we have

$$m_{ir} = z_i/z_r, \qquad |m_{ir}| \leq 1, \tag{43}$$

the inequality following from the choice of r'. If $x_{r'} = 0$ we take $M^{(r)}$ to be I. Hence if we use $M^{(r)}I^{(r,r')}$ instead of $M^{(r)}$ the danger of a breakdown is avoided and also all elements of $M^{(r)}$ are bounded. We refer to the combination $M^{(r)}$ and $I^{(r,r')}$ as a *stabilized elementary* matrix. The element $x_{r'}$ is referred to as a *pivotal* element and the process itself as *pivoting*.

In practice stabilized elementary matrices provide algorithms which are almost as stable as those based upon unitary matrices and are usually a good deal simpler, but unfortunately one cannot usually provide rigorous *a priori* error bounds when they are used.

8. Algorithms for Hermitian Matrices

The case for using unitary transformations is so strong when the matrix is Hermitian that algorithms of this kind are used in almost all cases except when A is very large and sparse. This last case is discussed briefly in §23. We shall describe detailed algorithms only for the case when A is real and symmetric but each of the algorithms extends immediately to the Hermitian case merely by using complex arithmetic. It is worth mentioning that the complex Hermitian case can be treated by a procedure designed for real symmetric matrices. If $A+iB$ is Hermitian with eigenvalues $\lambda_1, \ldots, \lambda_n$, the matrix C given by

$$C = \begin{bmatrix} A & -B \\ \hline B & A \end{bmatrix} \tag{44}$$

has the eigenvalues $\lambda_1, \lambda_1, \lambda_2, \lambda_2, \ldots, \lambda_n, \lambda_n$. If $(\mathbf{u} \mid \mathbf{v})$ is any eigenvector of C then $\mathbf{u}+i\mathbf{v}$ is an eigenvector of $A+iB$. However, it is more economical as regards speed and storage to treat $A+iB$ as a complex matrix provided one is prepared to write the program.

9. Jacobi's Method

The method of Jacobi (1846) is one of the few efficient methods which existed before 1950. It is based on the use of plane rotations, the original matrix $A^{(0)}$ being transformed into a sequence of matrices $A^{(r)}$ which tend to diagonal form as r tends to infinity.

Jacobi's original algorithm may be described as follows. Let $a_{pq}^{(r)}$ be the off-diagonal element of $A^{(r)}$ of maximum modulus. Then define $A^{(r+1)}$ by the relation

$$A^{(r+1)} = R(p, q)A^{(r)}(R(p, q))^T, \tag{45}$$

where $R(p, q)$ is a rotation in the (p, q) plane and the angle of the rotation is chosen so that $a_{pq}^{(r+1)} = 0$. Since we have

$$a_{pq}^{(r+1)} = (a_{qq}^{(r)} - a_{pp}^{(r)}) \cos \theta \sin \theta + a_{pq}^{(r)}(\cos^2 \theta - \sin^2 \theta) = a_{qp}^{(r+1)}, \qquad (46)$$

the angle of rotation must be chosen so that

$$\tan 2\theta = 2a_{pq}^{(r)}/(a_{pp}^{(r)} - a_{qq}^{(r)}). \qquad (47)$$

It is convenient to choose θ to be in the range $\left(-\dfrac{\pi}{4}, \dfrac{\pi}{4}\right)$ and if $a_{pp}^{(r)} - a^{(r)} = 0$ to take $\theta = \pm\dfrac{\pi}{4}$, the sign agreeing with that of $a_{pq}^{(r)}$. The remaining elements of $A^{(r+1)}$ are given by

$$a_{pp}^{(r+1)} = a_{pp}^{(r)} \cos^2 \theta + 2a_{pq}^{(r)} \cos \theta \sin \theta + a_{qq}^{(r)} \sin^2 \theta, \qquad (48)$$

$$a_{qq}^{(r+1)} = a_{pp}^{(r)} \sin^2 \theta - 2a_{pq}^{(r)} \cos \theta \sin \theta + a_{qq}^{(r)} \cos^2 \theta, \qquad (49)$$

$$\left. \begin{array}{l} a_{ip}^{(r+1)} = a_{ip}^{(r)} \cos \theta + a_{iq}^{(r)} \sin \theta = a_{pi}^{(r+1)} \\ a_{iq}^{(r+1)} = -a_{ip}^{(r)} \sin \theta + a_{iq}^{(r)} \cos \theta = a_{qi}^{(r+1)} \end{array} \right\}, \quad i \neq p, q. \qquad (50)$$

Only the elements in the upper triangle of each $A^{(r)}$ are computed.

The off-diagonal elements always tend to zero since if

$$S^{(r)} = \sum_{p \neq q} (a_{pq}^{(r)})^2$$

equations (50) show that

$$S^{(r+1)} = S^{(r)} - 2(a_{pq}^{(r)})^2, \qquad (51)$$

and as $a_{pq}^{(r)}$ is the maximum off-diagonal element

$$S^{(r+1)} \leq \left(1 - \frac{2}{n(n-1)}\right) S^{(r)} \quad \text{giving} \quad S^{(r+N)} < e^{-1} S^{(r)}, \quad N = \tfrac{1}{2}n(n-1). \quad (52)$$

The process is essentially iterative because an element reduced to zero in one step becomes non-zero again in later steps. It is terminated when the off-diagonal elements are negligible to working accuracy. It is convenient to refer to a set of N consecutive transformations as a "sweep". In practice it is rare for more than five sweeps to be necessary to reduce off-diagonal elements to less than 2^{-40} times their original values. It has been shown (Schönhage 1961, 1965) that the process is ultimately quadratically convergent in the sense that for sufficiently large r

$$S^{(r+N)} < K(S^{(r)})^2 \qquad (53)$$

for some constant K. This is true for all distributions of eigenvalues.

In practice the time taken to search for the largest off-diagonal element in the Jacobi process is time-consuming and it is faster to take the off-diagonal elements in the fixed order $(1, 2), (1, 3), \ldots, (1, n); (2, 3), \ldots, (2, n); \ldots;$ $(n-1, n)$; returning then to $(1, 2)$. (This is the origin of the term "sweep" for a set of N transformations.) This is called the *serial Jacobi* method and Henrici (1958) has shown that it is convergent, while Wilkinson (1962b, 1965) has shown that if there are no eigenvalues of multiplicities greater than two it is ultimately quadratically convergent.

A further improvement follows from the observation that $S^{(r)}$ is reduced by $2(a_{pq}^{(r)})^2$ in the rth step, where $a_{pq}^{(r)}$ is the element reduced to zero. There is little to be gained by annihilating any of the smaller off-diagonal elements and hence during each sweep only those elements greater than a prescribed threshold are treated, the threshold being reduced before each sweep. The *serial-threshold* variant is the one normally used; for discussions see Pope and Tompkins (1957) and Wilkinson (1965).

10. Methods of Givens and Householder

In Givens' method (1954) plane rotations are again used, but the aim is now to reduce $A^{(0)}$ to a symmetric tri-diagonal form rather than diagonal form. This can be done by means of $\frac{1}{2}(n-1)(n-2)$ plane rotations, the process being "direct" in contrast to the "iterative" Jacobi method. The zeros are introduced in pairs (because symmetry is maintained), the elements $(1, 3)$, $(1, 4), \ldots, (1, n)$; $(2, 4), \ldots, (2, n)$; $\ldots$; $(n-2, n)$ being annihilated by rotations in planes $(2, 3)$, $(2, 4), \ldots, (2, n)$; $(3, 4), \ldots, (3, n)$; $\ldots$; $(n-1, n)$ respectively. It will readily be verified that zeros introduced in any step are left unchanged by later transformations. If the rth rotation is in plane (p, q) and annihilates $a_{p-1, q}^{(r-1)}$ we have

$$\tan \theta = a_{p-1,q}^{(r-1)} / a_{p-1,p}^{(r-1)}, \tag{54}$$

the transformation being skipped if $a_{p-1, q}^{(r-1)}$ is already zero. The modified elements are given by

$$a_{p-1,p}^{(r)} = [(a_{p-1,p}^{(r-1)})^2 + (a_{p-1,q}^{(r-1)})^2]^{\frac{1}{2}}, \quad a_{p-1,q}^{(r)} = 0, \tag{55}$$

$$a_{pp}^{(r)} = a_{pp}^{(r-1)} \cos^2 \theta + 2a_{pq}^{(r-1)} \cos \theta \sin \theta + a_{qq}^{(r-1)} \sin^2 \theta, \tag{56}$$

$$a_{pq}^{(r)} = (a_{qq}^{(r-1)} - a_{pp}^{(r-1)}) \cos \theta \sin \theta + a_{pq}^{(r-1)}(\cos^2 \theta - \sin^2 \theta) = a_{qp}^{(r)}, \tag{57}$$

$$a_{qq}^{(r)} = a_{pp}^{(r-1)} \sin^2 \theta - 2a_{pq}^{(r-1)} \cos \theta \sin \theta + a_{qq}^{(r-1)} \cos^2 \theta, \tag{57a}$$

$$\left. \begin{aligned} a_{pi}^{(r)} &= a_{pi}^{(r-1)} \cos \theta + a_{qi}^{(r-1)} \sin \theta = a_{ip}^{(r)} \\ a_{qi}^{(r)} &= -a_{pi}^{(r-1)} \sin \theta + a_{qi}^{(r-1)} \cos \theta = a_{iq}^{(r)} \end{aligned} \right\}, \quad i > p \text{ and } \neq q. \tag{58}$$

Since the zeros persist the volume of work decreases as the reduction progresses. The complete Givens' reduction involves about $\frac{2}{3}$ of the amount of computation in one Jacobi sweep. We still have to compute the eigenvalues of the tri-diagonal matrix but this is quite economical as we show in §11.

In Householder's reduction (Householder and Bauer 1959) the matrix $A^{(0)}$ is reduced to tri-diagonal form by elementary Hermitians rather than plane rotations. The zeros in the rth row and column are introduced in one step by means of a transformation with matrix $P^{(r)}$. In terms of our discussion of §6 it is the rth column of $A^{(r-1)}$ which is the appropriate **x**. Writing $P^{(r)}$ in the form

$$P^{(r)} = I - \mathbf{u}^{(r)}(\mathbf{u}^{(r)})^T / H_r, \tag{59}$$

we have

$$S_r^2 = (a_{r+1,r}^{(r-1)})^2 + \ldots + (a_{nr}^{(r-1)})^2, \tag{60}$$

$$H_r = S_r^2 + |a_{r+1,r}^{(r-1)}| S_r, \tag{61}$$

$$(\mathbf{u}^{(r)})^T = (0, \ldots, 0, a_{r+1,r}^{(r-1)} \pm S_r, a_{r+2,r}^{(r-1)}, \ldots, a_{nr}^{(r-1)}). \tag{62}$$

In the calculation of $A^{(r)}$ it is important to take full advantage of symmetry. We have

$$A^{(r)} = P^{(r)}A^{(r-1)}P^{(r)}$$

$$= A^{(r-1)} - \mathbf{u}^{(r)}(\mathbf{p}^{(r)})^T - \mathbf{p}^{(r)}(\mathbf{u}^{(r)})^T + \alpha\mathbf{u}^{(r)}(\mathbf{u}^{(r)})^T/H_r, \qquad (63)$$

where

$$\mathbf{p}^{(r)} = A^{(r-1)}\mathbf{u}^{(r)}/H_r, \qquad \alpha = (\mathbf{u}^{(r)})^T\mathbf{p}^{(r)}. \qquad (64)$$

The vector $\mathbf{p}^{(r)}$ has its first $r-1$ components equal to zero. If we introduce $\mathbf{q}^{(r)}$ defined by

$$\mathbf{q}^{(r)} = \mathbf{p}^{(r)} - \tfrac{1}{2}\alpha\mathbf{u}^{(r)}/H_r \qquad (65)$$

we have

$$A^{(r)} = A^{(r-1)} - \mathbf{u}^{(r)}(\mathbf{q}^{(r)})^T - \mathbf{q}^{(r)}(\mathbf{u}^{(r)})^T \qquad (66)$$

and the symmetry of $A^{(r)}$ is immediately exposed.

Householder's reduction involves about half as many multiplications and divisions as that of Givens and only $n-2$ square roots against $\tfrac{1}{2}(n-2)(n-1)$ in Givens' method. It has the additional advantage that inner-products can be accumulated giving higher accuracy.

11. Eigenvalues of Symmetric Tri-Diagonal Matrices

To complete the Givens or Householder methods the eigenvalues of a symmetric tri-diagonal matrix C are required. This is an important problem in its own right since symmetric tri-diagonal matrices arise directly in many contexts. The method of Lanczos (1950) also gives rise to such matrices. It is convenient to write

$$c_{ii} = \alpha_i, \qquad c_{i,i+1} = c_{i+1,i} = \beta_{i+1}. \qquad (67)$$

There is a very accurate and convenient method due to Givens (1953, 1954) for finding the eigenvalues, which depends on the following theorem.

For any value λ the number of eigenvalues of C which are greater than λ is equal to the number $s(\lambda)$ of agreements in sign between consecutive members of the sequence of numbers $p_i(\lambda)$ $(i = 0, \ldots, n)$ given by the leading principal minors of $C - \lambda I$. The polynomials $p_i(\lambda)$ in fact form a *Sturm sequence*. The principal minors may be evaluated by the simple recurrence relations

$$p_0(\lambda) = 1, \qquad p_1(\lambda) = \alpha_1 - \lambda, \qquad (68)$$

$$p_r(\lambda) = (\alpha_r - \lambda)p_{r-1}(\lambda) - \beta_r^2 p_{r-2}(\lambda). \qquad (69)$$

This theorem enables us to compute any eigenvalue, the kth say, without computing any other. The method used is that of bisection. Suppose it is known that $s(a) \geq k$ and $s(b) < k$ so that λ_k is in the interval (a, b). The integer $s(\lambda)$ is then computed for $\lambda = \tfrac{1}{2}(a+b)$ from the Sturm sequence. If $s(\lambda) \geq k$ then λ_k is between $\tfrac{1}{2}(a+b)$ and b. Otherwise it is between a and $\tfrac{1}{2}(a+b)$. Continuing this process λ_k can be located in an interval of width

$2^{-p}(b-a)$ in p bisections. Since all the eigenvalues lie in the interval $(-x, x)$ where

$$x = \max_{i=2}^{n-1} [(|\alpha_1| + |\beta_2|), (|\beta_i| + |\alpha_i| + |\beta_{i+1}|), (|\beta_n| + |\alpha_n|)], \qquad (70)$$

initial values for a and b are readily computed.

This method is extremely stable. It has been shown by Wilkinson (1960) that using floating point arithmetic with t digits in the mantissa each eigenvalue can be determined with a maximum error of $4 \times 2^{-t} \max (|\alpha_i|, |\beta_i|)$. Notice that this bound is independent of n.

We have discussed the location of a single eigenvalue. In fact each evaluation of a Sturm sequence gives us information about all eigenvalues. If we take advantage of this all members of a group of multiplicity p are determined in the same time as that taken to find one isolated root. We have the unusual feature that coincident and pathologically close roots actually lead to an increase in speed. Givens (1954) has given a very detailed account of these points in his classical paper on the subject.

When there are severe clusters of eigenvalues the sequence $p_r(\lambda)$ may have some very small numbers for values of λ close to such eigenvalues. This does not affect the accuracy of the process unless the floating point exponent of the computer is inadequate. In this case the computer will probably replace the very small numbers by zeros and the sign determination will be incorrect. There is a simple modification of the process which avoids this danger of "underspill" (and the corresponding danger of "overspill"). If we write

$$q_r(\lambda) = p_r(\lambda)/p_{r-1}(\lambda), \qquad (71)$$

$$q_1(\lambda) = (\alpha_1 - \lambda), \qquad q_r(\lambda) = (\alpha_r - \lambda) - \beta_r^2/q_{r-1}(\lambda) \qquad (72)$$

we may work with the n values of $q_r(\lambda)$ rather than the $n+1$ values of $p_r(\lambda)$ and we have

$$s(\lambda) = \text{number of positive } q_r(\lambda). \qquad (73)$$

At first sight this looks dangerous since a $q_r(\lambda)$ may be zero. In fact when $q_{r-1}(\lambda)$ is zero we need only replace $-\beta_r^2/q_{r-1}(\lambda)$ by $-2^t\beta_r$ and the error analysis of Wilkinson (1960) is virtually unaltered. Overspill and underspill cannot occur with the $q_r(\lambda)$.

12. Reduction of a Matrix to Hessenberg Form

The development of a general purpose algorithm for non-Hermitian matrices presents severe difficulties. We have seen that in any case the eigenvalue problem can be almost arbitrarily ill-conditioned so that with computation of a prescribed precision we cannot expect to be able to solve all problems accurately even if we restrict ourselves to matrices of an order that can be accommodated by our computer. We present here the methods which experience has shown to be the most generally useful.

Several of the more satisfactory algorithms depend for their success on the initial similarity reduction of a general matrix A to a matrix H of Hessenberg form, that is to a matrix such that $h_{ij} = 0$ $(i > j+1)$. This comparatively modest reduction in the number of independent elements, from n^2 to $\frac{1}{2}(n^2 + 3n - 2)$, leads to a remarkable simplification in the eigenvalue problem. The reduction may be achieved by elementary unitary transformations or the stabilized non-unitary transformations.

13. Reduction using Stabilized Transformations

The reduction to Hessenberg form using stabilized transformations takes place in $n-2$ major steps in the rth of which the zeros are introduced in the rth column. Suppose at the beginning of the rth major step $A^{(0)}$ has been reduced to the form $A^{(r-1)}$, illustrated when $n = 6$, $r = 3$ by

$$
\begin{bmatrix}
X & X & X & X & X & X \\
X & X & X & X & X & X \\
  & X & X & X & X & X \\
  &   & X & X & X & X \\
  &   &   & X & X & X \\
  &   &   & X & X & X
\end{bmatrix},
\tag{74}
$$

so that $A^{(r-1)}$ is already of Hessenberg form in its first $r-1$ columns. The rth transformation is based on the rth column of $A^{(r-1)}$ and may be described as follows. (The name of each element is determined by its current position in the array.)

Let $(r+1)'$ be the smallest integer for which $|a^{(r-1)}_{(r+1)',\,r}| = \max\limits_{i > r} |a^{(r-1)}_{i,\,r}|$.

Interchange rows $(r+1)'$ and $(r+1)$ of $A^{(r-1)}$.

Pre-multiply the resulting matrix by $M^{(r+1)}$ where the relevant elements are defined by $m^{(r+1)}_{i,\,r+1} = a^{(r-1)}_{i,\,r}/a^{(r-1)}_{r+1,\,r}$ so that $|m^{(r+1)}_{i,\,r+1}| \leq 1$. This has the effect of subtracting $(m^{(r+1)}_{i,\,r+1} \times \text{row } (r+1))$ from row i for each value of i from $r+2$ to n.

Interchange columns $(r+1)'$ and $(r+1)$.

Post-multiply the resulting matrix by $(M^{(r+1)})^{-1}$. This has the effect of replacing column $(r+1)$ by column $(r+1) + \sum\limits_{i=r+2}^{n} m^{(r+1)}_{i,\,r+1} \times \text{column } (i)$.

The effect is to produce zeros in the appropriate elements of column r without destroying those in the first $r-1$ columns. A total of $\frac{5}{6}n^3$ additions and multiplications is involved. In general the process is remarkably stable. The effect of the pivoting is to re-order the rows and columns of $A^{(0)}$ by the same interchanges in such a way that with the re-ordering no multipliers of modulus greater than unity are required.

If we ignore the interchanges and denote the final Hessenberg matrix by H we have

$$
M^{(n-1)} \ldots M^{(3)} M^{(2)} A^{(0)} (M^{(2)})^{-1} (M^{(3)})^{-1} \ldots (M^{(n-1)})^{-1} = H, \tag{75}
$$

and if we write

$$
(M^{(2)})^{-1} \ldots (M^{(n-1)})^{-1} = M \tag{76}
$$

this becomes

$$
A^{(0)} M = MH \tag{77}
$$

where M is a unit lower-triangular matrix with its first column equal to that of the identity matrix. This decomposition can be achieved directly without deriving the intermediate matrices $A^{(r)}$. If we equate successive columns in equation (77) we find that equating the rth column enables us to determine the rth column of H and the $(r+1)$th column of M. In fact we have

$$
\left.
\begin{aligned}
a_{ir}+ \sum_{k=r+1}^{n} a_{ik}m_{kr} &= \sum_{k=2}^{i-1} m_{ik}h_{kr}+h_{ir} \quad (i = 1,\ldots,r+1) \\
&= \sum_{k=2}^{r+1} m_{ik}h_{kr} \quad\quad (i = r+2,\ldots,n)
\end{aligned}
\right\},
\tag{78}
$$

where the sum is zero if the upper limit is less than the lower limit. For $i = 1,\ldots,r+1$ the equations determine the h_{ir} and for $i = r+2,\ldots,n$ they determine the $m_{i,r+1}$. Notice that the h_{ir} are given directly in terms of two inner-products and the $m_{i,r+1}$ in terms of two inner-products divided by $h_{r+1,r}$. This is an advantage if inner-products can be accumulated.

Pivoting is essential for numerical stability and can best be described in terms of the array stored in the computer. The array stored at the beginning of the rth step is illustrated when $n = 6$, $r = 3$ by

$$
\begin{bmatrix}
h_{11} & h_{12} & a_{13} & a_{14} & a_{15} & a_{16} \\
h_{21} & h_{22} & a_{23} & a_{24} & a_{25} & a_{26} \\
m_{32} & h_{32} & a_{33} & a_{34} & a_{35} & a_{36} \\
m_{42} & m_{43} & a_{43} & a_{44} & a_{45} & a_{46} \\
m_{52} & m_{53} & a_{53} & a_{54} & a_{55} & a_{56} \\
m_{62} & m_{63} & a_{63} & a_{64} & a_{65} & a_{66}
\end{bmatrix}.
$$

The a_{ij} are elements of the original matrix but in general will have been subjected to interchanges in the earlier steps. The rth step is then as follows.

For each value of i from 1 to r compute h_{ir} defined by

$$
h_{ir} = a_{ir}+ \sum_{k=r+1}^{n} a_{ik}m_{kr} - \sum_{k=2}^{i-1} m_{ik}h_{kr}
\tag{79}
$$

and overwrite on a_{ir}.

For each value of i from $r+1$ to n compute s_i defined by

$$
s_i = a_{ir}+ \sum_{k=r+1}^{n} a_{ik}m_{kr} - \sum_{k=2}^{r} m_{ik}h_{kr}
\tag{80}
$$

and overwrite on a_{ir}.

Let $(r+1)'$ be the minimum integer for which $|s_{(r+1)'}| = \max_{i>r} |s_i|$. Then interchange rows $r+1$ and $(r+1)'$ and columns $r+1$ and $(r+1)'$. The element $s_{(r+1)'}$ is $h_{r+1,r}$ and is now in position $(r+1, r)$. For each value of i from $r+2$ to n compute $m_{i,r+1}$ defined by

$$
m_{i,r+1} = a_{ir}/a_{r+1,r}
\tag{81}
$$

and overwrite on a_{ir}. Note that $|m_{i,r+1}| \leq 1$.

Apart from rounding error this gives the same factorization and interchanges as the method using elementary stabilized matrices. The same number of multiplications and additions are involved in the two methods.

14. Unitary Reduction to Hessenberg Form

Givens (1958) has described a reduction to Hessenberg form using plane rotations and Householder and Bauer (1959) a reduction using elementary Hermitians. These are the exact analogues of those used for the reduction of a symmetric matrix to tri-diagonal form but since there is now no symmetry a zero introduced into position (i, j) does not simultaneously give a zero in position (j, i). We shall describe only the Householder reduction because it is needed for the QR algorithm and because in any case it is twice as efficient as the Givens reduction.

There are $n-2$ major steps in the rth of which the required zeros are introduced by means of a $P^{(r)}$ matrix in the rth column. The transformation is therefore based on the rth column of $A^{(r-1)}$ and if we write

$$P^{(r)} = I - \mathbf{u}^{(r)}(\mathbf{u}^{(r)})^T/H_r \qquad (82)$$

in the usual way, the elements of $\mathbf{u}^{(r)}$ and H_r are again defined by equations (60)–(62).

The computation of $A^{(r)}$ proceeds differently since there is now no symmetry. We write

$$B^{(r)} = P^{(r)}A^{(r-1)} = A^{(r-1)} - \mathbf{u}^{(r)}(\mathbf{p}^{(r)})^T/H_r, \qquad (83)$$

where

$$(\mathbf{p}^{(r)})^T = (\mathbf{u}^{(r)})^T A^{(r-1)} \qquad (84)$$

and has zero components in positions 1 to $r-1$. The matrix $A^{(r)}$ is then given by

$$A^{(r)} = P^{(r)}A^{(r-1)}P^{(r)} = B^{(r)}P^{(r)} = B^{(r)} - \mathbf{q}^{(r)}(\mathbf{u}^{(r)})^T/H_r, \qquad (85)$$

where

$$\mathbf{q}^{(r)} = B^{(r)}\mathbf{u}^{(r)}. \qquad (86)$$

In general $q^{(r)}$ has no zero components.

There are $\frac{5}{3}n^3$ multiplications and additions in this reduction compared with $\frac{10}{3}n^3$ in the Givens reduction and $\frac{5}{6}n^3$ in stabilized reduction or the equivalent direct reduction. Householder's reduction is superior to that of Givens in all respects but the choice between Householder's reduction and the direct reduction is more open. The Householder is a little safer in theory from the point of view of numerical stability since it can be shown that the computed H is always exactly similar to $A + \delta A$ where a small bound for δA can be guaranteed. For the stabilized reduction the rigorous bound for δA is rather large but this bound is unlikely to be approached in practice. On the contrary it is my experience that if inner-products can be accumulated the stabilized reduction is almost invariably slightly the more accurate and it is simpler and requires only half as much computation. On the whole I have preferred the stabilized reduction. For a detailed comparison see Wilkinson (1965).

15. Eigenvalues of Hessenberg Matrices

There are a number of methods for finding the eigenvalues of a Hessenberg matrix H which are based on the fact that det $(H - \lambda I)$ and its derivatives can be accurately evaluated by a very simple algorithm. The elements $h_{i+1,i}$ play a special role and it is convenient to rename them k_i. We observe that we may assume that no k_i is zero since otherwise H can be replaced by the direct sum of smaller Hessenberg matrices.

For any value of λ the determinant of $H - \lambda I$ is unaltered if multiples x_i of columns 1 to $n-1$ are added to the nth column. The x_i may be chosen so that the last column of the modified matrix is null except in the $(1, n)$ position. The relevant x_i are given by

$$k_{i-1}x_{i-1} + (h_{ii} - \lambda)x_i + h_{i,i+1}x_{i+1} + \ldots + h_{i,n-1}x_{n-1} + h_{in} = 0$$
$$(i = n, \ldots, 2). \quad (87)$$

The modified $(1, n)$ element is $f(\lambda)$ where

$$f(\lambda) = (h_{11} - \lambda)x_1 + h_{12}x_2 + \ldots + h_{1,n-1}x_{n-1} + h_{1n}. \quad (88)$$

Obviously we have

$$\det(H - \lambda I) = (-1)^{n-1}k_1 k_2 \ldots k_{n-1} f(\lambda), \quad (89)$$

so that the zeros of $\det(H - \lambda I)$ are those of $f(\lambda)$. This method of evaluation is due to Hyman (1957). The derivative of $f(\lambda)$ can be determined by differentiating the relations for x_i. We have for example

$$k_{i-1}x'_{i-1} + (h_{ii} - \lambda)x'_i + h_{i,i+1}x'_{i+1} + \ldots + h_{i,n-1}x'_{n-1} - x_i = 0, \quad (90)$$

where primes denote derivatives, and

$$f'(\lambda) = (h_{11} - \lambda)x'_1 + h_{12}x'_2 + \ldots + h_{1,n-1}x'_{n-1} - x_1. \quad (91)$$

Similar relations give the higher derivatives of $f(\lambda)$. This method of evaluation is extremely stable in spite of the fact that each x_i and its derivative are computed by dividing by k_i and this may be "small". It can be shown that the computed $f(\lambda)$ is always the exact value corresponding to some $H + \delta H$ where δH is very small for all relevant λ. If inner-products can be accumulated we have the remarkable result (Wilkinson 1963) that

$$|(\delta H)_{ij}| \leq 2^{-t}|H_{ij}|.$$

The simplest technique using Hyman's method of evaluation is based on successive linear interpolation and extrapolation. In this method starting from arbitrary z_1 and z_2 an eigenvalue is found as the limit point of the sequence z_r defined by

$$z_{r+1} = (f_r z_{r-1} - f_{r-1} z_r)/(f_r - f_{r-1}), \quad (92)$$

where $f_r = f(z_r)$, etc. Convergence to a simple eigenvalue λ is ultimately such that $|z_{r+1} - \lambda| \sim K|z_r - \lambda|^{1.62}$ for constant K. When s eigenvalues have been located $f(\lambda)$ is replaced by $f(\lambda)/\prod_{i=1}^{s}(\lambda - \lambda_i)$ in order to avoid converging to an eigenvalue which has already been found. A disadvantage of linear interpolation is that when H is real but has some complex eigenvalues, if z_1 and z_2 are real all subsequent z_r are real, and a complex eigenvalue cannot be located.

In the method of Muller (1956) successive quadratic interpolation replaces linear interpolation. Each eigenvalue is found as a limit of a sequence z_r, where z_{r+1} is determined by putting a quadratic in z through the points (z_r, f_r), (z_{r-1}, f_{r-1}), (z_{r-2}, f_{r-2}). The two possible values of z_{r+1} are given by

$$z_{r+1} = z_r - 2f_r/[p \pm (p^2 - 4f_r q)^{\frac{1}{2}}], \qquad (93)$$

where
$$p = f[z_r, z_{r-1}] + (z_r - z_{r-1}) f[z_r, z_{r-1}, z_{r-2}], \qquad (94)$$

$$q = f[z_r, z_{r-1}, z_{r-2}], \qquad (95)$$

using the usual notation for divided differences. The sign is chosen so that $|z_{r+1} - z_r|$ has the smaller value. Convergence to a simple root λ is ultimately such that $|z_{r+1} - \lambda| \sim K|z_r - \lambda|^{1.84}$. This method has the advantages that convergence "in the large" is better than with linear interpolation and complex roots may be determined starting from real z_1, z_2, z_3. Again $f(\lambda)$ is replaced by $f(\lambda)/\prod_{i=1}^{s}(\lambda - \lambda_i)$ when s roots have been determined.

16. Methods of Newton and Laguerre. Comparison of Methods

In the methods of Newton and Laguerre derivatives of $f(\lambda)$ are used in addition to function values. In the former an eigenvalue is found as the limit of the sequence z_r defined by

$$z_{r+1} = z_r - f_r/f_r'. \qquad (96)$$

Convergence to a simple root λ is ultimately such that $|z_{r+1} - \lambda| \sim K|z_r - \lambda|^2$. When λ is a root of multiplicity k convergence is merely linear, but with the modified formula

$$z_{r+1} = z_r - kf_r/f_r' \qquad (97)$$

convergence is again quadratic. Unfortunately the multiplicity must be inferred from iterates derived from the unmodified formula and the appropriate switch made. This presents considerable practical difficulties. When s roots have been found $g(\lambda)$ defined as $f(\lambda)/\prod_{i=1}^{s}(\lambda - \lambda_i)$ is used instead of $f(\lambda)$, and we have

$$g'/g = f'/f - \sum_{i=1}^{s} (\lambda - \lambda_i)^{-1}. \qquad (98)$$

In Laguerre's method the first two derivatives are used and the sequences of z_r are defined by the relations

$$\left. \begin{array}{l} z_{r+1} = z_r - nf_r/(f_r' \pm H_r^{\frac{1}{2}}) \\ H_r = (n-1)^2(f_r')^2 - n(n-1)f_r f_r'' \end{array} \right\}, \qquad (99)$$

where

the sign being chosen so that $z_{r+1} - z_r$ takes the smaller value. Convergence to a simple zero λ is ultimately such that $|z_{r+1} - \lambda| \sim K|z_r - \lambda|^3$. If λ is of multiplicity k convergence is merely linear but the modified formula

$$z_{r+1} = z_r - nf_r \bigg/ \left[f_r' + \left\{ \frac{n-k}{k}(n-1)(f_r')^2 - nf_r f_r'' \right\}^{\frac{1}{2}} \right] \qquad (100)$$

gives cubic convergence. Again, as with Newton's method, the multiplicity must be inferred from the iterates and the appropriate switch made. When s roots have been found we work with $g(\lambda)$ instead of $f(\lambda)$ and we have

$$(g'/g)^2 - g''/g = (f'/f)^2 - f''/f - \sum_{i=1}^{s} (\lambda - \lambda_i)^{-2}. \tag{101}$$

With Laguerre's method a complex zero of a real function may be located starting from a real z_1 but Newton's method gives a real sequence of z_r if z_1 is real.

Each of the methods we have discussed gives very accurate eigenvalues. Note the contrast with the superficially related unstable method of §2 which was also based on accurate determinant evaluations. The main danger in practice is the failure of a sequence to converge from arbitrary starting values. If all the eigenvalues are known to be real, convergence of linear interpolation is assured if we start with z_1 and z_2 larger than λ_1, the maximum eigenvalue. Convergence of Newton's method is assured if z_1 is greater than λ_1, while Laguerre's method has the remarkable property of converging if we start from any z_1.

The calculation of each derivative involves about as much work as the calculation of a function value. On this basis successive linear interpolation is more efficient than Newton's method and in my experience Muller's method is superior to both because of better convergence in the large. In spite of the fact that it uses two derivatives, Laguerre's method is much more effective than any of the others, the convergence in the large being remarkably impressive. A very detailed account of Laguerre's method has been given by Parlett (1964a). It includes discussions of the choice of starting values, criteria for terminating the iteration, the recognition of multiple eigenvalues, and scaling problems. Several of these points are of interest in a much wider context. A detailed comparison of algorithms based on Hyman's evaluation is given by Wilkinson (1965, Ch. 7).

17. The LR Algorithm

In 1955 Rutishauser introduced a new algorithm for the solution of the general eigenvalue problem. Starting from $A^{(1)}$ a sequence of similar matrices $A^{(s)}$ is produced, defined by the relations

$$A^{(s)} = L^{(s)} R^{(s)}, \qquad R^{(s)} L^{(s)} = A^{(s+1)}, \tag{102}$$

where $L^{(s)}$ is unit lower-triangular and $R^{(s)}$ is upper-triangular. Rutishauser (1958) showed first that if the $|\lambda_i|$ are distinct, $A^{(s)}$ tends to upper-triangular form and, in general, its diagonal elements are the λ_i in order of decreasing modulus. The proofs are based on the relations

$$A^{(s+1)} = (L^{(s)})^{-1} A^{(s)} L^{(s)}$$
$$= (L^{(1)} L^{(2)} \ldots L^{(s)})^{-1} A^{(1)} (L^{(1)} L^{(2)} \ldots L^{(s)}), \tag{103}$$
$$(L^{(1)} L^{(2)} \ldots L^{(s)})(R^{(s)} \ldots R^{(2)} R^{(1)}) = (A^{(1)})^s, \tag{104}$$

which are simple deductions from the definition of the $L^{(s)}$ and $R^{(s)}$. Coincident eigenvalues corresponding to linear divisors do not affect the convergence adversely but if there is a group of unequal eigenvalues $\lambda_r, \lambda_{r+1}, \ldots, \lambda_t$ of equal modulus, $A^{(s)}$ does not tend to upper triangular form as far as rows and columns r to t are concerned, but the matrix of order $t-r+1$ at their intersection has eigenvalues which tend to $\lambda_r, \ldots, \lambda_t$ respectively. The most important case is when $A^{(1)}$ is real but has a number of pairs of complex conjugate eigenvalues. Each such pair gives rise to a 2×2 diagonal matrix with eigenvalues tending to a complex conjugate pair. A detailed treatment of the convergence behaviour is given by Wilkinson (1965).

Rutishauser and others have produced a series of papers providing a progressive extension of the power of the LR algorithm and the following is a brief summary of the present position.

The convergence of the LR algorithm in its basic form is unsatisfactory since the sub-diagonal element of $A^{(s)}$ in the (i, j) position tends to zero as $(\lambda_i/\lambda_j)^s$ when $\lambda_i \neq \lambda_j$. (However, coincident eigenvalues do not give slow convergence.)

This weakness is overcome by using a modified form of the algorithm defined by

$$A^{(s)} - k^{(s)}I = L^{(s)}R^{(s)}, \qquad R^{(s)}L^{(s)} + k^{(s)}I = A^{(s+1)}, \qquad (105)$$

where $k^{(s)}$ is suitably chosen for each iteration. The matrices $A^{(i)}$ are still similar to $A^{(1)}$ but now the effect of the sth step is ultimately to reduce the (i, j) element in the ratio $(\lambda_i - k^{(s)})/(\lambda_j - k^{(s)})$. If $k^{(s)}$ can be chosen near to λ_n, the eigenvalue of smallest modulus, this means that all the sub-diagonal elements in the nth row will be greatly reduced in the sth iteration. However, if λ_n is a simple root $a_{nn}^{(s)}$ is tending to λ_n and hence ultimately $a_{nn}^{(s)}$ provides a good value of $k^{(s)}$.

The work involved in the factorization of $A^{(s)}$ when $A^{(1)}$ is a full matrix is very substantial, but if $A^{(1)}$ is of Hessenberg form the work required is far less and it may readily be verified that in this case all $A^{(s)}$ are of Hessenberg form. Hence in practice the use of the LR algorithm is always preceded by a reduction of the original matrix to Hessenberg form.

The only sub-diagonal elements in a Hessenberg matrix are those in the $(i+1, i)$ positions. When $a_{n, n-1}^{(s)}$ is negligible to working accuracy $a_{nn}^{(s)}$ may be accepted as an eigenvalue and the remaining eigenvalues are those of the leading principal submatrix of order $n-1$ of $A^{(s)}$. This submatrix is itself of Hessenberg form. The method therefore automatically provides a means of *deflating* the order of the matrix as the eigenvalues are found. If at any stage $a_{n-1, n-2}^{(s)}$ is negligible the eigenvalues of the 2×2 matrix in the bottom right-hand corner of $A^{(s)}$ are effectively eigenvalues of $A^{(s)}$ and the last two rows and columns may be discarded giving a *double deflation*.

The choice $k^{(s)} = a_{nn}^{(s)}$ is unsatisfactory when $A^{(1)}$ is real but has complex conjugate eigenvalues λ and $\bar{\lambda}$. In this case complex values of $k^{(s)}$ near to λ and $\bar{\lambda}$ are required. To deal with this we make a further modification. At each stage the roots of the 2×2 matrix at the bottom of $A^{(s)}$ are computed. If they are real then $k^{(s)}$ is taken to be that one which is nearer to $a_{nn}^{(s)}$. If they are complex conjugate and equal to p and $\bar{p}$ then two steps of LR are performed, one with $k^{(s+1)} = p$ and the next with $k^{(s+2)} = \bar{p}$.

In theory the final matrix should again be real but in practice this may not be so. There is an alternative method of doing two steps of LR which ensures that the final matrix is real (Wilkinson 1965), but this modification is unsatisfactory for reasons which we now discuss.

The main weakness of the LR algorithm is that it requires the LR factorization of a matrix. This may not exist and even if it does exist it may be numerically unstable. The LR factorization is important in the solution of linear equations and there instability is overcome by "pivoting". As a result of pivoting the factorization of A is replaced by that of PA where P is a permutation matrix.

The classical LR algorithm can be replaced by a modified version in which pivoting is used but this destroys the theoretical basis of the proof of convergence (Parlett 1964b, Wilkinson 1965). In practice the modified version converges well, but the lack of a supporting theory is disturbing and simple examples can be constructed for which convergence does not take place. More important, the process referred to in the last paragraph but one in which two steps are performed with complex conjugate values of $k^{(s)}$ completely loses its justification. Finally it has been my experience with large matrices that even when pivoting is used there can be a slow but steady loss of accuracy and over some 100–200 iterations this can be quite serious. These difficulties are overcome in a related algorithm which we now describe.

18. The QR Algorithm

The QR algorithm was developed by Francis and after a long experimental period was published in 1961, 1962. The same basic algorithm was also developed independently by Kublanovskaya (1961) but without many of the additional features which form an essential part of Francis' contribution. It is a natural analogue of the LR algorithm, the elementary non-unitary transformations involved in the latter being replaced by their unitary counterparts. The advantages of the unitary transformations are, however, more marked in this particular instance than is usually the case and these advantages were brilliantly exploited by Francis. The basic algorithm is defined by the relations

$$A^{(s)} = Q^{(s)}R^{(s)}, \qquad R^{(s)}Q^{(s)} = A^{(s+1)}, \qquad (106)$$

where $Q^{(s)}$ is a unitary matrix and $R^{(s)}$ is upper-triangular. The behaviour is closely related to that of the LR algorithm, the $A^{(s)}$ tending to upper-triangular form with λ_i on the diagonal in the case when the $|\lambda_i|$ are distinct. The super-diagonal elements of $A^{(s)}$ do not necessarily tend to a strict limit, but may change from one iteration to the next by a factor which is ultimately of modulus unity; since the diagonal elements are the main concern and these *do* tend to a limit this is not an important point. We shall say that $A^{(s)}$ tends "essentially" to a fixed upper-triangular matrix when the $|\lambda_i|$ are distinct. There are no cases of breakdown or numerical instability such as were met in the LR algorithm.

Multiple eigenvalues corresponding to linear divisors do not affect the convergence adversely but corresponding to a group of unequal λ_i of the same modulus we have diagonal blocks in the limiting form analogous to those discussed with the LR algorithm.

Again shifts of origin may be used giving the algorithm

$$A^{(s)} - k^{(s)}I = Q^{(s)}R^{(s)}, \qquad R^{(s)}Q^{(s)} + k^{(s)}I = A^{(s+1)}, \qquad (107)$$

and the $k^{(s)}$ may be determined from the 2×2 matrix in the bottom right-hand corner of $A^{(s)}$.

When $A^{(1)}$ is real and it is known that all eigenvalues are real the QR algorithm can be used in a fairly straightforward manner. In practice we do not actually factorize $A^{(s)} - k^{(s)}I$ into $Q^{(s)}$ and $R^{(s)}$ but rather we determine $(Q^{(s)})^H$ such that

$$(Q^{(s)})^H(A^{(s)} - k^{(s)}I) = R^{(s)}. \qquad (108)$$

Further the matrix $Q^{(s)}$ is determined as a produce of elementary unitary transformations and is not computed explicitly.

Basically then the requirement is "Given a matrix B (say), to determine a unitary matrix Q such that $QB = R$ is upper triangular". Such a Q may be determined as the product of $n-1$ elementary Hermitian matrices of types $P^{(0)}, P^{(1)}, \ldots, P^{(n-2)}$ defined in (29), (30), the zeros in B being introduced column by column. Those in the rth column result from a pre-multiplication by an appropriate $P^{(r-1)}$, which is itself determined from the current rth column of the transformed B matrix. We shall not describe the process in more detail because we shall never require it for a full matrix B.

If the factors of $(Q^{(s)})^H$ determined by $A^{(s)} - k^{(s)}I$ are $P^{(0)}, P^{(1)}, \ldots, P^{(n-2)}$ then

$$A^{(s+1)} = R^{(s)}P^{(0)}P^{(1)} \ldots P^{(n-2)} + k^{(s)}I. \qquad (109)$$

As with the LR algorithm we first reduce the original matrix A to a matrix $A^{(1)}$ of Hessenberg form. In this case all the $A^{(s)}$ produced by the QR algorithm are also of Hessenberg form and the factorization of $A^{(s)}$ is very much simpler. We find in fact that plane rotations of types $R(1, 2), R(2, 3) \ldots R(n-1, n)$ defined in §6 can be determined so that

$$R(n-1, n) \ldots R(1, 2)(A^{(s)} - k^{(s)}I) = R^{(s)}. \qquad (110)$$

In other words $(Q^{(s)})^H$ is so simple in this case that it can be produced by $n-1$ plane rotations instead of $n-1$ elementary Hermitians. This is immediately apparent since in reducing $A^{(s)} - k^{(s)}I$ to $R^{(s)}$ there is only one non-zero sub-diagonal element in each column to be treated. We have therefore

$$A^{(s+1)} = R^{(s)}(R(1, 2))^T \ldots (R(n-1, n))^T + k^{(s)}I. \qquad (111)$$

Only $4n^2$ multiplications and additions and $n-1$ square roots are involved in a QR step.

In the case when all roots of A are real the algorithm is therefore as follows.

(i) Reduce A to Hessenberg form $A^{(1)}$ by the direct process.

(ii) Perform the QR algorithm on $A^{(1)}$ using at each stage a shift of origin $k^{(s)}$ determined from the eigenvalues $p^{(s)}$ and $q^{(s)}$ of the bottom 2×2 sub-matrix of $A^{(s)}$. If $p^{(s)}$ and $q^{(s)}$ are real, take $k^{(s)}$ to be $p^{(s)}$ or $q^{(s)}$ according as

$|p^{(s)} - a_{nn}^{(s)}|$ or $|q^{(s)} - a_{nn}^{(s)}|$ is the smaller. Otherwise take $k^{(s)}$ to be the real part of $p^{(s)}$.

(iii) When $a_{n,n-1}^{(s)}$ is negligible to working accuracy, accept $a_{nn}^{(s)}$ as an eigenvalue, omit row n and column n of $A^{(s)}$ and continue. The average number of iterations per eigenvalue is remarkably low in practice, in my experience of the order of 2, and it should be remembered that because of deflation we are working with matrices of progressively decreasing orders.

If the original matrix A is symmetric then we can reduce it to symmetric tri-diagonal form by Householder's method (§10), the latter form being a special case of Hessenberg form. Now it is easy to see that the QR algorithm preserves symmetry since

$$A^{(s+1)} = (Q^{(s)})^H A^{(s)} Q^{(s)}. \tag{112}$$

Hence if $A^{(1)}$ is symmetric and tri-diagonal, since the QR algorithm preserves the Hessenberg form it must preserve the symmetric tri-diagonal form. The volume of work is therefore enormously reduced and the QR algorithm with shifts gives a very effective method of completing the symmetric eigenvalue problem.

19. Francis' Double QR Algorithm

In general if A is real and non-Hermitian it will have some complex conjugate eigenvalues. Hence inevitably complex values of $k^{(s)}$ will be required. If two successive steps with shifts k and $\bar{k}$ were performed exactly the final matrix would be real, but although the QR algorithm is very stable in that it preserves eigenvalues accurately, rounding errors may prevent the final matrix from having a negligible imaginary part. (For a discussion see Wilkinson 1965.) Francis has described a remarkably effective procedure for performing two such steps without leaving the real field.

Let us denote the original Hessenberg matrix by A (ignoring its upper suffix) and suppose that two steps with shifts k and $\bar{k}$ are described by the relations

$$A - kI = Q_1 R_1, \qquad R_1 Q_1 + kI = A_2, \tag{113}$$

$$A_2 - \bar{k}I = Q_2 R_2, \qquad R_2 Q_2 + \bar{k}I = A_3. \tag{114}$$

Then it can be shown that

$$A_3 = (Q_1 Q_2)^H A(Q_1 Q_2) \quad \text{and} \quad (Q_1 Q_2)(R_2 R_1) = (A - kI)(A - \bar{k}I). \tag{115}$$

The matrices Q_1, Q_2, R_1, R_2 will be complex but if we write $Q_1 Q_2 = Q$, $R_2 R_1 = R$, Q and R are real since they correspond to the factorization of the real matrix $(A - kI)(A - \bar{k}I)$. Hence $A_3 = Q^H A Q$ is also real. Francis effectively determines Q in factorized form and A_3 without computing Q_1, R_1, Q_2, R_2 or A_2. His method is based on the theorem that if

$$A\tilde{Q} = \tilde{Q}H, \tag{116}$$

where H is of Hessenberg form, and $\tilde{Q}$ is orthogonal and has the same first column as Q, then $\tilde{Q} = Q$ and $H = A_3$. Francis' algorithm therefore derives a Hessenberg matrix H from A via an orthogonal $\bar{Q}$ and merely ensures that $\bar{Q}$ has the same first column as Q. This guarantees that H is in fact A_3.

The correct Q is the orthogonal matrix such that

$$QR = (A-kI)(A-\bar{k}I) \quad \text{or} \quad R = Q^T(A-kI)(A-\bar{k}I). \tag{117}$$

We are interested in the first column of Q, that is the first row of Q^T. Now Q^T can be derived as a product $P^{(n-2)}\ldots P^{(0)}$ of elementary Hermitian matrices and it is easy to see that the first row of $P^{(n-2)}\ldots P^{(0)}$ is the first row of the single factor $P^{(0)}$. But $P^{(0)}$ is the matrix that introduces zeros into the first column when triangularizing the real matrix $(A-kI)(A-\bar{k}I)$ and it is determined solely by the first column of the latter matrix. This column is of the form

$$(x_0, y_0, z_0, 0, \ldots, 0), \tag{118}$$

where

$$\left.\begin{aligned} x_0 &= (a_{11}-k)(a_{11}-\bar{k})+a_{12}a_{21} = a_{11}^2 - a_{11}(k+\bar{k})+k\bar{k}+a_{12}a_{21} \\ y_0 &= a_{21}(a_{11}+a_{22}-k-\bar{k}) \\ z_0 &= a_{32}a_{21} \end{aligned}\right\}. \tag{119}$$

Because this first column is of special form the appropriate $P^{(0)} = I - 2w^{(0)} \times (w^{(0)})^T$ has only three non-zero elements in $w^{(0)}$, these being the first three.

Consider now the matrix $P^{(0)}AP^{(0)}$. We know that *any* matrix may be reduced to Hessenberg form using unitary similarity transformations. Householder's method (§14) in fact performs this reduction using matrices of type $P^{(1)}, P^{(2)}, \ldots, P^{(n-2)}$ respectively. (These $P^{(i)}$ are not those arising in the reduction of $(A-kI)(A-\bar{k}I)$ to upper-triangular form.) Hence applying Householder's process to $P^{(0)}AP^{(0)}$ we have

$$P^{(n-2)}\ldots P^{(1)}(P^{(0)}AP^{(0)})P^{(1)}\ldots P^{(n-2)} = H \tag{120}$$

for some Hessenberg matrix H. All the $P^{(r)}$ are, of course, real since no complex numbers are used anywhere, and we have finally

$$P^{(n-2)}\ldots P^{(0)}A = HP^{(n-2)}\ldots P^{(0)}. \tag{121}$$

Now the first row of $P^{(n-2)}\ldots P^{(0)}$ is the first row of $P^{(0)}$ which is itself the first row of Q^T as we have already shown. Therefore H is the matrix A_3 obtained by two steps of the QR algorithm.

20. Practical Details of the Double QR Method

Because the vector $w^{(0)}$ associated with $P^{(0)}$ has only three non-zero elements the matrix $P^{(0)}AP^{(0)}$ is still almost in Hessenberg form. In fact it is of the form illustrated when $n = 7$ by

$$\begin{bmatrix} X & X & X & X & X & X & X \\ X & X & X & X & X & X & X \\ X & X & X & X & X & X & X \\ X & X & X & X & X & X & X \\ & & & X & X & X & X \\ & & & & X & X & X \\ & & & & & X & X \end{bmatrix}. \tag{122}$$

Consequently the Householder reduction of $P^{(0)}AP^{(0)}$ to Hessenberg form is much simpler than that of a general matrix. In general we find that just before the rth stage of the reduction the matrix is of the form illustrated when $n = 8$, $r = 3$ by

$$
\begin{bmatrix}
X & X & X & X & X & X & X & X \\
X & X & X & X & X & X & X & X \\
  & X & X & X & X & X & X & X \\
  &   & x_r & X & X & X & X & X \\
  &   & y_r & X & X & X & X & X \\
  &   & z_r & p_r & X & X & X & X \\
  &   &   &   & & X & X & X \\
  &   &   &   & & & X & X
\end{bmatrix}. \tag{123}
$$

Apart from the three elements indicated by y_r, z_r, p_r the matrix is in Hessenberg form. Hence the $P^{(r)}$ used in the Householder reduction of $P^{(0)}AP^{(0)}$ has an associated vector $\mathbf{w}^{(r)}$ which has only three non-zero components, these being in positions $r+1, r+2, r+3$. Only $8n^2$ *real* multiplications are involved in the Francis double QR step, though this performs the equivalent of two ordinary QR steps requiring complex arithmetic. The non-zero elements of $\mathbf{w}^{(r)}$ are determined by the elements marked x_r, y_r, z_r and are given by the same formulae as those used to derive $\mathbf{w}^{(0)}$ from x_0, y_0, z_0. The first step of the Francis QR algorithm, the derivation of $P^{(0)}$ and the computation of $P^{(0)}AP^{(0)}$ is therefore of exactly the same form as the remaining steps. Once x_0, y_0, z_0 have been determined the whole process is uniform.

The motivation for the double QR algorithm came from the need to deal efficiently with complex conjugate shifts. But if λ and $\bar{\lambda}$ are both real the process is, of course, unaltered.

A complete step of the double QR algorithm is therefore as follows.

(i) The sum $\lambda + \bar{\lambda}$ and product $\lambda\bar{\lambda}$ of the eigenvalues of the 2×2 submatrix at the bottom of $A^{(s)}$ are determined.

(ii) The quantities x_0, y_0, z_0 are computed and used to determine $P^{(0)}$ and $P^{(0)}A^{(s)}P^{(0)}$.

(iii) $P^{(0)}A^{(s)}P^{(0)}$ is reduced to Hessenberg form using Householder's method, taking full advantage of its special form.

At the end of each step $a_{n,n-1}^{(s)}$ is examined. If it is negligible, $a_{nn}^{(s)}$ is accepted as an eigenvalue and the last row and column are deleted. If $a_{n-1,n-2}^{(s)}$ is negligible the eigenvalues of the bottom 2×2 submatrix are accepted as eigenvalues of $A^{(s)}$ and the last two rows and columns deleted. One or two other important techniques for improving the speed are described by Francis (1961, 1962) and these and some further points are elaborated by Wilkinson (1965). The speed of convergence attained in practice is quite phenomenal; for the matrices dealt with at the National Physical Laboratory to date the average number of iterations is about 1·6 per eigenvalue!

21. Further Reduction of a Hessenberg Matrix

A matrix of Hessenberg form may be reduced to tri-diagonal form using *non-stabilized* elementary matrices (Strachey and Francis 1961). No simple reduction exists using stabilized elementary matrices or unitary matrices. We consider first the reduction of a *lower-Hessenberg* matrix H, that is, of one for which $h_{ij} = 0$ ($j > i+1$). (All the Hessenberg matrices we have considered so far are of *upper Hessenberg* form.)

In fact if we apply the first method of §13 to a lower Hessenberg matrix and *omit* the interchanges we find that it gives a tri-diagonal matrix. The form of the matrix at the beginning of the rth step is illustrated when $n = 6$, $r = 3$ by the array

$$\begin{bmatrix} X & X & & & & \\ X & X & X & & & \\ 0 & X & X & X & & \\ 0 & 0 & X & X & X & \\ 0 & 0 & X & X & X & X \\ 0 & 0 & X & X & X & X \end{bmatrix}. \tag{124}$$

The matrix $M^{(r+1)}$ of the rth transformation is determined by the rth column of this array but *pivoting cannot be used* or the pattern of zeros above the diagonal will be destroyed. In this step multiples of the rth row are taken from rows $r+1$ to n and at this stage the rth row has only three non-zero elements. The similarity transformation is completed by adding multiples of each of columns $r+2$ to n to column $r+1$. Note that column i has only $n+2-i$ non-zero elements.

The complete reduction from Hessenberg form to tri-diagonal form involves only $n^3/6$ multiplications but since pivoting cannot be used the process can be unstable or even break down. The nature of the instability has been analyzed in detail by Wilkinson (1962a). We therefore have a two-stage reduction of a matrix A to tri-diagonal form. It is first reduced to upper-Hessenberg form H using stabilized elementary transformations. The lower-Hessenberg matrix H^T is then reduced to tri-diagonal form using the same process but no stabilization, and taking advantage of the Hessenberg form. To minimize the potential instability of the second half of the reduction it should be performed to higher precision than the first.

This reduction to tri-diagonal form is related to the Lanczos algorithm (see, for example, Strachey and Francis 1961) but is much more economical.

An upper Hessenberg matrix H can be reduced to the Frobenius canonical form by non-stabilized elementary transformations but not by the stabilized variants or by unitary transformations. However, it is simpler and just as accurate to pass directly from H to the polynomial form by means of the recurrence relations between leading principal minors $p_r(\lambda)$ of $H - \lambda I$. Writing $p_0(\lambda) = 1$ we have

$$p_r(\lambda) = (h_{rr} - \lambda)p_{r-1}(\lambda) - k_{r-1}h_{r-1,r}p_{r-2}(\lambda) + k_{r-1}k_{r-2}h_{r-2,r}p_{r-3}(\lambda) - \cdots$$
$$\cdots (-1)^{r-1}k_{r-1}k_{r-2}\ldots k_1 h_{1r}p_0(\lambda), \tag{125}$$

each polynomial being determined explicitly. There are $n^3/6$ multiplications and additions involved here but because of the sensitivity of the explicit polynomial form the calculation should be performed to higher precision than the preceding reduction to H. On the whole this reduction is more dangerous from the point of view of numerical stability than that to tri-diagonal form.

22. Eberlein's Method

The method of Jacobi is based on the fact that any Hermitian matrix can be reduced by a unitary transformation to a real diagonal matrix. This method may be extended to cover all normal matrices, that is matrices which are unitarily similar to real *or complex* diagonal matrices. As far as general matrices are concerned a theorem of Schur shows that every matrix is unitarily similar to a triangular matrix and the natural extension of Jacobi's method would be to attempt to reduce a general matrix to such a form by a sequence of plane rotations. Algorithms based on this idea have been con-spicuously unsuccessful.

Eberlein (1962) has described a related method which is based on the theorem that for any matrix A there exists a non-singular P such that $P^{-1}AP$ is arbitrarily close to a normal matrix and that inf $\|P^{-1}AP\|_F = \sum_i |\lambda_i|^2$.

The class of normal matrices includes all unitary and Hermitian matrices and has the advantage that its eigenvalue problem is always well conditioned. (In fact the original theorem of Hoffman and Wielandt (equation (10)) applies to all normal matrices and not merely to Hermitian matrices.) A normal matrix is characterized by the fact that $AA^H - A^H A = 0$.

In the classical Jacobi process each plane rotation is chosen so as to minimize the sum of the squares of off-diagonal elements. Eberlein uses elementary 2×2 matrices P defined by

$$\left.\begin{array}{ll} p_{kk} = e^{-i\beta}\cos z, & p_{km} = e^{-i\alpha}\sin z \\ p_{mk} = e^{-i\alpha}\sin z, & p_{mm} = e^{i\beta}\cos z \\ \multicolumn{2}{c}{p_{ij} = \delta_{ij} \quad \text{otherwise}} \end{array}\right\} \qquad (125a)$$

where α, β are real and z is complex. A natural extension of the Jacobi technique is to choose the transformation P_s at the sth stage so as to minimize $\|P_s^{-1}A^{(s-1)}P_s\|_F^2$. The determination of such a P_s is very tedious but Eberlein found a simpler modification of the procedure which actually reduces to the Jacobi process when A is Hermitian, and has the advantage of producing in the real case a limiting matrix which, in general, is partly diagonal and partly block diagonal with 2×2 diagonal blocks of the form

$$\begin{bmatrix} a_{ii} & a_{ij} \\ -a_{ij} & a_{ii} \end{bmatrix}.$$

For the details of this process the reader is referred to the original paper by Eberlein (1962). Eberlein's method, like Jacobi's, has the advantage of using one uniform program which gives both the eigenvalues and eigenvectors.

The indications are that it performs well but no complete error analysis exists. The final matrix is normal to working accuracy and therefore well-conditioned even if A is ill-conditioned, but it is possible (though perhaps unlikely since we are aiming at normality throughout) that in the early stages of the process $A^{(r)}$ are obtained which are more ill-conditioned than the original A.

23. The Power Method

When the original matrix A is of high order but very sparse there is much to be gained by working throughout with A itself if possible. This is the principal merit of the power method, one of the few methods used before 1950 which still has an important range of application. It is based on the observation that if A is not defective and has eigenvalues λ_i and normalized eigenvectors x_i an arbitrary vector $u^{(0)}$ may be expressed in the form

$$u^{(0)} = \sum \alpha_i x_i. \tag{126}$$

Hence
$$u^{(r)} = A^r u^{(0)} = \sum \alpha_i \lambda_i^r x_i, \tag{127}$$

and the sequence of $u^{(r)}$ may be determined from the relations

$$u^{(s+1)} = A u^{(s)}. \tag{128}$$

If the $|\lambda_i|$ are in decreasing order then

$$u^{(r)} = \lambda_1^r [\alpha_1 x_1 + \sum_2^n \alpha_i (\lambda_i/\lambda_1)^r x_i], \tag{129}$$

and if $|\lambda_1| > |\lambda_2|$

$$u^{(r)} \sim \lambda_1^r \alpha_1 x_1. \tag{130}$$

Since we are not interested in constant multipliers we can normalize each $u^{(r)}$ as we proceed and ultimately we obtain the normalized x_1.

The speed of convergence depends on the speed at which $(\lambda_2/\lambda_1)^r \to 0$. If $|\lambda_2|$ is close to $|\lambda_1|$ this may be slow. Many stratagems have been devised for accelerating convergence. The simplest is based on iterating with $A - k^{(r)}I$ at each stage rather than A itself. If the $k^{(r)}$ are chosen suitably the speed of convergence may be improved since $A - k^{(r)}I$ has the eigenvalues $\lambda_i - k^{(r)}$. We shall not discuss the other stratagems in detail but refer to the paper by Wilkinson (1954).

24. Inverse Iteration

The speed of convergence attainable with the classical power method is somewhat limited in practice though it is still a useful method for very large sparse matrices when a few dominant eigenvalues are wanted and these are not too close to each other. There is an important variant of the method, however, in which one iterates with $(A - pI)^{-1}$ for some value of p. We may express this in the form

$$u^{(s+1)} = (A - pI)^{-1} u^{(s)}, \quad \text{or} \quad (A - pI) u^{(s+1)} = u^{(s)}. \tag{131}$$

Hence $u^{(s+1)}$ may be found from $u^{(s)}$ by solving a system of equations with matrix $(A - pI)$.

Now the eigenvalues of $(A-pI)^{-1}$ are $(\lambda_i-p)^{-1}$. If p is "close" to λ_k but not to any other eigenvalue, $(\lambda_k-p)^{-1}$ is much larger than the other eigenvalues and hence iteration with $(A-pI)^{-1}$ gives rapid convergence to $\mathbf{x}_k$ since this is the corresponding eigenvector of $(A-pI)^{-1}$ as well as that of A. This method was first proposed by Wielandt (1944) and is usually called Wielandt iteration or inverse iteration.

To iterate with $(A-pI)^{-1}$, we are effectively solving systems of equations with matrix of coefficients $A-pI$, but with a succession of right-hand sides. If we have the triangular factorization LR of $A-pI$ then we may express the relevant equations in the form

$$LR\mathbf{u}^{(s+1)} = \mathbf{u}^{(s)}, \tag{132}$$

and these may be solved at each stage by a forward substitution followed by a back-substitution. For stability pivoting is used so that we have a permutation matrix P such that

$$P(A-pI) = LR. \tag{133}$$

The iteration therefore requires the solution of the systems

$$LR\mathbf{u}^{(s+1)} = P\mathbf{u}^{(s)} \tag{134}$$

and $P\mathbf{u}^{(s)}$ is merely $\mathbf{u}^{(s)}$ with the order of its elements permuted.

Suppose we have computed an accurate approximation $\bar{\lambda}_k$ to λ_k; then in $(A-\bar{\lambda}_kI)^{-1}$ the eigenvalue $(\lambda_k-\bar{\lambda}_k)^{-1}$ will completely dominate the others unless there are other eigenvalues close to λ_k. Starting with an arbitrary $\mathbf{u}^{(0)}$, we will expect two iterations to give a very good approximation to $\mathbf{x}_k$ unless $\mathbf{u}^{(0)}$ happened to be pathologically deficient in $\mathbf{x}_k$. Notice that inverse iteration can be used even when λ_k is complex, though complex arithmetic is then involved. There does not appear to be any technique for choosing $\mathbf{u}^{(0)}$ which can be *guaranteed* to avoid deficiency in $\mathbf{x}_k$ but the following is extremely effective in practice.

From equation (134) we have

$$R\mathbf{u}^{(1)} = L^{-1}P\mathbf{u}^{(0)} \tag{135}$$

and $\mathbf{u}^{(0)}$ is at our disposal. Let us assume that $\mathbf{u}^{(0)}$ has been chosen so that $L^{-1}P\mathbf{u}^{(0)} = (1, 1,\ldots, 1)$. The first iteration can then be completed merely by performing a back-substitution. The forward substitution is avoided. In our experience one further complete iteration to obtain $\mathbf{u}^{(2)}$ defined by

$$LR\mathbf{u}^{(2)} = P\mathbf{u}^{(1)} \tag{136}$$

gives an eigenvector which is as good as is attainable with the precision of computation that is being used. Notice that it effectively involves only about $1\frac{1}{2}$ true iterations!

Although $(A-\bar{\lambda}_kI)$ is almost singular when $\bar{\lambda}_k$ is close to λ_k this does not affect the accuracy of the process. It has been shown by Wilkinson (1963) that although the computed $\mathbf{u}^{(r)}$ are very inaccurate solutions of the equations which are solved they are almost exactly true multiples of the correct solutions and we are not worried by arbitrary scaling factors.

25. Inverse Iteration with Hessenberg and Tri-Diagonal Matrices

Although inverse iteration is extremely effective even with a full matrix A, it is far more efficient when A is of Hessenberg form since the amount of work involved in the LR factorization is then drastically reduced. The LR factorization with interchanges is equivalent to Gaussian elimination of A with partial pivoting. At each stage of the Gaussian reduction there are only two rows containing the current variable to be eliminated. There is therefore only one sub-diagonal element in each column of the unit lower-triangular matrix L. Triangular factorization involves only $\frac{1}{2}n^2$ multiplications and additions compared with $\frac{1}{3}n^3$ for a full matrix, while one step of inverse iteration involves only $\frac{1}{2}n^2$ multiplications and additions instead of n^2.

Turning now to tri-diagonal matrices (which are specialized Hessenberg matrices) we have a further simplification. When pivoting is included we find that each row of R has either two or three non-zero elements. In the rth row these occupy positions (r, r), $(r, r+1)$, if there are two, and also $(r, r+2)$ if there are three. As with full Hessenberg matrices L has only one non-zero sub-diagonal element in each column. The number of multiplications and additions is of order n and not n^2. This is true whether or not the tri-diagonal matrix is symmetric, and indeed when interchanges are used symmetry is irrelevant.

Inverse iteration is an extremely powerful and accurate technique for the computation of eigenvectors, and used in connexion with Hessenberg or tri-diagonal matrices after their eigenvalues have been determined it is extremely economical. Its main weakness is in connexion with multiple or pathologically close eigenvalues. As we have described it, it provides only one eigenvector corresponding to a given value of $\bar{\lambda}_k$. Now if an upper Hessenberg matrix has a root λ of multiplicity r and is not defective, the matrix $(H - \lambda I)$ must be of rank $n - r$ and this means that at least $r - 1$ of the line of sub-diagonal elements must be zero. Hence, if a matrix A having an eigenvalue of multiplicity r were reduced to Hessenberg form H using *exact* arithmetic, H would have at least $r - 1$ zero subdiagonal elements and this would make it easy to find r independent eigenvectors.

Unfortunately, although the reductions to Hessenberg form are stable in that eigenvalues are well preserved, one cannot rely on any subdiagonal element of H being pathologically small when A has multiple eigenvalues. In practice one finds that if A has linear divisors and two very slightly different approximations $\lambda_k^{(1)}$ and $\lambda_k^{(2)}$ to a double eigenvalue λ_k (or two pathologically close eigenvalues) are used, inverse iteration usually gives two very different eigenvectors and these span the required subspace. Similar remarks apply to eigenvalues of greater multiplicity or to pathologically dense clusters.

However, it cannot be denied that the process is aesthetically unsatisfactory; there remains the danger that two or more vectors $\mathbf{x}_k^{(1)}$, $\mathbf{x}_k^{(2)}$ may be obtained which agree in several of their leading figures, and then the direction in the invariant subspace orthogonal to $\mathbf{x}_k^{(1)}$ is poorly determined.

Lest this criticism should appear to be too damaging, it is worth emphasizing that the vectors given by inverse iteration are of a more consistently high accuracy than those given by any other method, and even in the case we have just discussed both $x_k^{(1)}$ and $x_k^{(2)}$ will usually be "better" eigenvectors, each judged on its own merit, than those given by alternative methods which ensure almost orthogonal eigenvectors.

26. Determination of Eigenvectors for Hermitian Matrices

We are now in a position to consider the determination of the eigenvectors when the eigenvalues have been found by the methods we have discussed. We take first the Hermitian case.

With Jacobi's method there is only one "natural" method for the computation of the eigenvectors. If the rotation matrices are $R_1, R_2, \ldots R_s$ and the final diagonal matrix is diag (λ_i) then we have

$$R_s \ldots R_2 R_1 A^{(0)} R_1^T R_2^T \ldots R_s^T = \text{diag}(\lambda_i). \tag{137}$$

Hence the columns of $R^T R_2^T \ldots R_s^T$ give the eigenvectors of $A^{(0)}$.

If all the eigenvectors are required the current product of the R_s^T matrices can be obtained after each transformation. If we are prepared to store the details of each R_s then we need only compute those eigenvectors of $A^{(0)}$ which correspond to the λ_i in which we are interested. If these are $\lambda_{i1}, \lambda_{i2}, \ldots, \lambda_{ik}$ we compute $(R_1^T R_2^T \ldots R_s^T)[e_{i_1} e_{i_2} \ldots e_{i_k}]$, where e_p is the pth column of I. If only a few vectors are required this saves a good deal of computation but the details of the R_s may make extensive demands on storage.

It has been shown (Wilkinson 1965) that the columns of $R_1^T \ldots R_s^T$ are always almost exactly orthogonal independent of the existence of multiple or pathologically close eigenvalues. The columns corresponding to pathologically close eigenvalues will not of course be accurate eigenvectors but they will be orthogonal vectors spanning the appropriate subspace (cf. §4) and this is often important in subsequent applications.

In the Givens and Householder methods we have

$$R_N \ldots R_2 R_1 A^{(0)} R_1^T R_2^T \ldots R_N^T = C_1, \qquad N = \tfrac{1}{2}(n-2)(n-1), \tag{138}$$

and

$$P^{(n-2)} \ldots P^{(2)} P^{(1)} A^{(0)} P^{(1)} P^{(2)} \ldots P^{(n-2)} = C_2 \tag{139}$$

respectively, where the R_i are the rotation matrices used by Givens, the $P^{(i)}$ are the elementary Hermitians used by Householder and C_1 and C_2 are the resulting tri-diagonal matrices. (It can be shown that with exact computation C_1 and C_2 are the same apart from signs of off-diagonal elements.)

Hence if x is an eigenvector of C_1 or C_2 the required eigenvectors of $A^{(0)}$ are

$$R_1^T R_2^T \ldots R_N^T x \quad \text{and} \quad P^{(1)} P^{(2)} \ldots P^{(n-2)} x \tag{140}$$

in the two cases.

The eigenvectors of C_1 and C_2 may be found from the eigenvalues by inverse iteration, taking advantage of the tri-diagonal form. This is very efficient and accurate. The only weakness is that we do not obtain orthogonal vectors corresponding to coincident or close eigenvalues and there is the slight danger that complete digital information on the relevant invariant subspaces will not be obtained in such cases.

In §18 we showed that the eigenvalues of a symmetric tri-diagonal matrix C_i may be obtained using the QR algorithm and that in general this gives very rapid convergence. Only $n-1$ plane rotations are involved in each QR step, indeed fewer as deflation proceeds. If the product R_k^T of the rotation matrices used in the QR algorithm is retained, the resulting matrix has as its columns the eigenvectors of C_i and from these we may obtain the eigenvectors of $A^{(0)}$ by pre-multiplying by the rotations or elementary Hermitians used to derive C_i. Like the Jacobi method this ensures automatically that the computed vectors are almost exactly orthogonal. It might be felt that this method is "extravagant" but the QR algorithm converges so rapidly in general that far fewer rotations are used than in the Jacobi process.

27. Eigenvectors for Non-Hermitian Matrices

In most of the methods we have discussed, A was first reduced to a Hessenberg matrix H. When the eigenvalues of H have been found by any of the methods we have discussed we can return to H and find the corresponding eigenvector by inverse iteration. The related eigenvector of A can then be found in the obvious way using the transformation derived in computing H from A. This method should be used even when H has subsequently been transformed to tri-diagonal form or to explicit polynomial form since it gives a measure of protection against the possible instability of these transformations. This method is accurate and economical but has the usual weakness of inverse iteration when A has multiple or pathologically close eigenvalues.

If either variant of the QR algorithm has been used to find the eigenvalues of the Hessenberg matrix this provides us with an alternative method for computing the eigenvectors. The ultimate result of performing the QR algorithm on H is to provide an orthogonal matrix R (the product of all the elementary orthogonal matrices which have been used) such that RHR^T is triangular except possibly for blocks of order two on the diagonal. When, for example, $n = 6$ and H has a triple root α, a simple root β and a complex conjugate pair $\gamma \pm i\delta$ the final matrix may be of the form

$$
T = \begin{bmatrix}
\alpha & X & X & X & X & X \\
 & \alpha & X & X & X & X \\
 & & \eta & q & X & X \\
 & & r & s & X & X \\
 & & & & \beta & X \\
 & & & & & \alpha
\end{bmatrix}, \tag{141}
$$

where the 2×2 matrix of elements p, q, r, s has the eigenvalues $\gamma \pm i\delta$.

The situation is complicated somewhat by the possibility that A may have non-linear divisors or may be pathologically close to a matrix which has them. If A has linear divisors then with exact computation this would reveal itself in T because the rank of $T-\alpha I$ would be $(6-3)$, that is 3. This implies, for example, that t_{12} should be zero. In practice it is best to leave this problem on one side and to determine vectors spanning the invariant subspace corresponding to a multiple eigenvalue. In our example the required vectors are obviously of the form

$$(1, 0, 0, 0, 0, 0),$$
$$(0, 1, 0, 0, 0, 0),$$

and $\qquad\qquad (0, 0, x_3, x_4, x_5, 1),$

where $(x_3, x_4, x_5, 1)$ is the eigenvector of the bottom 4×4 submatrix of T.

From the invariant subspaces of T we can find those of A and then test whether we have true eigenvectors corresponding to multiple eigenvalues or A has non-linear divisors. This alternative process is aesthetically more satisfying than inverse iteration in the case of multiple eigenvalues.

28. Final Assessment of Algorithms

For Hermitian matrices, the Jacobi, Givens and Householder methods all give very accurate eigenvalues. Error analyses have shown that in every case each computed eigenvalue is exact for some $A + \delta A$ where δA is very small. Since Householder's method is closely related to that of Givens and is faster and more accurate there is little point now in using Givens' method, though historically it occupies a key position in the development of modern algorithms. Using the Sturm sequence method we have great flexibility as regards which eigenvalues are determined. Generally if eigenvalues only are wanted Householder's method is the best, particularly if only a few eigenvalues of a large matrix are required.

As far as vectors are concerned the Jacobi method is very compact, has a simple, unified program and gives almost exactly orthogonal vectors. Householder's method with inverse iteration gives accurate eigenvectors and we need determine only those which are actually required, but eigenvectors corresponding to multiple or pathologically close eigenvalues may be far from orthogonal. Householder's method with the QR algorithm overcomes this difficulty and in my opinion is the best method if all the vectors are required and orthogonality is important.

For non-Hermitian matrices there are two outstanding methods in which A is first reduced to Hessenberg form by the second method of §13. The more impressive of the two in my experience has been the double QR algorithm of Francis for the eigenvalues, the eigenvectors being produced either by inverse iteration applied to H or directly from the QR transformations and the final triangular form as described in §27.

The second choice is the Laguerre method based on Hyman's evaluations as expounded by Parlett, the eigenvectors being found via H using inverse iteration.

The method of Eberlein does not involve preliminary reduction to Hessenberg form and experience suggests that it performs well in practice. Further research in this field might well lead to an algorithm which is superior to either of those which we have recommended.

3*

REFERENCES

COURANT, R. AND HILBERT, D. 1953. *Methods of Mathematical Physics*, Vol. 1. Interscience Publishers, New York.

EBERLEIN, P. J. 1962. A Jacobi-like method for the automatic computation of eigenvalues and eigenvectors of an arbitrary matrix. *J. Soc. Industr. Appl. Math.* **10**, 74–88.

FOX, L. 1964. *An Introduction to Numerical Linear Algebra*. Oxford University Press, London.

FRANCIS, J. G. F. 1961, 1962. The QR transformation, Parts I and II. *Computer J.* **4**, 265–271, 332–345.

GIVENS, W. 1953. A method of computing eigenvalues and eigenvectors suggested by classical results on symmetric matrices. *Appl. Math. Ser. Nat. Bur. Stand.* **29**, 117–122.

GIVENS, W. 1954. Numerical computation of the characteristic values of a real symmetric matrix. Oak Ridge National Laboratory, ORNL–1574.

GIVENS, W. 1958. Computation of plane unitary rotations transforming a general matrix to triangular form. *J. Soc. Industr. Appl. Math.* **6**, 26–50.

HENRICI, P. 1958. On the speed of convergence of cyclic and quasicyclic Jacobi methods for computing eigenvalues of Hermitian matrices. *J. Soc. Industr. Appl. Math.* **6**, 144–162.

HOFFMAN, A. J. AND WIELANDT, H. W. 1953. The variation of the spectrum of a normal matrix. *Duke Math. J.* **20**, 37–39.

HOUSEHOLDER, A. S. AND BAUER, F. L. 1959. On certain methods for expanding the characteristic polynomial. *Num. Math.* **1**, 29–37.

HYMAN, M. A. 1957. Eigenvalues and eigenvectors of general matrices. *Twelfth National meeting A.C.M., Houston, Texas*.

JACOBI, C. G. J. 1846. Über ein leichtes Verfahren die in der Theorie der Säculärstörungen vorkommenden Gleichungen numerisch aufzulösen. *Crelle's J.* **30**, 51–94.

KUBLANOVSKAYA, V. N. 1961. On some algorithms for the solution of the complete eigenvalue problem. *Zh. vych. mat.* **1**, 555–570.

LANCZOS, C. 1950. An iteration method for the solution of the eigenvalue problem of linear differential and integral operators. *J. Res. Nat. Bur. Stand.* **45**, 255–282.

MULLER, D. E. 1956. A method for solving algebraic equations using an automatic computer. *Math. Tab., Wash.* **10**, 208–215.

PARLETT, B. 1964a. Laguerre's method applied to the matrix eigenvalue problem. *Math. Computation*, **18**, 464–485.

PARLETT, B. 1964b. The development and use of methods of LR type. *Soc. Industr. Appl. Math. Reviews*, **6**, 275–310.

POPE, D. A. AND TOMPKINS, C. 1957. Maximizing functions of rotations—experiments concerning speed of diagonalization of symmetric matrices using Jacobi's method. *J. Ass. Comp. Mach.* **4**, 459–466.

RUTISHAUSER, H. 1958. Solution of eigenvalue problems with the LR-transformation. *Appl. Math. Ser. Nat. Bur. Stand.* **49**, 47–81.

SCHÖNHAGE, A. 1961. Zur Konvergenz des Jacobi-Verfahrens. *Num. Math.* **3**, 374–380.

SCHÖNHAGE, A. 1965. Zur quadratischen Konvergenz des Jacobi-Verfahrens. *Num. Math.* **6**, 410–412.

STRACHEY, C. AND FRANCIS, J. G. F. 1961. The reduction of a matrix to co-diagonal form by eliminations. *Comp. J.* **4**, 168–176.

WIELANDT, H. 1944. Bestimmung höherer Eigenwerte durch gebrochene Iteration. *Ber. B44/J/37 der Aerodynamischen Versuchsanstalt, Göttingen.*

WILKINSON, J. H. 1954. The calculation of the latent roots and vectors of matrices on the pilot model of the ACE. *Proc. Camb. Phil. Soc.* **50**, 536–566.

WILKINSON, J. H. 1960. Error analysis of floating-point computation. *Num. Math.* **2**, 319–340.

WILKINSON, J. H. 1962a. Instability of the elimination method of reducing a matrix to tri-diagonal form. *Comp. J.* **5**, 61–70.

WILKINSON, J. H. 1962b. Note on the quadratic convergence of the cyclic Jacobi process. *Num. Math.* **4**, 296–300.

WILKINSON, J. H. 1963. *Rounding Errors in Algebraic Processes. Notes on Applied Science No. 32.* H.M. Stationery Office, London; Prentice-Hall, New Jersey.

WILKINSON, J. H. 1965. *The Algebraic Eigenvalue Problem.* Oxford University Press, London.

Chapter 4

The Numerical Solution of Ordinary Differential Equations

J. C. P. MILLER

University Mathematical Laboratory, Cambridge

1. Introduction and Statement of the Basic Problem. Definitions

The numerical solution of ordinary differential equations has been developing for over a century, and the mathematical solution for even longer. Early workers in the numerical field were largely dynamical astronomers; more lately developments have proliferated with the advent of automatic computers.

The basic problem is similar in both mathematical and numerical cases, with the latter severely complicated by the presence of rounding errors, and by the necessity to develop solutions individually.

1.1 *An Ordinary Differential Equation* is of the type

$$f(x, y, y', \ldots, y^{(n)}) = 0 \qquad (1.1)$$

between an independent variable x, a dependent variable y, and its first n derivatives $y^{(r)} = \mathrm{d}^r y / \mathrm{d}x^r$, $r = 1, 2, \ldots, n$. The *order* of this equation is n.

In numerical work, and in the theory of existence of solutions, the equation is almost invariably written in the explicit form

$$y^{(n)} = g(x, y, y', \ldots, y^{(n-1)}). \qquad (1.2)$$

We shall start by assuming this to be the case (but not in §12 and after).

We often approximate to a differential equation in numerical work by means of a *difference equation*, expressed in terms of function values $y_r = y(x_r)$, where $x_r = a + rh$, $x_0 = a$ being some suitable starting value, and h some suitable interval in x.

$$F(x_r, y_r, y_{r+1}, \ldots, y_{r+m}) = 0 \qquad (1.3)$$

is a difference equation of order m, which we shall (except when the contrary is explicitly stated) assume written in the form

$$y_{r+m} = G(x_r, y_r, y_{r+1}, \ldots, y_{r+m-1}). \qquad (1.4)$$

The orders m and n need not be the same, even when we use (1.3) or (1.4) to obtain an approximate solution of (1.1).

Differential and difference equations both have infinitely many solutions, involving a number of degrees of freedom (which usually appear as arbitrary

63

constants) equal to the order. In numerical work, as well as in much mathematical work, we seek one particular solution, satisfying the equation concerned and a certain set of *boundary conditions*. Such a combination, normally defining a unique solution, will be called a *system* (differential or difference).

1.2 *Types of Boundary Conditions*. Mathematical and numerical methods for obtaining solutions to differential systems depend fundamentally on the types of boundary conditions. The main categories that have been widely considered are

  (i) One-point boundary conditions
  (ii) Two-point boundary conditions
  (iii) Other boundary conditions.

If boundary conditions are given all at one point, it is natural to start at that point and work away from it. Such systems are known widely as *Initial Value Problems*, and have been called *Marching Problems* by L. F. Richardson.

Problems with distributed boundary conditions are known as *Boundary-Value Problems*, or *Jury Problems* (L. F. Richardson).

Two-point boundary-value problems may be further subdivided into problems with

  (ii*a*) General two-point boundary conditions

  (ii*b*) Eigenvalue problems (the singular case when, e.g. boundary conditions are such that the only possible solution is $y \equiv 0$, except when some parameter in the differential equation takes certain special values, the eigenvalues, which have to be determined along with the corresponding non-zero solutions $y(x)$).

It is also useful, though not yet a recognized category, to consider cases that correspond to the frequent physical condition that solutions remain finite as $x \to x_0$, some particular special value. We shall consider only one case

  (ii*c*) Two-point boundary conditions where all specific numerical conditions are given at one point, with the added condition that the solution remain finite at the second boundary point.

The second point will be assumed to be at infinity, and the condition, simply stated, may involve several degrees of freedom. A change of variable can always move the second point to infinity, though it may not be necessary or convenient in numerical practice to make the change. This category will be referred to in discussing and commenting on various methods later.

1.3 *Linear and Non-linear Equations*. An equation which involves linearly the complete set of dependent variable and derivatives $y, y', \ldots, y^{(n)}$, or the complete set of function values $y_r, y_{r+1}, \ldots, y_{r+m}$, or a combination of function values and derivatives, is called a *linear equation*. Such equations have many useful and simple mathematical properties that do not apply to other *non-linear equations*.

It may be noted that difference equations used to replace differential equations for numerical work are often linear.

1.4 *Conditioning and Stability*. The major difference between mathematical and numerical developments lies in the inevitability of rounding and truncation errors, made because numerical processes must be finite.

Thus a differential system defines *mathematically* a unique solution, "the" solution of the system. This applies generally, apart from such special cases as, for example, non-linear equations having singular solutions, or in eigenvalue problems. When, however, a differential system is given *numerically*, the equation and the boundary conditions normally involve one or more rounded constants, which have a permissible range of variation; these correspond to a set (or pencil) of permissible solutions. Likewise, the numerical processes of obtaining a solution involve further truncation and rounding errors, increasing further the variation in the possible set of "solutions". The numerical work simply picks out a single member of this set.

We must ask how closely the possible members of such a set of solutions remain together. This is the general problem of *stability*. If they remain closely bunched together so that any one of them gives an adequate solution to the problem, we can say that the determination is *stable*; if the variation is so great that not all possible solutions are acceptable the determination is *unstable*. Errors in data, and those made during the computation, are distinct in the sense that the latter are capable of control during the computation whereas the former may not be so. If then all solutions originating from the boundary conditions, under reasonable rounding-error variations, are adequate, we say the problem is *well-conditioned*; if the dispersal is too wide to be satisfactory, the problem is *ill-conditioned* or *not well-conditioned*. Other terms used are *inherently stable* and *inherently unstable*.

We may also say a well-conditioned system is *well-posed*, and an ill-conditioned system is *badly-posed*, except that an *exactly-posed system* (yielding a unique mathematical solution) may also be ill-conditioned.

Any instability that is introduced by the particular method of computation used is regarded as *induced instability*.

2. Types of Computational Method

Methods used for obtaining numerical solutions to differential systems will be subdivided into groups in two ways.

2.1 The first grouping is concerned with truncation error. We have

(1) Methods with no truncation error,† in which the differential equations are rewritten in a form exactly equivalent to the original equation, but expressed in a manner suitable for computational use, e.g. as an infinite series involving differences, derivatives, or orthogonal polynomials, etc.

(2) Methods in which the differential equation is replaced by another finite equation, usually a difference equation, or an equation involving only the depen-

---

† Truncation error is taken to mean a systematic error incurred whenever a formula involving a series is curtailed at a fixed term, or in a fixed manner; the more random error incurred when the series is curtailed only when the estimated residual error is bounded by a fixed tolerance constant is regarded as part of the rounding error.

dent variable and its first derivative at several adjacent equally-spaced points. This *replacement equation* is chosen to have one of its solutions very close to the solution of the original system.

The methods are supposed expressed in terms of an equation in which one value y_p is isolated on the left and determined numerically from the remainder of the formula, written on the right of the equation.

2.2 Our second grouping is according to whether (a) the formula for the method is used *directly* (i.e. once) or (b) the formula is used *iteratively*.

This chapter is concerned almost exclusively with *marching methods*, i.e. those starting at $x = a$, and proceeding in succession to $a+h, a+2h,\ldots$ as far as necessary. These are methods most appropriate for initial-value problems; they are also of importance for boundary-value problems of type (ii*c*), with the second boundary point involving only a condition of boundedness (the method needs to be iterative in this case); they may also be used in other boundary-value problems, particularly when linear equations are involved (see §15).

The use of backward marching, $h < 0$, should also be mentioned. Change of sign in x turns this into forward marching, but is not always convenient, while use of both directions in the same problem is sometimes very effective.

Iteration may arise in two ways:

(i) With some methods we may iterate each step to completion (i.e. to adequate convergence) before starting the next, as recommended with the corrector in predictor-corrector methods (see §4.1). This is often necessary when the equation used involves y_n and $y' = f_n = f(x_n, y_n)$, so that the equation for y_n is implicit. Following Hartree, and Dahlquist, we may call this an "algebraic" equation; it is solved independently for each step, by methods which are usually iterative, but can be direct, e.g. if $y' = f(x, y)$ is linear. Such *algebraic* or *single-step iterative methods* will be regarded as normal in direct forward use of the differential or difference equation for numerical solution.

(ii) Alternatively we may obtain an approximation $y_n^{(p)}$ over a wide or moderately wide range of x, and use this to obtain the next iterate $y_n^{(p+1)}$; this is necessary when difference-correction methods involving high-order differences are used (cf. §§12, 13). It is, however, almost always best to progress a relatively small number of steps at a time, and to estimate further new forward values at intervals as convergence progresses, since the convergence is slower the further we are from the start. Only if improvement at each step is substantial is it worth while to take many new steps at a time. Such methods will be called *multi-step iterative* or simply *iterative methods*.

2.3 It is useful here to mention some requirements of methods for practical use; these should be borne in mind, although other considerations, particularly the possibility and ease of analysis of error and method, are not negligible and will enter into the account that follows.

Requirements are largely based on the use of automatic computers to carry out the arithmetic, and in some cases the algebra, involved in obtaining numerical solutions.

(1) We require a method to be safe to use, without too much thought, in circumstances as widely varying as possible.
(2) We require the calculation to be reasonably rapid—very rapid if many simultaneous differential equations are involved.
(3) We require the method to be available on the computer, either because it is easy to program, or because a suitable subroutine employing the method has been written.
(4) Methods must be usable by many people, of all kinds, some numerical analysts, but most of them not familiar with numerical work, or even with mathematics beyond elementary levels.

Clearly many methods and programs are needed to meet these requirements. For small problems (1) is paramount (because of (4)); for large problems (2) is predominant, and this needs a *program* to be available, so the method may be sophisticated and programmed by an expert.

2.4 We now list certain methods described in subsequent sections.

Methods with No Truncation Error. The following methods will be described:
  (i) The Adams-Bashforth method, using a series of backward differences (§3.1).
  (ii) The Numerov method, typifying the use of a series of central differences (§3.2).
  (iii) The Taylor series method, using a series of derivatives (§3.4).

More modern developments, which make the evaluation of successive derivatives more systematic and easier to carry out are described in §11.

  (iv) Clenshaw's method for expansions in series of Chebyshev polynomials (§3.5).

These are typical of several possibilities using orthogonal polynomials or functions.

  (v) The deferred-correction methods of Fox and Goodwin (§12).
  (vi) Some new iterative methods and ideas (§13).

Methods Replacing the Original Equation
  (i) Runge-Kutta methods (§4.2).
  (ii) Predictor-corrector methods using difference equations and typified by Milne's method (§4.1).

3. Methods Without Truncation Error

These involve series curtailed by rounding error only. The early developments, involving series of differences, may be exemplified by two methods, the Adams-Bashforth and Numerov methods.

Other methods described or mentioned in this section are generally of more recent development, at least in their most effective forms. These are the

Taylor series method, and Clenshaw's methods involving series of Chebyshev polynomials.

3.1 The Adams-Bashforth Method. In this, the differential equation

$$y' = f(x, y) \tag{3.1}$$

is converted into

$$\Delta y_n = y_{n+1} - y_n = F_n + \tfrac{1}{2}\nabla F_n + \tfrac{5}{12}\nabla^2 F_n + \tfrac{3}{8}\nabla^3 F_n + \ldots, \quad F_n = hf_n, \tag{3.2}$$

where h is the step-length of the calculation, $y_n = y(a+nh)$, etc., $x_0 = a$ being some convenient starting point.

We suppose that enough of the terms on the right are known when $y_r, r = 0, 1, \ldots, n$, is known. However, the coefficients on the right decrease slowly, and the convergence is poor and badly affected by rounding error.

This slow convergence can be improved by using the *corrector formula*

$$\Delta y_n = y_{n+1} - y_n = F_{n+1} - \tfrac{1}{2}\nabla F_{n+1} - \tfrac{1}{12}\nabla^2 F_{n+1} - \tfrac{1}{24}\nabla^3 F_{n+1} - \ldots, \tag{3.3}$$

with F_{n+1} calculated by using y_{n+1} obtained from (3.2). This is a single-step iteration method, though iteration should not normally be necessary beyond using (3.2) and (3.3) in succession.

However, for automatic computing—which I mention now for convenience —it is often sufficient to use (3.2) only, with full single-length accuracy on the machine and a reasonably small value of h, since this use is non-iterative and safe.

3.2 The Numerov Method. This is also known amongst astronomers as the Gauss-Jackson method and is called by Kopal (1955) the "Royal Road" method. It is applied to second-order differential equations with first derivative absent; such equations are common in astronomical motion. One form is as follows:

If

$$y'' = f(x, y), \tag{3.4}$$

we use

$$\delta^2 y_n = F_n + \tfrac{1}{12}\delta^2 F_n - \tfrac{1}{240}\delta^4 F_n + \ldots, \quad F_n = h^2 f_n, \tag{3.5}$$

in terms of central differences.

We suppose y_r and hence F_r and enough of its backward differences to be known already for $r = 0, 1, \ldots, n$. We then estimate $\delta^2 F_n, \delta^4 F_n$ by judicious estimating of higher-order differences, at an order where these depend only on rounding errors, or, except for these, would vary very slowly. This provides a value of $\delta^2 y_n$ from which y_{n+1} can be obtained, and hence F_{n+1} and a revised value of $\delta^2 F_n$, and a revised guess of $\delta^4 F_n$. Because of the small coefficient quite large errors in the estimate of $\delta^4 F_n$ have negligible effect on $\delta^2 y_n$ and y_{n+1}; we may, however, iterate the process if, as rarely, it should be necessary.

The Numerov method is highly efficient and has been used with high-order differences—up to $\delta^8 F_n$ or $\delta^{10} F_n$—and with correspondingly large values of h.

Though a multi-step iterative method, it is usually used more or less directly as a single-step method, with forward estimates of differences made independently at each step.

3.3 *Comment*. These two early methods, Adams-Bashforth and Numerov, remain useful and powerful, particularly for exploratory desk calculation. They both need special methods for starting since a difference table is used. This is often done by expansion in a Taylor series about the starting-point. This is virtually equivalent to the method of Taylor's series, of perennial usefulness.

3.4. *The Taylor Series Method*. This is a further, and very powerful, method involving series, this time of derivatives.

We consider a second-order equation as an example:

$$y'' = f(x, y, y'). \tag{3.6}$$

This yields $y^{(p)} = d^p y/dx^p$, and hence $T_p = y^{(p)} h^p/p!$, $p \geq 2$, by repeated differentiation at any point x_n where y_n, y_n are known. We then have

$$\left.\begin{array}{l} y_{n+1} = y_n + T_1 + T_2 + T_3 + T_4 + \ldots \\ hy'_{n+1} = T_1 + 2T_2 + 3T_3 + 4T_4 + \ldots \end{array}\right\}, \tag{3.7}$$

while the equations obtained by changing the sign of h,

$$\left.\begin{array}{l} y_{n-1} = y_n - T_1 + T_2 - T_3 + T_4 - \ldots \\ hy'_{n-1} = T_1 - 2T_2 + 3T_3 - 4T_4 + \ldots \end{array}\right\}, \tag{3.8}$$

yield valuable checks a step back. Here as before $y_n = y(x_n)$ where $x_n = a + nh$, and similarly for y'_n; the suffix n is omitted from the T_p for clarity.

From the values of y_{n+1} and hy'_{n+1}, the new T_1, we can then take another step by computing T_p at $x = x_{n+1}$.

This method using Taylor's series is sound and desirable, being based on a series with powerful and well-known properties of convergence. It has been used successfully for many years; later developments making it even more useful and easier to apply are given in §11.

3.5 *Expansion in Series of Chebyshev Polynomials*. Such expansions are proving very valuable for general use in automatic computers. They provide approximations to given precision over a given interval of x with a higher rate of convergence, i.e. with fewer terms, than any other expansion in polynomials. This is achieved by having a uniform rate of convergence over the whole interval of validity; if we compare with the Taylor series, based on the middle of the interval as origin, we find the latter to have superior convergence towards the origin—perfect convergence, i.e. with one term, at the origin—but to be less rapidly convergent at the ends of the range.

A number of methods have been developed in recent years to provide Chebyshev expansions directly from the differential equation and boundary conditions. Such methods are akin to the method of Frobenius for obtaining power series solutions to differential equations, but differ in detail. The treatment of singularities is, in particular, undeveloped.

The first method to be produced was the τ-method of Lanczos, described first in his highly readable and fascinating paper (Lanczos 1938). In this method a suitable linear differential equation is slightly varied by adding an extra term $\tau T^*_{n+1}(x)$ (or possibly a *few* consecutive such terms), and is solved *exactly* as a finite series $\sum a_r T^*_r(x)$ over the range $0 \le x \le 1$. Here the $T^*_r(x)$ are Chebyshev polynomials normalized to the interval $(0, 1)$.

Clenshaw (1957) obtains solutions in Chebyshev series for suitable equations by assuming series for each derivative of y that occurs, in particular for the *highest* derivative present, and then equating coefficients of Chebyshev polynomials, after substitution in the differential equation and reduction by means of the relations satisfied by the polynomials $T_n(x)$ normalized to the interval $(-1, 1)$ that he uses,

$$
\left.
\begin{aligned}
2x T_n(x) &= T_{n+1}(x) + T_{n-1}(x) \\
\int T_r(x)\, dx &= \tfrac{1}{2}\left(\frac{T_{r+1}(x)}{r+1} - \frac{T_{r-1}(x)}{r-1} \right), r > 1
\end{aligned}
\right\}.
\qquad (3.9)
$$

Fox 1962a discusses the relation between these two methods.

Clenshaw and Norton (1963) extend the method of Chebyshev series to non-linear equations by using a Picard iteration. Norton (1964) considers the application of the Newton iteration formula to the same problem. Scraton (1965) gives an approach to the solution of linear equations with non-polynomial coefficients.

These papers are concerned mainly with the determination of Chebyshev series valid over a single finite, but considerable, range. It would be helpful also to use Chebyshev expansions for several successive ranges of validity as a step-by-step process. The Chebyshev series is not only more rapidly convergent than the Taylor series, it also has a more convenient region of convergence. The Taylor series has a circle of convergence limited in radius by the nearest singularity (which usually depends on the particular solution in non-linear equations). The Chebyshev expansion has a basically *elliptic* region of convergence, with the ends of the normal Chebyshev interval as foci—that is, the series has uniform convergence on the straight line between the foci, and also converges for a region surrounding this line, a region that may be highly restricted near the foci in many cases. It is clearly much easier to get a large step with elliptic regions than with circles—though convergence may well be slow if there is a singularity near the line joining the foci.

3.6 *Comments on Convergence, etc.* The four methods just described all involve series that are curtailed by consideration of rounding error. Those involving differences are relatively slowly converging, representing almost the possible extremes—using differences at fixed interval (the same in each case)—of slow convergence with the Adams-Bashforth method, and of relatively rapid convergence with the Numerov method. The Taylor series method is better than either, producing a series with thoroughly well-known, and good, convergence properties. Chebyshev expansions are better still, being chosen for maximum possible rapidity of convergence over a given interval.

This means that maximum possible intervals h for a convenient speed of convergence are small for differences, larger for derivatives and largest of all for Chebyshev expansions. On the other hand, the work needed to obtain the coefficients in the expansions is small for differences, moderate for derivatives (but see §11) and, with present methods, considerable for Chebyshev expansions. All are useful in different circumstances. It is probable that, when the derivation is fully developed, the Chebyshev expansions will prove most powerful. At present, for substantial interval h, and for ease in changing interval, the Taylor series method seems most worth cultivation.

All these methods are safe to use—the only error incurred at each step is rounding error, and so instability cannot be induced, but must arise from ill-conditioning if at all, since lack of convergence is not permitted.

4. Methods Involving Fixed Truncation Error

Two examples will be given of such formulae.

4.1 *Milne's Method.* For this the differential equation

$$y' = f(x, y) \tag{4.1}$$

is replaced by two finite-difference equations. One of these,

$$y_{n+1} = y_{n-3} + \tfrac{4}{3}h(2f_n - f_{n-1} + 2f_{n-2}), \tag{4.2}$$

is used as a *predictor* formula for y_{n+1}, given y_p, $p \le n$. This gives f_{n+1}, by use of (4.1), and we can follow with the use of the second formula

$$y_{n+1} = y_{n-1} + \tfrac{1}{3}h(f_{n+1} + 4f_n + f_{n-1}) \tag{4.3}$$

(Simpson's rule) as a *corrector*, with an iteration (regarded as "algebraic") of this last step to secure convergence if necessary. We then continue by use of (4.2) and (4.3) again, with n increased by unity.

4.2 *Runge-Kutta Methods.* There are many variants; just one will be considered here. Starting again with equation (4.1) from a known point (x, y), we compute in succession

$$\left.\begin{aligned}
k_0 &= hf(x, y) \\
k_1 &= hf(x + \tfrac{1}{2}h, y + \tfrac{1}{2}k_0) \\
k_2 &= hf(x + \tfrac{1}{2}h, y + \tfrac{1}{2}k_1) \\
k_3 &= hf(x + h, y + k_2)
\end{aligned}\right\} \tag{4.4}$$

and use as the new value of y

$$y(x + h) = y(x) + \tfrac{1}{6}(k_0 + 2k_1 + 2k_2 + k_3). \tag{4.5}$$

This method gives $y(x + h)$ with a fixed truncation error of order h^5 (i.e. it is regarded as an overall fourth-order process) in the sense that, when expanded in powers of h, the series for the right of (4.5) agrees with the correct Taylor series for $y(x + h)$ as far as the term in h^4.

4.3 *Comment.* Milne's method is only one of many suggested predictor-corrector methods, and (4.3) only one of many ways of replacing the original differential equation by an approximating difference equation. Such difference equations are often of higher order than the original differential equation; this results in severe stability limitations, some of which are discussed in §9.1.

The main virtues of the Runge-Kutta methods are that they require the evaluation of $f(x, y)$ only, four times at each step in the method described, and that change of interval is easy (as it is when using Taylor series). Several third- and fourth-order methods have been devised (Kopal 1955, Chapter IV, §L), culminating in that of Gill (1951). Higher-order methods are almost prohibitively difficult to devise; this tends to limit the maximum size of h.

Merson (1957) has described a process of Runge-Kutta type involving five function evaluations, which provides also an estimate of the truncation error for a very restricted class of differential equations.

Scraton (1964) gives a similar process of wider validity which may be converted to yield a fifth-order process for a single first-order equation, though not linear in the quantities evaluated.

The Runge-Kutta-Gill process has had wide currency as the basis of computer programs since its first derivation by Gill for use on EDSAC 1. The resulting satisfactory and generally applicable *program*, coming early in the history of automatic computers as it did, may have delayed development of other methods, capable of yielding even better programs.

5. Stability and Convergence. Definitions

It is useful now to consider stability and convergence, before describing methods of recent development and suggestions for further study, since stability considerations have played a part in the search for new methods.

Although stability and convergence have been quite widely discussed in recent years, *all* the various terms and ideas do not seem to have been fully and precisely defined anywhere, and there is a certain amount of variation in the definitions given. It seems useful to attempt a more comprehensive and precise statement of definitions than has appeared hitherto.

5.1 *The Desired Solution.* With an exactly-posed mathematical problem, a unique solution exists; we may call this *the solution*. As mentioned, however, in §1.4, a practical problem usually involves rounded constants, and so leads to a pencil of solutions. If the original system is nevertheless well-conditioned, the solution is not unique, but the pencil of solutions remains adequately bundled together, and the *desired solution* is adequately defined. If the original system is, however, ill-conditioned, we shall suppose this is because it is badly-posed, and that other criteria exist by which the desired solution can be picked out from amongst the pencil of solutions given by *all* allowable sets of boundary conditions, however widely the solutions may become dispersed.

Thus we suppose the desired solution is adequately defined in all cases within suitable error limits. We ignore the case where an ill-conditioned system is all we have, and any solution, however discrepant from others, is equally undistinguished; such cases cannot be improved.

The extra criterion in ill-conditioned cases merits comment. It may be called "physical intuition" or some similar term. It consists very often of a condition of boundedness, as in §1.2 (iic), and, although vaguely stated, may often be precise and easy to use, e.g. by simply rejecting solutions when we find that $|y| > M$ for some suitable M. As we shall see, such conditions may be introduced when we replace a differential equation by an approximate difference equation of higher order. A single criterion of this form may comprise several normal boundary conditions.

5.2 *Revised and Replacement Equations. Method.* Methods without truncation error (§2.1 (1)) use the original equation, but in a revised form; this will be called the *revised equation.* Methods involving fixed truncation error use a new equation which will be called the *replacement equation.* Replacement boundary conditions are also needed to provide the *replacement system.* When the replacement equation is of higher order than the original equation extra boundary conditions are needed; it is important to note that, even if the original system is a one-point boundary system, some of the new conditions may nevertheless involve boundedness at infinity, so that the problem may be converted into a two-point boundary problem; this will be of type (iic) in §1.2, a type quite readily dealt with by iterative marching methods.

The replacement system has as its solution the *desired solution of the replacement system.* It is also helpful to define the *intermediate equation* or *system* in an iterative method; this is the part involving the new $(p+1)$st iterate, obtained by ignoring in the equation all terms depending on the previous, pth, iteration.

A *method* is simply a precise manner for using a particular equation, revised or replacement, to obtain the desired solution. There may be many methods applied to the same equation, e.g. forward progression, backward progression, or iterative use based on evaluation of an intermediate function value in terms of those on either side and using the latest available value in each case.

Error and stability analysis will depend on method, and not on equation alone.

5.3 *Stability and Convergence.* Stability is concerned with the use of a particular method to obtain the desired solution of the revised or replacement equation. If rounding errors propagate and accumulate in such a way that all possible numerical results given by the system remain adequately bundled together, the method is said to be *effective for that solution,* that is, the particular calculation is stable. Otherwise the method is *ineffective* for the solution concerned. More precision than there is in the phrase "adequately bundled together" will be given below in §7.3.

Convergence is of two kinds, which will usually not be easily confused. *Convergence with h* occurs when the desired solution of the replacement system, adequately computed, converges as $h \to 0$ to the desired solution of the original system. *Convergence with iteration* applies to the use of an iterative method to obtain a desired solution, whether of a revised or a replacement system.

6. Stability. General Discussion

Before continuing with methods, it is useful to give some general ideas.

6.1 The first key idea is the following:

Suppose we are computing a particular solution of a particular (revised or replacement) equation, and we make an error at any particular step, e.g. a rounding error or a truncation error. This alters the solution into a *neighbouring solution* of the same equation at the point where the error is made. The change can be completely represented by appropriate changes in the particular values to be given to the parameters of the general solution of the equation. Further similar errors at subsequent steps cause further jumps to other neighbouring solutions.

If we confine attention to the original equation, as with the Taylor series method or any other method where the truncation error is swamped by the rounding error (so that the equation used is a revised one), these rounding errors will cause random jumps from solution to solution, whilst on the other hand a *fixed truncation error* (corresponding to a replacement equation) causes systematic drift, which may nevertheless be reasonably controlled on occasion. With a difference equation replacing the original equation, the jump will bring in parts of any parasitic solution (i.e. a solution of the replacement equation with no counterpart amongst those of the original equation), thus yielding obvious non-solutions of the original equation when a parasitic solution is dominant.

6.2 The next point to note is that, when a revised equation is used, either directly or iteratively, the result (*provided we achieve convergence* in the iterative case) satisfies the original equation within rounding error at each point of the calculation. Thus the stability analysis depends, using the principle of §6.1, only on the behaviour of solutions of the original equation.

The intermediate equation in the iterative case may, if it introduces parasitic solutions, delay or prevent convergence; it may also turn an ill-conditioned system into a well-conditioned one, if we choose the initial iterate in such a way as to keep out an unwanted dominant solution. See §13 for an example of this, and a proof of its efficacy.

6.3 When a replacement equation is used, this may be of order different from that of the original equation, so that new boundary conditions, appropriate to the desired solution of the replacement equation, are needed.

If the order of the replacement equation is greater, extra boundary conditions are needed. Now the new equation has extra parameters in its set of solutions, and has parasitic solutions. For one-point boundary systems in the original, it is usual to try to obtain the extra boundary conditions at the same point. The work of Dahlquist (see §8) shows the danger of this procedure, which may convert a well-conditioned original system into a badly-conditioned replacement system. In fact, the extra boundary conditions that properly define the desired solution of the replacement equation may well include several (e.g. involving boundedness) at a second point (often at infinity), thus converting to a well-conditioned two-point boundary system.

If the order of the replacement system is less than that of the original (see, for instance, the examples in §14), this usually implies the existence of boundedness conditions in the original system, corresponding to a zero value of one or more of the parameters of the original. Thus the replacement system needs *fewer* boundary conditions, and this may convert an ill-conditioned one-point boundary system into a well-conditioned one.

We note that the stability of methods using the replacement equation depends on the behaviour of solutions of *this* equation, leaving studies of convergence as the only link between solutions of the two systems, replacement and original.

6.4 It seems worth while to mention here, as a subject for further study, that a replacement system may be a very good approximation to the original, in the sense that the desired solutions of both are almost identical, and yet suffer awkward instability in use. If this is the case, it may be preferable to use a revised form of the replacement equation in iterative fashion, as this may be simpler than any suitable revised form of the original equation (e.g. if this involves very high differences). This would appear to be quite a possible and even a promising approach, perhaps as an intermediate stage in approximating to the desired solution.

6.5 It is, of course, easiest to study the stability and behaviour of solutions for linear equations, particularly those with constant coefficients.

This suggests a useful method for studying local stability behaviour as follows. The differential equation, e.g. $y' = f(x, y)$, is slightly varied to give $\delta y' = f_y \delta y$. Locally we now take f_y to be virtually a constant, and then substitute $\delta y = \varepsilon\, e^{k(x-x_0)}$ into the formula for the method, and so obtain an equation for k. The values of k that satisfy this equation exhibit the local stability structure of the method with this equation.

7. Stability. Examples and Further Definitions

In order to clarify, examples are given below of some of the points outlined previously. Specific and usually very simple systems will be used, just complicated enough to exhibit the ideas considered.

7.1 Consider the differential equation

$$y'' = P^2 y, \qquad P \text{ constant}, \tag{7.11}$$

with general solution

$$y = A\, e^{Px} + B\, e^{-Px} = Au + Bv. \tag{7.12}$$

If the solution is known at $x = a$, say, we can solve the equation numerically to find $y(a+h)$ and $y'(a+h)$. Rounding or truncation errors will, however, give us $y^*(a+h)$ and $y^{*\prime}(a+h)$, slightly different values. This causes a shift to a neighbouring solution $A^*u + B^*v$ which is such that

$$\left. \begin{aligned} A^*u(a+h) + B^*v(a+h) &= y^*(a+h) \\ A^*u'(a+h) + B^*v'(a+h) &= y^{*\prime}(a+h) \end{aligned} \right\}. \tag{7.2}$$

Thus $\delta A = A^* - A$, $\delta B = B^* - B$ satisfy

$$\left.\begin{array}{l} \delta A . u(a+h) + \delta B . v(a+h) = \delta y = y^*(a+h) - y(a+h) \\ \delta A . u'(a+h) + \delta B . v'(a+h) = \delta y' = y^{*\prime}(a+h) - y'(a+h) \end{array}\right\}. \quad (7.3)$$

In general $\delta A . u$ and $\delta B . v$ are each of order δy and $\delta y'$ and so small.

We readily see that it is important to know whether the two solutions $Au + Bv$, $A^*u + B^*v$ (which are sufficiently close at $x = a$, $x = a+h$ to be considered virtually identical) approach one another more closely, or diverge from one another as x progresses further to $a+2h$, $a+3h$, etc. This is the problem of *error propagation*.

We must also examine how the error changes with the continued occurrence of new rounding or truncation errors at successive steps. This is the problem of *accumulation of error*.

These two kinds of error, when combined, give us the material for the study of *stability* of numerical solutions. A similar brief discussion, applied to the equation $y'' = xy$, appears in Miller (1946, p. B13), where it is extended to the case $x < 0$, yielding a pair of oscillatory solutions.

If we replace the *differential equation* (7.11) by a *difference* equation, by writing

$$h^2 y''(x) \simeq y(x+h) - 2y(x) + y(x-h), \quad (7.4)$$

we obtain, writing $y_r = y(a+rh)$,

$$y_{n+1} - (2 + h^2 P^2) y_n + y_{n-1} = 0, \quad (7.51)$$

or

$$y_{n+1} - (k + 1/k) y_n + y_{n-1} = 0. \quad (7.52)$$

This has the solution

$$y_n = \alpha k^n + \beta k^{-n}, \quad (7.53)$$

where $k + 1/k = 2 + h^2 P^2$, so that k and $1/k$ are real, and we may take $k > 1$.

Solutions clearly correspond to those of the original equation, but k and e^{Ph} are only approximately equal. The manner in which a solution of the difference equation tends to one of those of the differential equation is the problem of *convergence*.

7.2 In the case of the equation

$$y' = Kx \quad (7.61)$$

with solution

$$y = A e^{Kx}, \quad (7.62)$$

we can write

$$hy_n' \simeq \tfrac{1}{2}(y_{n+1} - y_{n-1}), \quad (7.63)$$

yielding on substitution the difference equation

$$y_{n+1} - 2hK y_n - y_{n-1} = 0 \quad (7.64)$$

with solution

$$y_n = \alpha \lambda^n + \beta(-\lambda)^{-n} \quad (7.65)$$

where $\lambda \simeq e^{Kh}$ if h is small.

In this case $\alpha\lambda^n$ corresponds to $A e^{Kx}$, but $\beta(-\lambda)^{-n}$ is a *parasitic solution* which has no counterpart in the original equation. If K is negative, and $\lambda < 1$, then the parasitic solution *dominates* the other, unless $\beta = 0$ exactly. This value of β cannot be maintained by forward recurrence (though if we work backwards with decreasing n, this does not matter, since $\alpha\lambda^n$ then dominates).

7.3 *Error Propagation and Precise Definitions of Effectiveness.* An error once made can (in the absence of further errors) grow, or diminish. It can also, as with solutions of $y'' = -Q^2 y$, $Q^2 > 0$, be oscillatory and remain of the same order over many steps of the calculation. However, which of these happens is not always the most important consideration. It is often more important to know the behaviour of the error *relative to the desired solution*; we need to know if the ratio grows or remains approximately constant—it is only rarely that the relative error diminishes, though it is possible.

Let us again consider $y_n = \alpha k^n + \beta k^{-n}$, $k > 1$. The solution k^n grows, whilst k^{-n} diminishes, as n increases. If we need $\alpha k^n + \beta k^{-n}$, $|\alpha| > 0$, then the relative behaviour of a single error is

$$\frac{\delta\alpha k^n + \delta\beta k^{-n}}{\alpha k^n + \beta k^{-n}} \sim \frac{\delta\alpha}{\alpha} = \eta \tag{7.71}$$

say, so that it is ultimately constant. Thus each individual error is nearly constant relative to the solution αk^n to which y tends; it is bounded by a constant, ε say.

Thus the accumulated relative error is bounded after n steps by $n\varepsilon$. Oliver (1965) introduces this as a standard or *basic error bound*, to provide a measure of normal behaviour, and we note that it increases steadily (and realistically) with the number of steps.

If we need βk^{-n} $(\alpha = 0, \beta \neq 0)$, then the relative error is

$$\frac{\delta\alpha k^n + \delta\beta k^{-n}}{\beta k^{-n}} \sim \frac{\delta\alpha}{\beta} k^{2n}, \tag{7.72}$$

which increases exponentially with n. This is *instability*. The solution k^n is *dominant*, k^{-n} is *dominated* or *subdominant*. Remember, however, that with two solutions, their roles are reversed if we work backwards, with decreasing n; this still leaves the problem, with some third- and higher-order equations, of determining solutions that are subdominant in both directions.

Oliver defines *effectiveness* thus:

If $$|\delta y/y| < Sn\varepsilon \tag{7.8}$$

where $n\varepsilon$ is the basic error bound, then, over an infinite range of x,

(i) if $S \leq 1$, the method is *strongly effective*† for that solution,
(ii) if $S \leq M$, $M > 1$ the method is *weakly effective* for that solution,
(iii) if S is unbounded, the method is *ineffective* for that solution.

† The word "stable" would fit better, if it were not for the variety of usage to which it has already been put. Likewise "ineffective" is perhaps too strong in (iii), since *some* useful results are obtainable—the error may grow fast, but it does not become instantaneously dominant.

Case (ii) is considered as essentially one of stability, since a *fixed* number of extra guarding figures in the calculation suffices to overcome the difficulty.

Effectiveness has been described in terms of error relative to the desired solution. It may be noted that sometimes absolute error, i.e. error relative to a constant, is more appropriate, or error relative to a particular function $u(x)$ for various solutions of a given equation. However, absolute and relative error are readily interchangeable by simple change of dependent variable; such change need not be applied practically, but its possibility removes the need to be precise on all occasions. The occasion when absolute error is most useful is in connection with errors at or near zeros of the desired solution; even then, e.g. as in Miller (1946, p. B13), relative error can often be suitably defined.

8. Dahlquist's Discussion of Linear Methods. Types of Instability

8.1 Dahlquist (1956) has given a valuable and stimulating analysis of the *direct* (one-step iterative) *forward use*† of recurrence relations

$$L(y) \equiv \rho(E)y_r - h\sigma(E)f_r = 0 \qquad (8.1)$$

where $\rho(E)$, $\sigma(E)$ are polynomials of degree k in the displacement operator E, for obtaining approximate solutions to systems

$$\frac{dy}{dx} = f(x, y), \qquad a \le x \le b, \qquad y(a) = y_0, \qquad (8.2)$$

at points with $x_r = a + rh$, $h = (b-a)/n$; $f_r = f(x_r, y_r)$, $y_r = y(x_r)$. Here $f(x, y)$ is restricted to functions satisfying suitable conditions regarding boundedness and existence of derivatives.

An important aim of his investigation was to discover replacement equations that have a solution agreeing closely with the desired solution of the original system, and for which one-point boundary conditions continue to give a well-conditioned problem in the replacement system. This is, in fact, a substantial restriction, since the extra boundary conditions needed for a replacement equation of higher order will usually transform a one-point boundary system rather naturally into a two-point boundary system, perhaps of type (iic) (§1.2).

The *order* of the operator, and of the method resulting from direct forward use, is defined to be k, and the *degree* p is that of the highest degree of polynomial $P(x)$ such that $L(P(x)) \equiv 0$, so that $L(y(x))$ is of the order $h^{p+1}y^{p+1}(\xi)$.

Dahlquist now defines *stable convergence*. The numerical solution y_r^*, approximating the exact solution of (8.1) corresponding to the solution of (8.2), is given by

$$\rho(E)y_r^* = h\sigma(E)f_r^* + \eta_r \qquad (8.3)$$

starting from

$$y_\kappa^* = y_\kappa + \theta_\kappa, \qquad \kappa = 0, 1, \ldots, k-1, \qquad (8.4)$$

† This must be emphasized, because it is unstated. Nomenclature and results are applicable only to this natural, but not unique nor always most successful, use of a recurrence relation. Results and names do not apply to iterative or backward use.

in which θ_κ, η_r are the *local perturbations* at each starting value and each step of the calculation.

Then y_r^* converges stably to $y(x)$, for direct forward use of (8.1), if the maximum value of $|y_r^* - y(x_r)|$ is less than $K\varepsilon$ as $h \to 0$, for all points x_r, and for all perturbations θ_κ, η_r satisfying

$$\sum_{\nu < n} |\eta_\nu| + \max |\theta_\kappa| < \varepsilon, \qquad n = (b-a)/h \tag{8.5}$$

where K is independent of h and ε $(0 < \varepsilon < \varepsilon_0)$.

Dahlquist then shows that stable convergence exists if and only if L is a *stable operator*, that is, if the zeros of $\rho(\zeta)$ are within or on the unit circle $|\zeta| = 1$, and if those on the unit circle are distinct. Otherwise the operator is said to be *unstable*.

A method using an unstable operator is said to exhibit *strong numerical instability* for direct forward use, since the determination of any solution to any system (8.2) is unstable, and in general† the instability gets worse as h is decreased. Such operators can only yield useful results by iterative use in a forward sense; such use remains to be investigated.

An alternative statement of the situation is to say that a replacement system involving an unstable operator yields either an ill-conditioned one-point boundary replacement system, or requires two boundary points for a well-posed restatement.

Dahlquist also shows that a stable operator of order k has maximum degree p equal to the next even integer exceeding k. If the degree is $k+2$, and the operator is stable, then all zeros of $\rho(\zeta)$ have unit modulus, and a method involving semi-direct forward use with (8.2) in this case exhibits *weak instability*. Here the method is stable for some equations $y' = f(x, y)$, and unstable for others; when there is instability it does not in this case get more severe as h diminishes. Milne's corrector formula (4.3) is of this type (see 9.1).

Dahlquist's ideas are discussed and extended in Henrici 1962.

8.2 Another type of instability is common to many methods; this is when the method is stable for small h, but becomes unstable when h exceeds some critical value h_0. This may happen when the approximation is so crude that the replacement equation has no solution approximating that of the original system. This kind of instability is not then of major importance, since it clearly arises only when the interval h is already so large that the solution provided by the replacement equation is unacceptable as an approximation to the desired solution; that is, the lack of correspondence with the desired solution (non-convergence) becomes apparent before instability.

Fox, however (1962, p. 49) gives an example of another type, also mentioned by Dahlquist, involving a complementary function, of rapid relative variation, which is absent from the desired solution. For the solution needed, a con-

---

† If the operator has all zeros with $|\zeta| \leq 1$, but has multiple roots with $|\zeta| = 1$, the instability is always present, but its quality seems to be more like that defined as weak instability below.

siderable interval in h would be possible but for the fact that such an interval, though giving a replacement equation with a reasonable counterpart to the desired solution, gives a highly unstable counterpart to the unwanted complementary function; this component swamps the desired solution unless h is very small. Thus, to give an exaggerated example, the equation

$$y'' + 101y' + 100y = 0 \tag{8.6}$$

has general solution

$$y = A\,e^{-x} + B\,e^{-100x}. \tag{8.7}$$

If $A = 1$, $B = 0$, we could obtain an approximately five-decimal solution with an interval $h = 0 \cdot 1$, using Taylor's series truncated at the fourth term. However, the solution e^{-100x} is represented by $(1 - 100h + 5000h^2 - 166666\tfrac{2}{3}h^3)^n$ after n steps, and the modulus exceeds unity unless $h \le 0 \cdot 0038$ approximately.

Fox classes both of these types under the name *partial instability*—where the existence of stability or instability depends on h. Equations such as (8.6) are sometimes called *stiff* equations. In §13.5 (vi) a suggestion for overcoming this difficulty in some cases is made.

9. Stability. Applications of Theory and Further Remarks

9.1 *Milne's Method.* This method (§4.1) arises from a stable operator giving

$$(E^2 - 1)y_r - \tfrac{1}{3}h(E^2 + 4E + 1)y_r' = 0 \tag{9.1}$$

of the type exhibiting weak instability mentioned in §8.1. The zeros of $\rho(\zeta)$ are $\zeta = \pm 1$, and closer examination is needed.

We consider the particular equation

$$y' = -\mu y, \tag{9.2}$$

which has general solution $y = a\,e^{-\mu x}$. Substitution in (9.1) gives, with $q = \mu h$,

$$(1 + \tfrac{1}{3}q)y_{n+1} + \tfrac{4}{3}qy_n - (1 - \tfrac{1}{3}q)y_{n-1} = 0. \tag{9.3}$$

This has general solution

$$y_n = \alpha\zeta_1^n + \beta\zeta_2^n, \tag{9.4}$$

where

$$\left.\begin{array}{l} \zeta_1 = 1 - q + \tfrac{1}{2}q^2 - \tfrac{1}{6}q^3 + \tfrac{1}{24}q^4 - \tfrac{1}{72}q^5 \ldots \simeq e^{-q} \\[4pt] \zeta_2 = -(1 + \tfrac{1}{3}q + \tfrac{1}{18}q^2 - \tfrac{1}{54}q^3 + \ldots) \simeq -e^{\frac{1}{3}q} \end{array}\right\}. \tag{9.5}$$

Thus if $x_n = nh$,

$$y_n \simeq \alpha\,e^{-\mu x_n} + (-1)^n\beta\,e^{\frac{1}{3}\mu x_n}. \tag{9.6}$$

The first term represents the desired solution, the second is an oscillatory parasitic solution.

Now if $\mu < 0$, $\zeta_2^n \to 0$ as $n \to \infty$ and the determination of the desired solution is stable. If, however, $\mu > 0$, ζ_1^n, representing $e^{-\mu x}$, diminishes, but ζ_2^n oscillates with increasing amplitude and eventually dominates; its order, however, is $e^{\frac{1}{3}\mu x_n}$ whatever h may be, so that it does not get worse as h diminishes. Thus Milne's method is weakly unstable.

Recently Milne and Reynolds (1959, 1962) have introduced the idea of using a stabilizing formula occasionally, in addition to the predictor and corrector.

9.2 *The Adams-Bashforth Method.* If we apply (3.2), truncated for example after the fourth term on the right, to the same equation $y' = -\mu y$, we obtain

$$y_{n+1} - y_n = -(1 + \tfrac{1}{2}\nabla + \tfrac{5}{12}\nabla^2 + \tfrac{3}{8}\nabla^3)h\mu y_n, \qquad (9.7)$$

with the general solution

$$y_n = \alpha\zeta_1^n + \beta\zeta_2^n + \gamma\zeta_3^n + \delta\zeta_4^n, \qquad (9.8)$$

where ζ_r satisfies

$$\zeta^4 - \zeta^3 + h\mu[\zeta^3 + \tfrac{1}{2}\zeta^2(\zeta-1) + \tfrac{5}{12}\zeta(\zeta-1)^2 + \tfrac{3}{8}(\zeta-1)^3] = 0. \qquad (9.9)$$

For $h = 0$ this yields $\zeta = 1, 0, 0, 0$.

The term $\alpha\zeta_1^n$ corresponds to the desired solution, the others to parasitic solutions. As h increases, the zeros drift steadily from the values for $h = 0$. It is clear that h will reach a considerable size before instability (here partial) can occur; before it becomes obvious, lack of convergence of the series will indicate the inadequacy of truncation after four terms. In fact, the Adams-Bashforth method involves using (3.2) until terms are negligible; if they do not become negligible, we use (3.3), which has better stability properties, repeatedly until the iteration converges, or we may reduce h. Instability will always involve failure of the difference formulae to converge. This discussion applies wherever we truncate the formula.

Thus we can say that the Adams-Bashforth method is always used directly and stably when it converges.

9.3 *Taylor Series Method.* This, like the Adams-Bashforth method proper, is used only when it converges, and it is then stable. If curtailed, partial instability can appear.

9.4 *Runge-Kutta Methods.* These exhibit partial instability (see Fox 1962, p. 50), but are normally usable with moderate intervals.

9.5 *General Remarks on Error Propagation and Stability.*

(i) It seems useful to note that stability is not always important. Over a finite range *any* method, however unstable, can provide a useful, even an adequate, solution if not too much accuracy is demanded, if the range is short enough, and if the working precision is high enough. This is sometimes virtually the only reasonable way to obtain a highly subdominant solution, and may well be the easiest way to carry out rough exploration.

(ii) Over a very large or infinite range nearly *every* method will eventually fail (a counter-example can be constructed, but it is rather a special case, though not uncommon). We thus need, as Oliver realized, a basic error bound that involves steady though not overwhelming deterioration.

(iii) We could also consider the accumulation of errors statistically. This is relevant only for stable solutions; in the case of instability, the first large error usually dominates subsequent ones. For very strongly stable solutions, likewise, the early errors die out, and only the few latest matter. In other cases, i.e. of weak stability, or of normal behaviour, with S having upper bound $b > 0$, we obtain a statistical error of order $\sqrt{n}\varepsilon$, which may be considerably less than the basic error bound.

10. Methods. Recent Developments and New Suggestions

The following sections describe methods that have arisen largely since the advent of automatic computing. This has led to a search for methods involving repetition without too much ingenuity, and particularly for methods not needing human intervention at frequent intervals. The lack of storage space in early computers led to methods using only a small amount of back information; this tended to reduce the attractiveness of differences (in any case more difficult to examine) and to promote rather drastic truncations.

However, the characteristics of some of the early methods are so good that it is a relief that modern computers can no longer be regarded as short of storage space, and methods using a good deal of back information can be considered again. There will always be problems involving very large numbers of simultaneous equations, but the limitations are now largely of time rather than of space.

Section 11 describes recent developments in the evaluation of derivatives that make Taylor's series attractive for machine use.

Section 12 discusses the deferred-correction methods of Fox and Goodwin.

Section 13 suggests the search for new methods involving iterative use of replacement difference equations, and gives a detailed error analysis demonstrating that effective use of an unstable operator is possible, provided the use is iterative and not direct.

Recently Gragg and Stetter (1964) and Butcher (1965) have discovered stable algorithms of high order, using equally-spaced points, together with one extra judiciously-chosen extraneous point, for which a special predictor is used.

11. Taylor Series Method. Calculation of Derivatives

We begin with two remarks.

(i) With the advent of computer programs capable of deriving automatically derivatives of many known functions in analytical form, it becomes feasible to use derivatives more readily than when the analysis and algebra has to be done by hand and brain.

(ii) It is not necessary for all derivatives to be expressed in terms of the starting values obtained at the beginning of each step, e.g. y_n and y'_n for a second-order equation. In fact it is sufficient to have expressions in terms of *any derivatives already known*. Thus one may develop a recurrence relation for the pth derivative that involves any or all derivatives up to the $(p-1)$st.

11.1 *Recurrence Relations for Derivatives.* The problem of obtaining recurrence relations to give higher derivatives easily from a given differential relation depends basically for its solution on the theorem of Leibnitz for differentiating a product. Its application is well known for linear differential equations.

Extension to more general equations is outlined in Gibbons 1960 and Moore 1965 (§9). It seems worth while to give a brief account here.

The basic operation is best expressed in terms of multiplication of power series, applied to Taylor expansions. For convenience we shall consider only the step a to $a+h$ (but remember that a is quite arbitrary, and that we may start from a, $a+h$,... in succession). For any function $u(x)$, we shall write

$$
\begin{aligned}
u(a+\theta h) &= u(a)+\theta h u'(a)+\ldots+\frac{(\theta h)^p}{p!}u^{(p)}(a)+\ldots \\
&= u_0+u_1 h\theta+\frac{u_2 h^2}{2!}\theta^2+\ldots+\frac{u_p h^p}{p!}\theta^p+\ldots \\
&= U_0+U_1\theta+U_2\theta^2+\ldots+U_p\theta^p+\ldots
\end{aligned}
\right\} \quad (11.1)
$$

where

$$
U_p = \frac{u_p h^p}{p!} = \frac{u^{(p)}h^p}{p!}, \quad (11.2)
$$

a *reduced derivative*. The relations (3.7), (3.8) are thus rewritten as

$$
\left.
\begin{aligned}
y_{\pm 1} &= Y_0 \pm Y_1 + Y_2 \pm Y_3 + \ldots \\
hy'_{\pm 1} &= Y_1 \pm 2Y_2 + 3Y_3 \pm 4Y_4 + \ldots
\end{aligned}
\right\}. \quad (11.3)
$$

Consider now the basic operation

$$
y = uv \quad (11.4)
$$

as a multiplication of Taylor series of reduced derivatives. Equating coefficients of θ^p gives immediately

$$
Y_p = U_p V_0 + U_{p-1}V_1 + \ldots + U_1 V_{p-1} + U_0 V_p, \quad (11.5)
$$

which may be used to give Y_p if U_r, V_r are known for $r = 0, 1,\ldots, p$, or to give, say, V_p if Y_r, U_r, $r = 0, 1,\ldots, p$, V_s, $s = 0, 1,\ldots, p-1$, are known. The latter corresponds to the determination of $v = y/u$. In addition to this basic step, we need only remark that it is obvious that the differentiated and integrated series are easily obtained by mutliplying or dividing the reduced derivatives by integers and h.

11.2 *Some Examples.* We now have to express elementary functions in terms of simple products of series. This is quite easy to do, using differential relations, as follows.

(i) $z = y^n$ yields $z' = ny^{n-1}y'$, whence $yz' = nzy'$. Equating coefficients of θ^p immediately gives Z'_p and so Z_{p+1}, assuming that Y_r, Z_s, $r \leq p+1$, $s \leq p$, are known, and hence Y'_r, Z'_s, $r \leq p$, $s \leq p-1$.

(ii) $z = e^y$ yields $z' = zy'$. Equating coefficients of θ^p gives Z_{p+1}, assuming Y_r, Z_s, $r \leq p+1$, $s \leq p$, known. Likewise the coefficients of θ^p give Y_{p+1}, if Z_s, Y_r, $s \leq p+1$, $r \leq p$, are known; this corresponds to

(iii) $y = \log_e z$.

(iv) $c = \cos y$, $s = \sin y$ are treated together. They yield

$$
c' = -sy', \qquad s' = cy',
$$

whence coefficients in the two series are obtained alternately.

These examples should be enough to make the idea behind the manipulation clear. It is worth remarking that the simplicity of (11.5), in which each term on the right is a product of two quantities, is slightly blemished if, as in all cases above, derivatives appear directly in the formula for the product of series, and coefficients in the series for the original function are used, since $Y'_{p-1} = (p/h) Y_p$, where Y'_r is the coefficient of θ^r in y'.

In these circumstances there is also a multiplying factor, linear in the suffix p of (11.5). This may be removed from the formula if the coefficients Y'_{p-1} are formed in advance; a useful device when writing computer programs in terms of subroutines.

The method is readily extended to functions with less simple differential relations. For example

(v) $t = \tan y = \sin y/\cos y$. Here we use $t = s/c$, $c' = -sy'$, $s' = cy'$.

(vi) $z = uvw$; we use $t = uv$, $z = tw$ in succession.

(vii) $j = J_0(y)$. This function satisfies

$$yj'' + j' + yj = 0$$

in which the primes denote differentiation with respect to y. This is composed of products and so, by equating coefficients of θ^p, assuming Y_s known, we can obtain J_p, $p = 2, 3, 4, \ldots$ in succession. We must remember, however, that $dj/dx = j'y'$, etc. It is now evident that any system of differential equations ultimately expressible in terms of elementary functions can be dealt with.

11.3 *Comment*. Two final complementary remarks are needed.

(1) The first term in each expansion usually needs special treatment; it is often the most difficult to compute. It may be obtained by use of subroutines for elementary functions, or from its Taylor series at any step after the first (possibly with increased error), since all derivatives needed will have been computed.

(2) As remarked above, with a good routine for obtaining automatically algebraic or analytic expressions for derivatives, some of these may be obtained more efficiently, and often with better known accuracy, by means of machine subroutines, whether for elementary functions normally provided, or for such special functions as may be available.

The program written by Gibbons (1960) automatically selects the auxiliary variables and sets up the subsidiary equations, given only the original differential equation and the initial conditions.

12. The Deferred-Correction Methods of Fox and Goodwin

Fox and Goodwin (1949) describe a very useful collection of methods whereby what we have called a replacement equation, with a solution corresponding reasonably with the solution of the original equation, is converted into a revised equation by the inclusion of a deferred correction Δ, usually expressed in terms of a series of differences of the required solution, but which we start by ignoring (i.e. take $\Delta = 0$) and then use iteratively; at each iteration the replacement or *leading* part is used directly, in a forward direction, while Δ is computed from the previous iteration. *If the process converges* we then have a solution of the original equation, even though the direct use of the replacement part is unstable (not too strongly—strong instability would prevent convergence). We would normally use such methods by proceeding several steps at a time and then iterating before appending a further sequence of steps. Convergence is normally progressive, i.e. quicker for steps near the start than for more remote ones.

The replacement part should not normally be of higher order than the original equation, but if it is so, great care must be taken to avoid badly-posed (i.e. wrong) initial conditions.

Three methods are now given as illustrations.

12.1 The first and simplest is an application of the trapezoidal rule for integrals. We have

$$\left. \begin{array}{l} y_{r+1} = y_r + \tfrac{1}{2}h(y'_{r+1} + y'_r) + \Delta \\ \Delta = (-\tfrac{1}{12}\delta^3 + \tfrac{1}{120}\delta^5 - \ldots)y_{r+\frac{1}{2}} \end{array} \right\}. \tag{12.1}$$

where

This is used iteratively, starting each iteration with y_0 given. The first takes $\Delta = 0$, and the result of each iteration is used to give Δ for the next. This is a simple formula, with satisfactory stability properties. (For sufficiently small h, no iteration is needed.)

12.2 Method III of Fox and Goodwin 1949 operates with $(1 + \tfrac{1}{6}\delta^2)$ on the equation

$$y' = f(x)y + g(x) \tag{12.2}$$

to give

$$(1 + \tfrac{1}{6}\delta^2)y' = (1 + \tfrac{1}{6}\delta^2)(fy + g), \tag{12.3}$$

whence

$$\left. \begin{array}{l} (1 - \tfrac{1}{3}hf_1)y_1 = \tfrac{4}{3}hf_0 y_0 + (1 + \tfrac{1}{3}hf_{-1})y_{-1} + \tfrac{1}{3}(g_1 + 4g_0 + g_{-1}) + \Delta \\ \Delta = (-\tfrac{1}{90}\mu\delta^5 + \tfrac{1}{315}\mu\delta^7 - \ldots)y_0 \end{array} \right\}. \tag{12.4}$$

with

Here each iteration starts with y_{-1}, y_0 given (y_{-1} may be computed by Taylor's series).

With the equation $y' = y$, $y(0) = 1$, $h = 0.2$, this method yields

$$y_1 = \tfrac{2}{7}y_0 + \tfrac{8}{7}y_{-1} + \tfrac{15}{14}\Delta, \tag{12.5}$$

Δ being given as above. About five figures are obtained at $x = 2$, taking $\Delta = 0$, with considerable improvement on the next iteration.

For $y' = -y$, $y(0) = 1$, $h = 0.5$, an example given by Fox and Goodwin, we find

$$y_1 = -\tfrac{4}{7}y_0 + \tfrac{5}{7}y_{-1} + \tfrac{6}{7}\Delta. \tag{12.6}$$

This time the difference equation (with $\Delta = 0$) is unstable for the desired solution k_1^n, with $k_1 \simeq e^{-\frac{1}{2}}$, having a parasitic solution $(-k_2)^n$ with $k_2 > 1$. This method thus exhibits weak instability in Dahlquist's sense.

12.3 Method VII of Fox and Goodwin is reminiscent of the Numerov method. We apply the operation $(1 + \frac{1}{12}\delta^2)$ to the equation

$$y'' = f(x)y, \tag{12.7}$$

and obtain

$$\left(1 - \frac{h^2}{12}f_1\right)y_1 = (2 + \tfrac{5}{6}h^2 f_0)y_0 - \left(1 - \frac{h^2}{12}f_{-1}\right)y_{-1} + \Delta \Bigg\}, \tag{12.8}$$

with $\qquad\qquad \Delta = (-\tfrac{1}{240}\delta^6 + \tfrac{13}{15120}\delta^8 - \ldots)y_0$

a formula of remarkable accuracy and power.

13. Iterative Forward Use of Formulae

The work of Dahlquist has shown that some difference equations, theoretically possible as replacement equations of high accuracy, exhibit instabilities that render them useless or difficult for direct forward use. The example in §12.2 also exhibits instability before the deferred correction can be brought into use.

Again, an ill-conditioned problem runs into trouble in forward use because of an unwanted dominant part that is introduced by rounding errors.

Likewise, in stiff equations, a rapidly varying part that is decreasing or has decreased to negligibility can cause trouble if the replacement equation does not represent the *unwanted and theoretically absent element* adequately.

It appears that most, if not all, of these troubles can be overcome, or at least minimized, by iterative use of the differential or difference equation. This is a subject that merits much further study. A price to be paid is that the calculation has to be repeated iteratively, instead of being direct, but the gain is that some solutions are obtainable that cannot be found at all by direct forward methods, and there is a possibility of large step-lengths in others.

In this section we shall merely demonstrate a practical example, and prove the effectiveness in one simple case. We shall not examine ways of choosing the iteration to give a good initial approximation, which is essential for reasonably rapid convergence.

An important point concerns boundary conditions. We suppose the problem (original or replacement) to be of type (iic) of §1.2, that is, basically a problem with two-point boundary conditions in a well-posed form, but where the conditions at the second point are simply conditions of boundedness. (This can often be achieved, as mentioned, by change of independent variable to put the second point at infinity, and by change of dependent variable to make the wanted solution diminish and unwanted ones increase as $x \to \infty$.)

The conditions of boundedness are introduced via the initial approximation in the iterative process, simply by starting with zero, or at least with an approximation diminishing as $x \to \infty$. If the initial approximation is not too good, and convergence is slow, it will also be progressive in general, that is, convergence will be delayed more and more as x increases; in such cases it is therefore useful to progress a moderate number of steps, to be increased as convergence becomes established at the near end.

13.1 *Dahlquist's Example Discussed.* We start first with Dahlquist's example for exhibiting strong instability. This applies the formula

$$y_{n+2} = -4y_{n+1} + 5y_n + h(4f_{n+1} + 2f_n) \qquad (13.11)$$

to the differential equation $y' = y$, $y(0) = 1$, with solution e^x. With $h = 0\cdot1$, substitution for f_n yields

$$y_{n+2} = -3\cdot6y_{n+1} + 5\cdot2y_n, \qquad y_0 = 1, \qquad n = 10x. \qquad (13.12)$$

This is second order, so Dahlquist needs y_1 also. In Table I the first column gives x, the second e^x, the third, y_a, gives the result using $y_1 = 1\cdot105171$, which is $e^{0\cdot1}$ to six decimal places. The fourth column gives the result y_b, using $y_1 = 1\cdot105168$; the positive root of $\lambda^2 + 3\cdot6\lambda - 5\cdot2 = 0$ is nearly $1\cdot1051678$ (the other root is $-4\cdot7051678$, which accounts for the instability). These two columns are taken from Dahlquist 1956.

We rewrite the equation in the form

$$5\cdot6y_{n+1} = 6\cdot2y_n - \delta^2 y_{n+1} \qquad (13.13)$$

and use this iteratively as follows

$$y_{n+1}^{(p+1)} = \frac{62y_n^{(p+1)} - 10\delta^2 y_{n+1}^{(p)}}{56}, \qquad (13.14)$$

starting with $y_n^{(0)} = 0$, $n > 0$, $y_0^{(p)} = 1$. The iterates for $p = 1, 2, \ldots, 5$ are given in the next five columns of Table I; the last of these agrees *throughout* with $(1\cdot1051678)^n$ to six decimals, within a unit in the last figure. The last column gives $e^x - y^{(5)}$.

The approximation $y^{(5)}$ is now ideal for application of a deferred correction. This involves rather clumsy evaluation of high differences, and estimates of these near the ends of the table, and this needs reasonably small and accurate values to work on.

13.2 *Detailed Error Analysis of a Case of Iterative Forward Use.* For a simple rigorous error analysis we revert to an equation discussed earlier (7.52),

$$y_{n+1} - \left(k + \frac{1}{k}\right)y_n + y_{n-1} = 0, \qquad (13.21)$$

with general solution

$$y_n = Ak^n + Bk^{-n}. \qquad (13.22)$$

We have seen that for recurrence with increasing n, the solution $A*k^n$ dominates even with $A = 0$ initially, since errors induce a perturbation δA. Likewise with decreasing n the solution $B*k^{-n}$ dominates similarly even if $B = 0$ initially. Much error analysis assumes, without explicit statement, that the equation is used in one of these two ways, for *both* of which the general solution given above is appropriate.

We now consider a simple forward method of using the equation iteratively, in the form

$$\left(k + \frac{1}{k}\right)y_n^{(p+1)} - y_{n-1}^{(p+1)} = y_{n+1}^{(p)}, \qquad (13.23)$$

J. C. P. MILLER

TABLE I. Results for Dahlquist's Example of §13.1.

x	e^x	y_a	y_b	$y^{(1)}$	$y^{(2)}$	$y^{(3)}$	$y^{(4)}$	$y^{(5)}$	$(e^x - y^{(5)}) \times 10^6$
0·0	1	1	1	1	1	1	1	1	
0·1	1·105171	1·105171	1·105168	1·107143	1·105093	1·105171	1·105168	1·105168	3
0·2	1·221403	1·221384	1·221395	1·225765	1·221226	1·221404	1·221396	1·221396	7
0·3	1·349859	1·349907	1·349852	1·357097	1·349559	1·349861	1·349847	1·349848	11
0·4	1·491825	1·491532	1·491787	1·502500	1·491373	1·491829	1·491807	1·491808	17
0·5	1·648721	1·650001	1·648797	1·663482	1·648083	1·648729	1·648697	1·648698	23
0·6	1·822119	1·815963	1·821623	1·841712	1·821253	1·822130	1·822086	1·822088	31
0·7	2·013753	2·042538	2·015902	2·039038	2·012612	2·013769	2·013710	2·013713	40
0·8	2·225541	2·089871	2·215192	2·257506	2·224069	2·225564	2·225487	2·225491	50
0·9	2·459603	+3·097662	2·507999	2·499382	2·457734	2·459635	2·459536	2·459541	62
1·0	2·718282	−0·284254	2·490202	2·767173	2·715939	2·718325	2·718199	2·718206	77

where we take $y_0^{(p)} = y_0$ for all p, $y_n^{(0)} = 0$ for $n > 0$. It will be shown that the condition $y_n^{(0)} = 0$ ensures that only the solution $y_0 k^{-n}$ can enter into the calculation, coupled with ever-decreasing error terms as n, p increase.

The errors at successive stages of the calculation satisfy the equation

$$\left(k + \frac{1}{k}\right)\varepsilon_n^{(p+1)} = \varepsilon_{n-1}^{(p+1)} + \varepsilon_{n+1}^{(p)} + \varepsilon_{n,p}, \tag{13.31}$$

where

$$\varepsilon_n^{(p)} = y_n^{*(p)} - y_n, \qquad y_n = y_0 k^{-n}. \tag{13.32}$$

Here $y_n^{*(p)}$ is the iterate actually computed, and $\varepsilon_{n,p}$ is the rounding error, bounded by $\eta_{n,p}$ say.

We shall study the error behaviour in two parts, and show that

(i) The initial error dies out with exact calculation, so that $y_n^{(p+1)}$ converges to $y_0 k^{-n}$,

(ii) The accumulation of the rounding errors introduced at each iteration is suitably bounded.

13.3 *Convergence*. The initial error of y_0 is zero. We suppose that all other initial errors in y_n are bounded by M_0. In an iteration carried out exactly, we have

$$\left.\begin{array}{l} \varepsilon_{n,p} = 0, \text{ all } n,p; \qquad \varepsilon_0^{(p)} = 0, \text{ all } p; \\ |\varepsilon_n^{(0)}| < M_0, \text{ all } n > 0. \end{array}\right\} \tag{13.4}$$

Thus if $E_n^{(p)}$ are corresponding maximum errors

$$\left(k + \frac{1}{k}\right)E_n^{(1)} = E_{n-1}^{(1)} + M_0, \tag{13.51}$$

whence

$$\left.\begin{array}{l} E_1^{(1)} = \dfrac{M_0}{k+1/k} = M_0\mu, \text{ say} \\ E_2^{(1)} = M_0(\mu + \mu^2) \\ \cdots\cdots\cdots\cdots\cdots\cdots\cdots\cdots \\ E_r^{(1)} = M_0(\mu + \mu^2 + \ldots + \mu^r) = M_0\mu\dfrac{1-\mu^r}{1-\mu} \end{array}\right\} \tag{13.52}$$

Thus

$$E_r^{(1)} < M_1 = \frac{1}{(k+1/k-1)} M_0 < M_0, \tag{13.53}$$

since $k + 1/k > 2$. Each iteration gives similarly a bound

$$M_{p+1} = \frac{M_p}{(k+1/k-1)}, \tag{13.54}$$

so that $M_p \to 0$. Convergence is thus assured. It is worth noting that convergence is more rapid for small n than for large n.

13.4 *Accumulation of Rounding Error*. In this case we start with

$$\varepsilon_n^{(0)} = 0, \qquad \varepsilon_0^{(p)} = 0, \qquad |\varepsilon_{n,p}| < \eta_{n,p}. \tag{13.6}$$

For suitable choice of $\eta_{n,p}$ we need a bound for $|\varepsilon_n^{(p)}|$, using (13.31) in the form

$$\left(k + \frac{1}{k}\right)\left|\varepsilon_n^{(p+1)}\right| \leq \left|\varepsilon_{n-1}^{(p+1)}\right| + \left|\varepsilon_{n+1}^{(p)}\right| + \eta_{n,p}. \tag{13.71}$$

If we choose $\eta_{n,p} = \varepsilon\lambda^p\mu^n$, and try $|\varepsilon_n^{(p)}| < C\varepsilon\lambda^p\mu^n$, $0 < \lambda \leq 1, 0 < \mu \leq 1$, we find on substitution that we must have

$$C\lambda\left\{\left(k + \frac{1}{k}\right) - \frac{1}{\mu} - \frac{\mu}{\lambda}\right\} \leq 1, \tag{13.72}$$

in which the coefficient of $C\lambda$ has to be positive. This is clearly possible.

We can take $\lambda = \mu = 1$, which corresponds to a constant rounding error bound ε. Then $C(\sqrt{k} - 1/\sqrt{k})^2 \leq 1$, or $C \leq 1/(\sqrt{k} - 1/\sqrt{k})^2$. This gives $|\varepsilon_n^{(p)}| < C\varepsilon$ for all n, p, and this excludes the solution Ak^n of the original difference equation as a contributor to the error; this is what we set out to demonstrate.

However, we can also take, for example, $1 > \lambda = \mu > \dfrac{1}{k + 1/k - 1}$, which will give us an error that diminishes with both n and p. This has a larger value of C, and requires adjustment of the rounding error with both n and p.

It will be noted that, by the definitions of stability in §7, these individual iterations are all ineffective. However, the instability is under control by successive iteration, and refers to error bounds. The bounds obtained are over-estimates of the error in practice, which accumulates in a statistical fashion, and may well converge rapidly to zero.

13.5 *General Comments on Iterative Forward Methods.* Such methods have not been extensively studied recently, in particular, error analysis is noticeable by its absence. The comments that follow are somewhat disconnected but may be helpful in use and further study.

(i) The iterative forward methods mentioned are those of Fox and Goodwin in §12, and the Numerov method of §3.2, and other central-difference methods. The latter are, in a sense, semi-direct, since the estimates of higher central differences are made anew for each step, and need be only rough, having small coefficients when used.

(ii) The use of an iterative method is usually more time-consuming than a direct method *if available*. The work of Dahlquist has shown that helpful, direct, replacement equations of higher order are not easy to come by, while any direct forward method has difficulty with any solution that does not dominate all others. We can cope with the dominant solution for decreasing x by backward use. In ill-conditioned problems, however, we are often unable to find any direct method of solution. Iterative methods of some sort are then essential.

(iii) In choosing an iterative method for solving a difference equation, we write it in the form

$$y_{n+1}^{(p+1)} = f_{n+1}^{(p+1)} + g_{n+1}^{(p)}, \tag{13.81}$$

where f_{n+1} involves y_r for $r \leq n$, and g_{n+1} may involve y_r for some $r > n$ as well.

For a differential equation we likewise write

$$\left[\frac{d^n y}{dx^n}\right]^{(p+1)} = f^{(p+1)} + g^{(p)} \tag{13.82}$$

at each point, where f involves $d^r y/dx^r$, $r < n$, while g may involve higher derivatives as well.

For mixed equations, involving differences and derivatives, such as those considered by Dahlquist, we have $y_{n+1}^{(p+1)}$ on the left, and we may allow f_{n+1} to involve one derivative (or more) of $y_{n+1}^{(p+1)}$, resulting in an algebraic equation to be solved at each step; $g^{(p)}$, involving as it does the previous iteration, is always known in full.

(iv) We wish our iterative method to converge, and to do so as rapidly as possible. Likewise we wish the calculations to be easy. Rapid convergence means that $g^{(p)}$ must be as small as convenient compared with $f^{(p+1)}$; this may mean that $g^{(p)}$ is rather cumbersome to compute, possibly because it involves high-order differences of $y_r^{(p)}$.

It is therefore useful to choose the leading part of the equation, involving $f^{(p+1)}$, in such a way that, even with $g^{(p)}$ neglected, it yields a good approximation to the desired solution of the original equation. Dahlquist's stable direct forward methods do just this. Deferred correction terms can then be included as $g^{(p)}$.

(v) It may be convenient to choose the leading part of the equation to correspond to an unstable direct forward method, but to use it iteratively if thereby a good approximation to y_r can be obtained easily, and then to apply the deferred correction in a further iteration.

This is equivalent to using only one or two terms in a deferred correction in the early iterations, and adding more terms as the iteration proceeds, but it may be more convenient if early iterates are expressed in terms of function values rather than of differences.

(vi) If in a revised equation the order is reduced, this means that higher-order derivative or difference terms are relegated to $g^{(p)}$. The reason for this is usually that we expect these higher-order terms to be small. It is thus evident that we are, in general, eliminating by this implication those solutions of the original equation for which the derivatives are relatively largest. This is, in fact, what appears to happen in practice, though rigorous proofs are needed. The order of successive disappearance of solutions as the order of the leading part of the revised equation is reduced merits study.

The solutions thus eliminated are (a) dominant solutions and (b) rapidly evanescent solutions; both types, exemplified by $e^{\pm Ax}$ with large A, have relatively large derivatives. A third type that may be removed consists of (c) rapidly oscillating solutions, corresponding to complex A with $|A|$ large.

Case (a) is demonstrated in §§13.2–13.4. For case (b), consider the "stiff" equation (8.6) which can be rewritten as

$$\left[\frac{dy}{dx}\right]^{(p+1)} = -\tfrac{100}{101} y^{(p+1)} - \tfrac{1}{100}\left[\frac{d^2 y}{dx^2}\right]^{(p)} \tag{13.9}$$

and solved iteratively, and successfully, at a reasonable interval, e.g. $h = 0.1$, immediately the term e^{-100x} becomes negligible.

Case (c) is illustrated in Olver 1950, where the solution with small derivatives is seen to be needed, others being highly oscillatory.

14. Extension to Systems of Equations and to Higher-order Equations

14.1 Attention has so far been confined mainly to single equations of first or second order. Extension to systems of first-order equations is immediate for all methods involving first-order equations, though stability discussions will need modification.

Likewise any higher-order equation can be replaced by a system of first-order equations by defining new variables. This may be done usually in several ways, with important differences in effect on the singularities and on stability behaviour.

It is worth remarking that it is not always desirable to have a system of first-order equations. A simple example will show how this reduction may have disastrous effects on stability.

Consider

$$y'' + (10x+1)y' + 10xy = 0. \tag{14.1}$$

This is equivalent to

$$\left.\begin{array}{l} y' = z \\ z' = -(10x+1)z - 10xy \end{array}\right\}. \tag{14.2}$$

Any errors in y and z are clearly magnified in z' and in higher derivatives, and h must be chosen to keep hz', h^2z'', etc. within reasonable bounds; particularly, truncation error must be kept reasonable. This is so in spite of the fact that the solution that causes this trouble is subdominant, approximately e^{-5x^2} compared with e^{-x}. This is another example of *stiffness* or *over-stability* (cf. §8.2); if we use too big a value of the interval h, the subdominant solution is represented by an approximation so bad that it becomes dominant, even if the particular solution concerned is initially absent from the complementary function satisfying the boundary conditions.

We can, however, use the *second-order* equation iteratively in the form

$$\left[\frac{dy}{dx}\right]^{(p+1)} = -y^{(p+1)} - \frac{1}{10x}\left\{\left[\frac{d^2y}{dx^2}\right]^{(p)} + \left[\frac{dy}{dx}\right]^{(p)}\right\}, \tag{14.3}$$

in which it is quite clear that the unwanted solution has no chance.

A similar device was used by Fox and Goodwin 1953 to solve an ill-conditioned integral equation of the form

$$\int_0^x k(x, y)f(y)\,dy = g(x) + f(x). \tag{14.4}$$

Differentiation gives

$$f(x) + \frac{1}{k(x, x)}\int_0^x \frac{\partial}{\partial x}k(x, y)f(y)\,dy = \frac{g'(x)}{k(x, x)} + \frac{f'(x)}{k(x, x)}. \tag{14.5}$$

Obvious direct methods have large error build-up if $k(x, x)$ is large and positive, but if $f(x)$ does not vary rapidly, so that $f'(x)$ is small, we can solve the differentiated equation by the iteration

$$f^{(p+1)}(x) + \frac{1}{k(x, x)} \int_0^x \frac{\partial}{\partial x} k(x, y) f^{(p+1)}(y) \, dy = \frac{g'(x)}{k(x, x)} + \frac{f'^{(p)}(x)}{k(x, x)},$$

$$f'^{(0)}(x) = 0, \quad (14.6)$$

with much better speed and accuracy.

See also Fox and Mitchell 1957 for suggestions about stiff equations.

14.2 For higher-order equations the Taylor series method is clearly readily adaptable, and likewise for systems. Predictor-corrector methods can also be readily devised.

It seems likely also that we can produce iterative versions as in §13, so that any desired solution can be brought into dominance of the leading part involving the iteration $(p+1)$, and others kept out of the deferred part involving iteration (p). Much more work is needed on the investigation of these cases.

In devising such equations for iteration we observe that convergence is, in general, linear, so that it is helpful to produce an iterative scheme in which the deferred correction, which we suppose behaves like Ck^p, has a small value of k, at the expense of a larger value of C.

Thus

$$y_{n+1} - \left(n + \frac{1}{n}\right)y_n + y_{n-1} = 0 \qquad (14.7)$$

might be replaced by

$$\left(n + \frac{1}{n}\right)y_n^{(p+1)} - y_{n-1}^{(p+1)} = y_{n+1}^{(p)}, \qquad (14.8)$$

with success for the solution diminishing with n.

The alternative form

$$ny_n^{(p+1)} - y_{n-1}^{(p+1)} = y_{n+1}^{(p)} - \frac{1}{n} y_n^{(p)} \qquad (14.9)$$

gives a smaller right hand side and so perhaps better convergence. Further improvements are possible.

15. Boundary-value Problems

15.1 The most successful methods so far developed for boundary-value problems are concerned with reduction to an approximately equivalent matrix equation, of form $Ay = b$, in which, for example, y^T is the vector $(y_1, y_2, \ldots, y_{n-1})$ of approximations to the desired solution, y_0 and y_n being known. Well-known methods for solving simultaneous equations may then be used; these will not be discussed here.

Such methods yield results which may be improved by use of deferred corrections, that is, the methods are essentially approximate, or iterative.

It is also possible to obtain solutions, in this way, to equations that are strongly unstable for forward recurrence. Direct methods for boundary-value problems are not common; we mention that of Ridley (1957) for a second-order equation.

For a comprehensive survey of boundary-value problems and their solution see Fox 1957.

15.2 Here we mention only that it is possible to solve some boundary-value problems by marching methods, though such methods in these cases involve iterative, or at least several, individual numerical calculations.

The methods described below are fairly straightforward, even obvious, in their ideas, but it seems useful to mention them. Fox 1957 contains more details and some error analysis.

For linear equations of order n we need to obtain n independent solutions of the equation over the interval $[a, b]$ between the two boundaries. These may then be combined linearly to satisfy the boundary conditions. The main difficulties that can arise are concerned with the choice of n independent solutions, and the determination of those that are subdominant for both forward and backward solution; these can occur when $n \geq 3$ (though not in all cases when n is small, e.g. 3 or 4).

Alternatively, for general equations, not necessarily linear, we may start at one end with the conditions known at that end and with estimates of as many further conditions as may be needed. If the number of estimated conditions is small enough, we may vary them and eventually satisfy conditions at the other end by trial and error. Otherwise we may work inwards from both ends and match solutions at some point in the interval (a, b). This has been used on a problem in stellar evolution with four degrees of freedom by Haselgrove and Hoyle (1956).

Variational methods are also useful for determining small perturbations. Having obtained one approximate solution in $[a, b]$, we can derive from the original differential equation an equation for a small variation δy such that $y + \delta y$ satisfies the original equation, with slightly varied boundary conditions. This may be used to improve the first approximate solution.

Similar variational methods may be used to obtain from the solution of one system the equation of a slightly varied system (the variations may be in the equation as well as in the boundary conditions). Eigenvalue problems come into this category.

15.3 Finally we mention an obvious iterative method suitable for choosing a bounded solution from a diverging pencil of solutions. We assume that it is possible to tell in which sense each solution is diverging, if we carry on far enough. For illustration, consider a second-order equation starting with given $y(a)$ that has diverging solutions as we march towards a prescribed $y(b)$. Start at $x = a$ with $y^{(1)} = y^{(2)} = y(a)$, $y^{(1)\prime} = y_0^{(1)\prime}$, $y^{(2)\prime} = y_0^{(2)\prime}$ and carry on with these, obtaining $y^{(1)}$ and $y^{(2)}$ until both clearly diverge from our requirements, and suppose that (by preliminary search if necessary) they diverge in opposite senses.

Choose now $y_0^{(3)'} = \frac{1}{2}(y_0^{(1)'} + y_0^{(2)'})$, or some preferable intermediate value if one can be obtained, and obtain $y^{(3)}$, *between* $y^{(1)}$ and $y^{(2)}$; continue until the sense of divergence is determined, and then use $y^{(3)}$ in place of $y^{(1)}$ or $y^{(2)}$, whichever has the same sense of divergence as $y^{(3)}$. Repeat the process.

We eventually arrive at a situation where $y_0^{(p)}$ and $y_0^{(p-k)}$ are indistinguishable— yet $y^{(p)}$ and $y^{(p-k)}$ still diverge on opposite sides of the desired value $y(b)$. However, divergence is gradual, and there will be some $x = c$, $a < c < b$, for which $y^{(p)}(c)$, $y^{(p-k)}(c)$ differ moderately, and such that linear interpolation between these solutions can be carried out in the neighbourhood of $x = c$. We then have a well-determined pair of solutions, linearly interpolable in $[a, c]$ but not in $[a, b]$.

We now repeat the interpolation process, but only in $[c, b]$, in order to obtain further approximations, and eventually reduce the working interval to $[d, b]$, $c < d < b$, and so on until the final boundary condition at b can be satisfied.

The complete solution can now be constructed.

This whole method is quite crude in principle, and time consuming in its many iterations, and because of the need not to assume the sense of divergence too quickly. It is, however, a useful last resort, and in fact was the first method ever to be used on an electronic computer for such a problem—by Hartree on ENIAC. It is useful for obtaining a finite solution at a singularity.

16. Choice and Change of Interval h

This is a major consideration in adapting methods to electronic computers, where it is so easy to use a time-consuming small interval (with some danger of accumulating undue statistical error, and even, on occasion, unsuspected systematic error, particularly in x itself).

16.1 *Choice of Interval.* The convergence properties of the Taylor series and Chebyshev series (particularly the latter) suggest that substantially larger values of h may be possible with these methods than with others. This is borne out in practice for the Taylor series, for which more experience is available. An interval in which a dominant function increased by a factor 10^6 at each step has been successfully used. The limitations on h when using Taylor series appear to be

(i) Lack of convergence near a singularity—h cannot exceed the distance to this singularity.

(ii) Cancellation in summing the Taylor series, which can seriously increase rounding-error effects relative to final results. This cancellation occurs both with oscillatory solutions and with rapidly diminishing exponential-type solutions. With oscillatory solutions, h can be up to about $\frac{1}{4}\lambda$, where λ is the "wavelength" (i.e. twice the distance between zeros). With $h \simeq \frac{1}{4}\lambda$, about one decimal digit is lost overall, and larger h results in loss of further digits; this is a case of weak effectiveness with $S \simeq 1$ for $h = \frac{1}{4}\lambda$, $S \simeq 10$ for $h = \frac{1}{2}\lambda$, etc. With rapidly descending exponentials the loss is more severe, and occurs even if the corresponding term of the complementary function is absent from the desired solution; this is due to *over-stability* or *stiffness* of the differential equation, mentioned in §8.2.

These problems of cancellation, and of proximity of singularities would appear to be less severe, and sometimes avoidable, with Chebyshev series, but experience is lacking. It is also worth noting that besides superior convergence properties over a prescribed range, compared with the Taylor series, the Chebyshev step h is the full range for the series, whereas the Taylor expansion has a range $-h$ to $+h$; this latter makes possible a useful check at the expense of some loss of rapidity of convergence.

Methods involving series of differences, such as those of §3 (Adams-Bashforth, etc.), also allow fairly large values of h to be used, depending on the last term retained. However, convergence is poorer than for the Taylor series, and the optimum value of h correspondingly smaller.

Other methods involving fixed truncation error (including use of Adams-Bashforth or the Taylor series in this way—cf. Nordsieck 1962) all require correspondingly smaller intervals h, varying with the method. It is also a disadvantage of methods that do not use a series *until negligible terms are reached* that it is much more difficult to determine whether h is small enough. Almost always h must either be too small, in order to be sure, or two distinct values of h must be used and the results compared. In this connection we note that the backward step in the Taylor series method is in fact redundant—it is used because it is a "free gift".

With deferred correction a larger step may be used, since the corrections are applied later, and h is then limited by the need for reasonably rapid convergence.

16.2 *Change of Interval.* For methods involving values at the most recent point only, such as Taylor series and Runge-Kutta, change of interval offers no difficulty; each step starts afresh and a new h may be used almost as easily as the old value.

For other methods depending on several earlier values, both starting and change of interval need special treatment. For starting it is a common practice to use Taylor's series, and to obtain several values from one such series (a clear indication that the Taylor series method can normally make use of relatively large values of h). It is also possible to start in a semi-iterative fashion by using the method intended for use later, but with a much smaller value of h, so that extreme truncation is possible; this interval is gradually increased—with fresh starts—until the working size is reached.

For changing the interval, doubling and halving are easiest, particularly the former. We may have to resort to interpolation at each change, but this is quite easily done automatically using Neville's process. It is clearly desirable to keep the number of such changes to a minimum. The method of Nordsieck (1962) is essentially an Adams-Bashforth method, coupled with the production of pseudo-derivatives at each step to allow complete flexibility in the choice of interval; it is an interesting idea, but both the Adams-Bashforth and Taylor series methods proper would seem to be more efficient in the size of step-length possible, and in the ease of testing its adequacy, and because they can avoid fixed truncation.

17. Concluding Remarks

These notes have been concerned mainly with marching problems (initial-value problems), but with discussion of iterative, deferred-correction methods which can cope with cases where the solution desired is dominated by others. This implies that we know which solution we want, and have criteria to detect when we are departing from it—this in turn implies that at least one boundary condition is *not* given at the start, i.e. that we have a jury problem (boundary-value problem).

No attempt has been made to cover boundary-value problems in general. For discussion of such problems see Fox 1957. We note also that they are often special cases of elliptic partial differential equations, reduced to one variable, and that the matrix theory and methods appropriate to elliptic equations can be specialized to deal with the one-dimensional case.

REFERENCES

BUTCHER, J. C. 1965. A modified multistep method for the numerical integration of ordinary differential equations. *J. Assoc. Comp. Mach.* **12**, 124–135.

CLENSHAW, C. W. 1957. The numerical solution of linear differential equations in Chebyshev series. *Proc. Camb. Phil. Soc.* **53**, 134–149.

CLENSHAW, C. W. AND NORTON, H. J. 1963. The solution of nonlinear ordinary differential equations in Chebyshev series. *Comp. J.* **6**, 88–92.

DAHLQUIST, G. 1956. Convergence and stability in the numerical integration of ordinary differential equations. *Math. Scand.* **4**, 33–53.

DAHLQUIST, G. 1959. Stability and error bounds in the numerical integration of ordinary differential equations. *K. Tekn. Hogsk. Handl.* **130**.

FOX, L. 1957. *The Numerical Solution of Two-point Boundary Problems in Ordinary Differential Equations.* Clarendon Press, Oxford.

FOX, L. 1962. *Numerical Solution of Ordinary and Partial Differential Equations.* Pergamon, Oxford.

FOX, L. 1962a. Chebyshev methods for ordinary differential equations. *Comp. J.* **4**, 318–331.

FOX, L. AND GOODWIN, E. T. 1949. Some new methods for the numerical integration of ordinary differential equations. *Proc. Camb. Phil Soc.* **45**, 373–388.

FOX, L. AND GOODWIN, E. T. 1953. The numerical solution of non-singular linear integral equations. *Phil. Trans.* A245, 501–534.

FOX, L. AND MITCHELL, A. R. 1957. Boundary-value techniques for the numerical solution of initial-value problems in ordinary differential equations. *Quart. J. Mech. and App. Math.* **10**, 232–243.

GIBBONS, A. 1960. A program for the automatic integration of differential equations using the method of Taylor series. *Comp. J.* **3**, 108–111.

GILL, S. 1951. A process for the step-by-step integration of differential equations in an automatic digital computing machine. *Proc. Camb. Phil. Soc.* **47**, 96–108.

GRAGG, W. B. AND STETTER, H. J. 1964. Generalized multistep predictor-corrector methods. *J. Assoc. Comp. Mach.* **11**, 188–209.

HASELGROVE, C. B. AND HOYLE, F. 1956. A mathematical discussion of the problem of stellar evolution, with reference to the use of an automatic digital computer. *Month. Not. Roy. Astron. Soc.* **116**, 515–526.

HENRICI, P. 1962. *Discrete Variable Methods in Ordinary Differential Equations.* Wiley, New York.

KOPAL, Z. 1955. *Numerical Analysis.* Chapman & Hall, London.

LANCZOS, C. 1938. Trigonometric interpolation of empirical and analytical functions. *J. Math. Phys.* **17**, 123–199.

MERSON, R. H. 1957. An operational method for the study of integration processes. *Proc. Symposium on Data Processing.* Weapons Research Establishment, Salisbury, S. Australia.

MILLER, J. C. P. 1946. *The Airy Integral.* British Association Mathematical Tables, Part Vol. **B.** University Press, Cambridge.

MILNE, W. E. AND REYNOLDS, R. R. 1959. Stability of numerical solution of differential equations. *J. Assoc. Comp. Mach.* **6**, 196–203.

MILNE, W. E. AND REYNOLDS, R. R. 1962. Fifth-order methods for the numerical solution of ordinary differential equations. *J. Assoc. Comp. Mach.* **9**, 64–70.

MOORE, R. E. 1965. The automatic analysis and control of error in digital computation based on the use of interval numbers. *Error in Digital Computation.* Vol. **1**, 61–130. Wiley, New York.

NATIONAL PHYSICAL LABORATORY. 1961. Notes on Applied Science **16**. *Modern Computing Methods.* H. M. Stationery Office, London.

NORDSIECK, A. 1962. On numerical integration of ordinary differential equations. *Math. Comp.* **16**, 22–49.

NORTON, H. J. 1964. The iterative solution of non-linear ordinary differential equations in Chebyshev series. *Comp. J.* **7**, 76–85.

OLIVER, J. 1965. *Numerical Solution of Linear Recurrence Relations.* Ph.D. thesis. Cambridge.

OLVER, F. W. J. 1950. A new method for the evaluation of zeros of Bessel functions and of other solutions of second-order differential equations. *Proc. Camb. Phil. Soc.* **46**, 570–580.

RIDLEY, E. C. 1957. A numerical method of solving second-order linear differential equations with two-point boundary conditions. *Proc. Camb. Phil. Soc.* **53**, 442–447.

SCRATON, R. E. 1964. Estimation of the truncation error in Runge-Kutta and allied processes. *Comp. J.* **7**, 246–248.

SCRATON, R. E. 1965. The solution of linear differential equations in Chebyshev series. *Comp. J.* **8**, 57–61.

Chapter 5

Elliptic and Parabolic Equations

J. WALSH

Department of Mathematics, The University, Manchester

1. Introduction. Example

Partial differential equations of elliptic and parabolic types arise in the mathematical analysis of many physical problems, for example, in fluid flow, neutron diffusion, and electromagnetic and gravitational phenomena. As a simple example, let us consider the problem of heat conduction in two space dimensions. In the steady state, the temperature u satisfies an equation of elliptic type

$$\operatorname{div}(K \operatorname{grad} u) + Q = 0, \tag{1}$$

where K is the conductivity, and Q the heat production per unit area. If K is constant over the region, we obtain Poisson's equation

$$K\left(\frac{\partial^2 u}{\partial x^2} + \frac{\partial^2 u}{\partial y^2}\right) + Q = 0. \tag{2}$$

We can represent this equation approximately by using the simplest finite-difference formulae for the second derivatives,

$$h^2\left(\frac{\partial^2 u}{\partial x^2}\right)_{(x,y)} = u(x+h,\,y) - 2u(x,\,y) + u(x-h,\,y) + E, \tag{3}$$

and similarly for the y-derivative. The error term E is of order h^4, and is bounded in modulus by $\frac{1}{12}h^4 M_4$, where M_4 is an upper bound for the modulus of the fourth derivative of u. Neglecting the errors, we obtain the following representation of (2)

$$K\{u(x+h,\,y) + u(x-h,\,y) + u(x,\,y+h) + u(x,\,y-h) - 4u(x,\,y)\}$$
$$+ h^2 Q(x,\,y) = 0. \tag{4}$$

This can be interpreted directly as the approximate equation for heat balance over a small square of side h with centre $(x,\,y)$, i.e.

$$\text{heat flowing in} + \text{heat produced} = 0. \tag{5}$$

In complicated problems, we may prefer to set up an equation of the form (4) as a direct approximation to the physical system, rather than to the differential equation. For example, in some problems the region is highly inhomogeneous, and applying a mathematical equation such as (2) is itself only an approximation to the physical situation. However, we shall not discuss such problems here.

The usual boundary conditions associated with an elliptic equation are of two kinds. We may have

either (a) specified values of u,
or   (b) a linear condition on the normal gradient of u, e.g.

$$\frac{\partial u}{\partial v} = h(u - u_0), \tag{6}$$

representing linear heat transfer into a medium at temperature u_0. It is characteristic of elliptic equations that boundary conditions of some type must be given at all points of a closed curve (or surface), in order to define a well-posed problem in the region which it encloses. This has a great influence on the numerical methods of solution.

Returning to our original example, in the case of unsteady heat flow the difference between the heat produced and the heat dissipated is non-zero, and the temperature at any point changes with time. Thus we obtain the typical parabolic equation

$$c \frac{\partial u}{\partial t} = K\left(\frac{\partial^2 u}{\partial x^2} + \frac{\partial^2 u}{\partial y^2}\right) + Q, \tag{7}$$

where c is the heat capacity per unit area. The boundary conditions required for a well-posed parabolic problem are specified values of u at all points of the space region when $t = 0$, and a condition such as (a) or (b) at all boundary points of the region when $t > 0$.

2. Non-linear Terms

The partial differential equations (2) and (7) are linear in u, and they can be solved analytically for many simple geometrical regions. However, the linear forms of the equations exclude some important physical features of the problem. For example, in practical cases the conductivity is often a function of the temperature, e.g.

$$K = k_1 + k_2 u, \tag{8}$$

where k_1, k_2 are constants. The boundary condition (6) does not cover the cases of radiative or convective heat transfer, where the normal gradient depends on some power of u. Similarly, in other types of problem, we often find that the coefficients in the equation or boundary conditions are functions of u.

Non-linearities such as these cannot be dealt with by the usual analytical methods of solution (Fourier series, Laplace transform, etc.). To some extent the problems are simplified when we use numerical techniques, but it should be noted that most of the recent work on numerical methods for elliptic and parabolic equations has been concerned with the linear case. Many non-linear equations are being solved successfully on computers, but the theoretical basis of the methods used is still incomplete, and such problems as optimum convergence and stability need further investigation.

3. Linear Elliptic Case. Finite-difference Equations

It is easily seen that an elliptic differential equation can be approximated by a set of linear algebraic equations of the form (4), by using finite differences. But the problem of obtaining a numerical solution by elementary methods is formidable, without the help of computers. In the 1940s, Southwell and his group developed the technique of relaxation, and applied it with great success to problems of considerable size and difficulty (Southwell 1946). This method was a non-systematic form of iteration, and its efficiency depended largely on the skill and experience of the user. When computing machines were intro-duced, it was found that experience was a very difficult thing to program, and interest shifted to more systematic methods.

The basic finite-difference equations are obtained by using simple approxi-mate formulae for the derivatives at the points of a mesh (usually rectangular) covering the region. Special modifications may be needed near the boundary to take account of general boundary conditions, but we shall not discuss the details (see Fox 1962, Chapter 21).

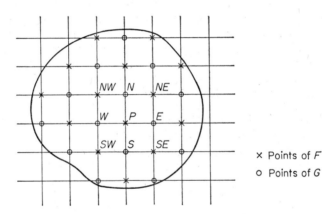

x Points of F
o Points of G

FIG. 1. Finite-difference mesh

At a point P, if we call the adjacent points N, S, W, E in an obvious nota-tion (Fig. 1), we have

$$h^2\left(\frac{\partial^2 u}{\partial x^2}\right)_P = u_E - 2u_P + u_W + 0(h^4),$$ (9)

$$2h\left(\frac{\partial u}{\partial x}\right)_P = u_E - u_W + 0(h^3),$$ (10)

and similarly for the y-derivatives. Thus any second-order differential expres-sion, which does not include a cross-derivative term, can be approximated at

P by a finite-difference expression involving only function values at the five points P, N, S, E, W. If cross-derivatives occur, we use the formula

$$4h^2\left(\frac{\partial^2 u}{\partial x\,\partial y}\right)_P = u_{NE} - u_{NW} + u_{SW} - u_{SE} + 0(h^4) \tag{11}$$

(assuming a square mesh), and our approximation involves up to nine points. We ignore this case for the moment.

The five-point finite-difference equations have the characteristic property that, if we divide the points of the mesh into the two sets shown in Fig. 1, the equations at points of one set involve only points of the other, and vice versa. The matrix of the linear equations is said to have Property A, a term first defined by Young (1954) in his analysis of iterative methods. If we call the two sets F and G, and arrange the equations so that those at points of F precede those at points of G, we see that the matrix can be written in the partitioned form

$$A = \begin{bmatrix} D_1 & B_1 \\ C_2 & D_2 \end{bmatrix}, \tag{12}$$

where D_1, D_2 are diagonal. This property is important in the theory.

The number of equations obtained is equal to the number of mesh-points, including any boundary points at which the value of u is not given explicitly. This number can be very large, of the order of thousands, and direct methods of solution such as Gaussian elimination (Chapter 2, §3) are not generally suitable, because of the storage space required. However, the special form of the equations makes iterative solution very simple.

4. Iterative Methods of Solution

The general results on iterative methods for linear equations are given in Chapter 2, §9. We consider now the application of these to elliptic difference equations. We start with the linear equations derived from (2),

$$u_N + u_S + u_W + u_E - 4u_P = -h^2 Q/K. \tag{13}$$

The Gauss-Seidel iterative method uses equations of the form

$$u_P^{(n+1)} = \tfrac{1}{4}(u_N^{(n+1)} + u_W^{(n+1)} + u_S^{(n)} + u_E^{(n)} - h^2 Q/K) \tag{14}$$

to obtain an improved solution $u^{(n+1)}$ from the preceding $u^{(n)}$. The points of the mesh are traversed in a fixed order, assumed in (14) to be the natural "reading order". If the *residual* R_P at P is defined by

$$R_P^{(n)} = \tfrac{1}{4}(u_N^{(n+1)} + u_W^{(n+1)} + u_S^{(n)} + u_E^{(n)} - 4u_P^{(n)} - h^2 Q/K), \tag{15}$$

then (14) is equivalent to

$$u_P^{(n+1)} = u_P^{(n)} + R_P^{(n)}. \tag{16}$$

The convergence of this iteration can be greatly improved by extrapolation, using in place of (16) the equation

$$u_P^{(n+1)} = u_P^{(n)} + \omega R_P^{(n)}, \tag{17}$$

where ω is some constant > 1. Young (1954) has given a general theory of this type of extrapolation for equations where the matrix has Property A.

As shown in Chapter 2, the rate of convergence of a linear iteration such as (17) is determined by the spectral radius of a certain matrix, i.e. by the maximum modulus of its eigenvalues. Let us write the linear equations as

$$Au = b, \qquad A = D - L - U, \tag{18}$$

where D is a diagonal matrix, and L and U are strictly lower and upper triangular respectively. Then the extrapolated Gauss-Seidel method (often called successive over-relaxation, or SOR) may be expressed in vector form as

$$\mathbf{u}^{(n+1)} = \mathbf{u}^{(n)} + \omega D^{-1}(L\mathbf{u}^{(n+1)} + U\mathbf{u}^{(n)} - D\mathbf{u}^{(n)} + \mathbf{b}). \tag{19}$$

This is equivalent to

$$\mathbf{u}^{(n+1)} = (I - \omega D^{-1}L)^{-1}\{(1-\omega)I + \omega D^{-1}U\}\mathbf{u}^{(n)} + \omega D^{-1}\mathbf{b}, \tag{20}$$

and hence the iteration matrix M is given by

$$M = (I - \omega D^{-1}L)^{-1}\{(1-\omega)I + \omega D^{-1}U\}. \tag{21}$$

If we write

$$E = D^{-1}L, \qquad F = D^{-1}U, \tag{22}$$

it is easily seen that the eigenvalues λ of M satisfy

$$\det\left[(\lambda + \omega - 1)I - \lambda\omega E - \omega F\right] = 0. \tag{23}$$

At this point we make use of Property A, and assume further that the equations are ordered so that the matrix A is of the form (12). Then, by expansion of the determinant, we can show that (23) is equivalent to

$$\det\left[(\lambda + \omega - 1)I - \sqrt{\lambda}\omega E - \sqrt{\lambda}\omega F\right] = 0, \tag{24}$$

provided $\lambda \neq 0$. This equation gives us a fundamental relation between the eigenvalues λ of M and those of the matrix $E + F$. If we call the latter μ, then μ satisfies

$$\det\left[\mu I - E - F\right] = 0, \tag{25}$$

and comparing with (24) we find that

$$\lambda\omega^2\mu^2 = (\lambda + \omega - 1)^2, \qquad \omega \neq 0. \tag{26}$$

From this equation, it is possible to determine the best choice of ω for extrapolation, and the resulting rate of convergence, in terms of μ. The derivation of (26) assumed that the matrix A had the form (12), but this restriction can be relaxed. The eigenvalues of M, and therefore the convergence properties of the iteration, are identical for any two consistent orderings, i.e. any two orderings which lead to identical results for the new iterate. The determinantal property used in obtaining (24) also holds for a matrix of the following more general form

$$A = \begin{bmatrix} D_1 & C_1 & & & \\ B_2 & D_2 & C_2 & & \\ & B_3 & D_3 & C_3 & \\ & & \cdot & \cdot & \cdot & \cdot & \cdot & \cdot \\ & & \cdot & \cdot & \cdot & \cdot & \cdot & \cdot & \cdot \end{bmatrix}, \tag{27}$$

in which the D_i are diagonal submatrices. Many orderings are consistent with the form (27), in particular the natural reading order used in (14).

The choice of the optimum value of ω depends on some knowledge of the eigenvalues μ. The simplest case occurs when the eigenvalues are all real, and less than unity in modulus. (This condition is satisfied in many practical problems, e.g. when A is symmetric and diagonally dominant.) The optimum ω is then given in terms of the eigenvalue of largest modulus, $\bar{\mu}$ say, by

$$\omega = \frac{2}{1+\sqrt{(1-\bar{\mu}^2)}},\tag{28}$$

and the corresponding maximum eigenvalue of M has modulus $\omega - 1$. A full analysis of the relation between λ and μ is given by Forsythe and Wasow (1960).

To show the effect of extrapolation on convergence, it is traditional to quote the example of the solution of Laplace's equation in a square of side π, with u specified on the boundary. This is rather trivial, but it gives an idea of the improvement obtained. It is easily shown that the rate of convergence, defined as $-\log|\bar{\lambda}|$, where $|\bar{\lambda}|$ is the spectral radius of M, is approximately h^2 for the Gauss-Seidel iteration, and $2h$ for the optimum extrapolated method, when h (the mesh-length) is small. Thus extrapolation gives an order-of-magnitude gain in convergence.

There have been many developments in the theory of iterative methods since Young's paper, some of which will be discussed in later sections. But first we must point out that the above results cannot always be applied directly to practical problems. Even when all the conditions are fulfilled (Property A, consistent ordering, real values of μ), we seldom have a good estimate of $\bar{\mu}$. In these circumstances, extrapolation is often applied semi-experimentally, using estimates of ω which are improved as the iteration proceeds. Some methods which work very well in practice are described by Carré (1961) and Kulsrud (1961).

5. Further Developments

Some people have suggested that, when the size and speed of computers increase sufficiently, direct methods will be preferred to iterative methods for solving large systems of difference equations. The matrices of the equations are of band type, and therefore direct solution takes considerably less time and space than it would for a general matrix of the same order. But the tendency is to use larger machines to solve larger problems, so that we are always likely to need methods which are economical in storage space. It has been found that certain mixed iterative and direct methods give improvements in convergence over the simple point iteration described in §4, without requiring appreciably more storage.

The matrix of the elliptic finite-difference equations on a rectangular grid admits a natural partitioning into submatrices, in which each row contains three submatrices relating function values on one line of the mesh to those on the two adjacent lines. Thus the equations can be written in block form as

$$
\begin{bmatrix}
A_1 & B_1 & & & \\
C_2 & A_2 & B_2 & & \\
& C_3 & A_3 & B_3 & \\
& & & \cdots & \\
& & & C_p & A_p
\end{bmatrix}
\begin{bmatrix}
\mathbf{u}_1 \\ \mathbf{u}_2 \\ \mathbf{u}_3 \\ \vdots \\ \mathbf{u}_p
\end{bmatrix}
=
\begin{bmatrix}
\mathbf{b}_1 \\ \mathbf{b}_2 \\ \mathbf{b}_3 \\ \vdots \\ \mathbf{b}_p
\end{bmatrix},
\tag{29}
$$

where each sub-vector $\mathbf{u}_i$ represents the function values along a single line of the mesh. In the case of five-point equations, the submatrices A_i are triple-diagonal, and B_i, C_i are diagonal. For the nine-point equations, all sub-matrices are triple-diagonal. We can write down immediately the equations for iteration with blocks instead of points, analogous to (14) and (19) above. Thus the block Gauss-Seidel method has the form

$$
A_i \mathbf{u}_i^{(n+1)} = -C_i \mathbf{u}_{i-1}^{(n+1)} - B_i \mathbf{u}_{i+1}^{(n)} + \mathbf{b}_i,
\tag{30}
$$

and the block extrapolated Gauss-Seidel method

$$
\mathbf{u}_i^{(n+1)} = \mathbf{u}_i^{(n)} - \omega A_i^{-1} \{ C_i \mathbf{u}_{i-1}^{(n+1)} + A_i \mathbf{u}_i^{(n)} + B_i \mathbf{u}_{i+1}^{(n)} - \mathbf{b}_i \},
\tag{31}
$$

with obvious modifications for $i = 1$ and p. To avoid having to find the inverse matrix A_i^{-1}, (31) is usually written in the more convenient form

$$
\left.
\begin{aligned}
A_i \mathbf{u}_i^{*(n+1)} &= -C_i \mathbf{u}_{i-1}^{(n+1)} - B_i \mathbf{u}_{i+1}^{(n)} + \mathbf{b}_i \\
\mathbf{u}_i^{(n+1)} &= \omega \mathbf{u}_i^{*(n+1)} + (1-\omega) \mathbf{u}_i^{(n)}
\end{aligned}
\right\},
\tag{32}
$$

where $\mathbf{u}_i^{*(n+1)}$ is an intermediate vector.

Methods of iteration using lines instead of points are discussed by Arms, Gates and Zondek (1956) and by Keller (1958). It is clear that both (30) and (32) require the direct solution on each line of a set of linear equations with matrix A_i. However, the tridiagonal form of A_i ensures that this part of the calculation is very simple, and in fact Cuthill and Varga (1959) have shown that, after suitable initial transformations, one step of line iteration can be carried out in exactly the same number of arithmetic operations as one step of point iteration.

The theory of extrapolation can be applied to block methods just as to point methods, provided the matrices have Property A in block form, i.e. regarding the submatrices as elements. This requirement is less stringent than "point Property A"; for example, the matrices obtained by using nine-point equations have Property A in blocks, but not in points. The increase in convergence obtained by iterating with lines instead of points for the example quoted above is a factor of $\sqrt{2}$ in two dimensions, or $\sqrt{1\cdot5}$ in three dimensions.

Varga (1962) discusses the general theory of the use of sub-blocks of the matrix as elements in the iteration. We can write any stationary iterative method for solving $A\mathbf{u} = \mathbf{b}$ in the form

$$
P\mathbf{u}^{(n+1)} = -Q\mathbf{u}^{(n)} + \mathbf{b},
\tag{33}
$$

where $A = P + Q$. For simple Gauss-Seidel iteration we have $P = D - L$, while for the block methods we include in P certain non-zero elements from above the diagonal of A. Varga shows that, for the class of irreducible Stieltjes matrices, the rate of convergence can always be increased by transferring non-zero super-diagonal elements of A into P. However, to take advantage of the improved convergence, we must ensure that P is of such a form that the equations (33) are easy to solve, and that the conditions for extrapolation are fulfilled. It seems that the "best" method does not involve solving for more than two lines simultaneously.

In the case where the eigenvalues of a stationary iterative method are real, we can improve its convergence by using the properties of the Chebyshev polynomial (see Chapter 2, §10). Suppose that the eigenvalues lie in the interval (a, b), where $|a|, |b| < 1$. We can show that the polynomial $p_n(x)$ of degree n with minimum maximum modulus in (a, b), normalized so that $p_n(1) = 1$, is given by

$$p_n(x) = \left\{ T_n\left(\frac{2x - a - b}{b - a}\right) \right\} \bigg/ \left\{ T_n\left(\frac{2 - a - b}{b - a}\right) \right\}. \tag{34}$$

Here $T_n(z)$ is the Chebyshev polynomial of the first kind.

Writing $M = -P^{-1}Q$, the general iterative method (33) becomes

$$\mathbf{u}^{(n+1)} = M\mathbf{u}^{(n)} + P^{-1}\mathbf{b}. \tag{35}$$

If M has eigenvalues λ_i and eigenvectors $\mathbf{y}_i$, we can expand the initial error in the form

$$\mathbf{u}^{(0)} - \mathbf{u} = \sum \alpha_i \mathbf{y}_i, \tag{36}$$

and we construct a sequence of iterates $\{\mathbf{v}^{(n)}\}$ such that

$$\mathbf{v}^{(n)} - \mathbf{u} = \sum \alpha_i p_n(\lambda_i)\mathbf{y}_i. \tag{37}$$

Since the Chebyshev polynomials satisfy a three-term recurrence relation, this can be done as follows:

$$\left. \begin{array}{l} \mathbf{u}^{(n+1)} = M\mathbf{v}^{(n)} + P^{-1}\mathbf{b} \\ \mathbf{v}^{(n+1)} = \mathbf{v}^{(n)} + \beta_n(\mathbf{u}^{(n+1)} - \mathbf{v}^{(n)}) + \gamma_n(\mathbf{v}^{(n)} - \mathbf{v}^{(n-1)}) \end{array} \right\}, \tag{38}$$

where β_n, γ_n are defined by

$$\left. \begin{array}{ll} \beta_n = \dfrac{4}{b - a} \dfrac{T_n(\rho)}{T_{n+1}(\rho)}, & \gamma_n = \dfrac{T_{n-1}(\rho)}{T_{n+1}(\rho)}, \qquad n \geq 1 \\[3mm] \beta_0 = \dfrac{2}{2 - a - b}, & \gamma_0 = 0, \qquad \rho = \dfrac{2 - a - b}{b - a}. \end{array} \right\} \tag{39}$$

A full discussion is given by Stiefel (1958).

Theoretically this method is very satisfactory, but its application depends on two conditions. First, the minimizing property of the Chebyshev polynomials requires the eigenvalues λ_i to be real, and it does not hold for general complex values. Wrigley (1963) discusses the case where some of the λ_i are complex, and shows that the polynomials (34) are optimal for values of λ_i lying within a certain ellipse in the complex plane. If some of the eigenvalues lie outside this ellipse, we do not obtain optimum convergence. Wrigley suggests a practical method for locating the eigenvalues corresponding to the dominant error terms, and hence improving the convergence, but this is not easy to carry out automatically.

Secondly, even when the eigenvalues are all real, we need good estimates of a and b, the lower and upper limits for λ_i, in order to obtain rapid convergence. Just as with successive over-relaxation, we can use a semi-experimental method to determine the convergence parameters (Wachspress 1957), but the process is quite elaborate.

Varga (1957, 1962) gives a detailed comparison of SOR and Chebyshev methods. For a general matrix with Property A, successive over-relaxation is preferable, but if the matrix has the form (12), it is possible to obtain faster *average* rates of convergence over a finite number of steps with Chebyshev methods, though the *asymptotic* convergence rates are the same. However, for large problems, Chebyshev acceleration suffers from the disadvantage that it requires the storage of two previous vectors for extrapolation, and on some computers time may be lost in transferring data from the backing store.

6. Parabolic Equations

A parabolic equation such as (7) is an initial-value problem in the time variable, and a boundary-value problem in the space variables. The numerical solution proceeds step by step in the time direction, and we have to consider problems of stability, as in Chapter 4.

To introduce the basic methods, we start by considering a problem in one space dimension, and take the simplest form of the equation,

$$\frac{\partial u}{\partial t} = \frac{\partial^2 u}{\partial x^2}, \tag{40}$$

where $u = u(x, t)$. We suppose that the associated boundary conditions are specified values of u on the line $t = 0$ for $0 \le x \le 1$, and on the lines $x = 0$, $x = 1$ for $t > 0$. One approach to the solution of (40) is to approximate the space derivative by finite differences, and thus obtain a system of coupled first-order ordinary differential equations in t. If we write $u_i = u(ih, t)$, these equations are

$$\frac{d}{dt}\begin{bmatrix} u_1 \\ u_2 \\ \vdots \\ u_n \end{bmatrix} = \frac{1}{h^2}\begin{bmatrix} -2 & 1 & & & \\ 1 & -2 & 1 & & \\ & 1 & -2 & 1 & \\ & & \ddots & \ddots & \ddots \\ & & & 1 & -2 \end{bmatrix}\begin{bmatrix} u_1 \\ u_2 \\ \vdots \\ u_n \end{bmatrix} + \frac{1}{h^2}\begin{bmatrix} u_0 \\ 0 \\ \vdots \\ u_{n+1} \end{bmatrix}, \tag{41}$$

or in vector form

$$\frac{d\mathbf{u}}{dt} = \frac{1}{h^2}(B\mathbf{u} + \mathbf{b}), \tag{42}$$

where $(n+1)h = 1$, B is the matrix in (41), and $\mathbf{b}$ is a vector depending on the boundary conditions. A method of integrating (42) analytically is described by Wadsworth and Wragg (1964), who also give other examples and numerical results. However, for more general problems we have to use numerical methods in both directions.

Equation (42) is a linear first-order equation, and its complementary function includes terms of the form $\mathbf{y}_i \exp(\lambda_i t/h^2)$, where λ_i is an eigenvalue and $\mathbf{y}_i$ an eigenvector of the matrix B. The eigenvalues, which are all negative, are given by

$$\lambda_i = -4\sin^2(\tfrac{1}{2}i\pi h), \qquad i = 1, 2, \ldots, n, \qquad (43)$$

and hence, for small h, the exponent of largest modulus in the complementary function is $0(1/h^2)$. Therefore if we use the Runge-Kutta method to solve (42), we have to take a very small step-length to represent the rapidly diminishing exponential terms adequately and avoid instability.

The problem of instability also arises if we replace both derivatives in (40) by the simplest finite-difference approximations, and obtain an explicit method for integration, i.e.

$$\frac{u(x, t+H) - u(x, t)}{H} \simeq \frac{u(x+h, t) - 2u(x, t) + u(x-h, t)}{h^2}, \qquad (44)$$

where H is the time-step. If we write $u_{i,j} = u(ih, jH)$, we have, neglecting the truncation error,

$$u_{i,j+1} = u_{i,j} + \frac{H}{h^2}(u_{i+1,j} - 2u_{i,j} + u_{i-1,j}), \qquad (45)$$

with suitable modifications at the ends of the range. This is an explicit formula for obtaining u at time $t+H$ from u at time t, but it can be shown that it is unstable for $H/h^2 > \tfrac{1}{2}$, so that we are again restricted to a very small time-step.

The implicit method of Crank and Nicolson (1947) was devised to overcome this difficulty. In place of (44), it uses the approximation

$$\frac{u(x, t+H) - u(x, t)}{H} \simeq \tfrac{1}{2}\frac{\delta_x^2 u(x, t+H) + \delta_x^2 u(x, t)}{h^2} \qquad (46)$$

for forward integration. We shall analyse a more general implicit method, given by

$$\frac{u(x, t+H) - u(x, t)}{H} \simeq \frac{\theta\delta_x^2 u(x, t+H) + (1-\theta)\delta_x^2 u(x, t)}{h^2}, \qquad 0 \le \theta \le 1. \quad (47)$$

If we neglect the truncation error, this is equivalent to

$$u_{i,j+1} - p\theta(u_{i+1,j+1} - 2u_{i,j+1} + u_{i-1,j+1})$$
$$= u_{i,j} + p(1-\theta)(u_{i+1,j} - 2u_{i,j} + u_{i-1,j}), \qquad (48)$$

where $p = H/h^2$. The value $\theta = 0$ gives the fully explicit method of (45). For $\theta > 0$, the finite-difference equations (48) give an implicit set for finding the values of u at $t+H$ from those at t. In vector form, we can express (48) as

$$(I - p\theta B)\mathbf{u}(t+H) = \{I + p(1-\theta)B\}\mathbf{u}(t) + p\mathbf{b}, \qquad (49)$$

where $\mathbf{u}$, B and $\mathbf{b}$ have the same meaning as in (42).

Now (49) is a linear difference equation in $\mathbf{u}$, and the condition for stability is that its complementary function must be non-increasing. This means that the eigenvalues μ_i of the matrix

$$M = (I - p\theta B)^{-1}\{I + p(1-\theta)B\} \qquad (50)$$

must not exceed unity in modulus. We can express μ_i in terms of λ_i (defined by (43)) by the equation

$$\mu_i = \frac{1+p(1-\theta)\lambda_i}{1-p\theta\lambda_i},\qquad(51)$$

and we see that we have stability for *all* values of p if $\theta \geq \frac{1}{2}$. Of course we still have to choose step-lengths h and H which are small enough to give the required *accuracy*, i.e. which make the truncation error of the finite-difference approximations negligible.

In one space dimension, implicit methods of the type (48) are very easy to apply, because the equations to be solved at each time-step have a matrix of simple triple-diagonal form. The best value for θ is generally $\theta = \frac{1}{2}$ (the value of Crank and Nicolson), because this gives the smallest truncation error. However, for certain mildly non-linear equations, Curtis has found that the value $\theta = 1$ has some advantages (Fox 1962, Chapter 29).

In two or three space dimensions, the problem of solving the equations at each time-step becomes much more difficult. As before, the simple explicit method, analogous to (45), has serious limitations of stability; in two dimensions we have to take $p \leq \frac{1}{4}$, and in three dimensions $p \leq \frac{1}{6}$. Again we can get unconditional stability by using implicit methods. For the parabolic equation

$$\frac{\partial u}{\partial t} = \frac{\partial^2 u}{\partial x^2} + \frac{\partial^2 u}{\partial y^2},\qquad u = u(x, y, t),\qquad(52)$$

we obtain the following implicit equation, corresponding to (48),

$$u_{i,j,k+1} - p\theta(\delta_x^2 u_{i,j,k+1} + \delta_y^2 u_{i,j,k+1}) = u_{i,j,k} + p(1-\theta)(\delta_x^2 u_{i,j,k} + \delta_y^2 u_{i,j,k}),\qquad(53)$$

where $u_{i,j,k} = u(ih, jh, kH)$. This gives a stable method for all p if $\theta \geq \frac{1}{2}$. The left-hand side of (53) is a finite-difference expression of elliptic type, involving the unknown values of u at time $t + H$, and so we have an elliptic equation to solve at each time-step. This can be done by using the iterative methods discussed earlier, but the whole procedure becomes rather long. More efficient methods have been developed for certain classes of equations, and these will now be described.

7. Alternating-direction Methods

A significant advance in the solution of problems in two space dimensions was made by Peaceman and Rachford (1955), who devised the method of alternating directions for solving the finite-difference equations arising from (52). In this method we use two forms of equation alternately in successive time-steps; in the first the finite-difference equations are implicit in the x-direction and explicit in the y-direction, and in the second the directions are interchanged. The equations for the two steps are

$$\left.\begin{array}{l} u_{i,j,2k+1} - p\delta_x^2 u_{i,j,2k+1} = u_{i,j,2k} + p\delta_y^2 u_{i,j,2k} \\ u_{i,j,2k+2} - p\delta_y^2 u_{i,j,2k+2} = u_{i,j,2k+1} + p\delta_x^2 u_{i,j,2k+1} \end{array}\right\},\qquad(54)$$

where $p = H/h^2$ as before. For each step, we solve a simple set of equations with triple-diagonal matrix, and no iteration is required.

We can show that, for a rectangular region, the complete two-step process is stable for all values of p. If we define matrices X and Y to represent the finite-difference operators in the x- and y-directions respectively, we can write X and Y in the forms

$$X = \begin{bmatrix} B & & \bigcirc \\ & B & \\ & & B \\ \bigcirc & & \ddots \end{bmatrix}, \qquad Y = \begin{bmatrix} -2I & I & & \bigcirc \\ I & -2I & I & \\ & I & -2I & I \\ \bigcirc & & \ddots & \ddots & \ddots \end{bmatrix}, \qquad (55)$$

where B is the matrix in (42). Equations (54) can then be expressed as

$$\left. \begin{array}{l} (I - pX)\mathbf{u}(t+H) = (I + pY)\mathbf{u}(t) + \mathbf{b} \\ (I - pY)\mathbf{u}(t+2H) = (I + pX)\mathbf{u}(t+H) + \mathbf{c} \end{array} \right\}, \qquad (56)$$

where the components of $\mathbf{u}$ are taken in order along successive x-rows. The vectors $\mathbf{b}$, $\mathbf{c}$ in (56) depend on the boundary conditions, and do not affect the stability of the method. The error $\varepsilon(t)$ satisfies the homogeneous form of (56), and so for the complete two-step process we have

$$\varepsilon(t+2H) = [(I - pY)^{-1}(I + pX)(I - pX)^{-1}(I + pY)]\varepsilon(t). \qquad (57)$$

For stability we require the eigenvalues μ_i of the matrix M, given by

$$M = (I - pY)^{-1}(I + pX)(I - pX)^{-1}(I + pY), \qquad (58)$$

to be less than unity in modulus. Now the eigenvalues ξ_i, η_j of X, Y are of the forms

$$\xi_i = -4\sin^2 \tfrac{1}{2} \frac{i\pi}{r+1}, \qquad \eta_j = -4\sin^2 \tfrac{1}{2} \frac{j\pi}{s+1}, \qquad (59)$$

where r, s are the numbers of internal points in the x-, y-directions respectively. Also X and Y have common eigenvectors, and so the eigenvalues of M are related to those of X and Y by

$$\mu = \frac{(\xi_i + p)(\eta_j + p)}{(\xi_i - p)(\eta_j - p)}. \qquad (60)$$

We see from (59) and (60) that $|\mu_i| < 1$ for all p, giving unconditional stability.

The idea of using alternating directions has been applied to the solution of elliptic equations in two dimensions (Peaceman and Rachford 1955), and it has also been extended to elliptic and parabolic equations in three space dimensions (Douglas and Rachford 1956, Douglas 1962). We shall give a brief outline of some results, and refer the reader to Varga (1962) for a full discussion.

Consider the two-dimensional elliptic case, over a rectangular region. An equation such as (2) can be approximated in finite differences by

$$\delta_x^2 u_{i,j} + \delta_y^2 u_{i,j} = b_{i,j}, \qquad (61)$$

where u is now a function of x and y only, and $u_{i,j} = u(ih, jh)$. Defining X and Y as in (55), this is equivalent to

$$(X + Y)\mathbf{u} = \mathbf{b}', \tag{62}$$

where $\mathbf{b}'$ depends on the right-hand side of (61) and the specified boundary values of u. Following the idea of (56), we set up the iteration equations

$$\left.\begin{aligned} (\alpha I - X)\mathbf{u}^{(n+\frac{1}{2})} &= (\alpha I + Y)\mathbf{u}^{(n)} - \mathbf{b}' \\ (\alpha I - Y)\mathbf{u}^{(n+1)} &= (\alpha I + X)\mathbf{u}^{(n+\frac{1}{2})} - \mathbf{b}' \end{aligned}\right\}, \tag{63}$$

where α is some extrapolation parameter. If the iteration converges, it is clear that we obtain the solution of (62). The iteration matrix for this scheme is

$$M = (\alpha I - Y)^{-1}(\alpha I + X)(\alpha I - X)^{-1}(\alpha I + Y), \tag{64}$$

which is almost the same as the matrix of (58). It follows that the iteration converges for any positive value of α.

The result is easily extended to equations of more general elliptic type. Over a rectangular region, we can show that the iteration of the form (63) converges for $\alpha > 0$ whenever the matrices X and Y are symmetric and negative definite. However, if we take the optimum value of α, we find that the asymptotic convergence rate for the example considered earlier (§4) is the same as that of successive over-relaxation (Varga 1962), so no advantage has been gained by the extra work involved in (63).

The convergence may be improved by allowing the parameter α to vary from step to step, giving a non-stationary iterative method. Peaceman and Rachford (1955) show that an average rate of convergence of $0(1/|\log h|)$ can be obtained for the simple model problem, by choosing a particular set of extrapolation parameters α_k. This compares favourably with SOR, where the optimum convergence rate is $0(h)$. Wachspress (1962) discusses the choice of optimum parameters when α is allowed to vary. An exact analysis is rather complicated, but he suggests methods which have proved very successful for large elliptic problems.

Most of the theoretical results about alternating-direction methods depend on having matrices X and Y with common eigenvectors, which are also the eigenvectors of M in (64). If X and Y are symmetric, the condition for a common set of eigenvectors is that X and Y commute, i.e. $XY = YX$. This property holds for quite a wide class of elliptic equations, but unfortunately only for rectangular regions (Birkhoff and Varga 1959). However, a number of numerical experiments have shown that alternating-direction methods are often superior to SOR for more general regions, provided the mesh-size is fairly small (Young and Ehrlich 1960).

8. Accuracy of Finite-difference Solutions

Our discussion so far has been concerned with methods for setting up and solving the finite-difference approximations to elliptic and parabolic equations. There has been much interest in the last few years in improved techniques for iterative solution of the linear equations, but less attention has been given to the relation between the solution and that of the original differential equation. It is of little value to solve the approximating equations efficiently unless we can make an estimate of the accuracy of the solution. Ideally, we would like to devise numerical methods which produce, along with the approximate solution, an upper bound or at least an estimate for the error. But we are a long way from achieving this in the field of partial differential equations. For methods of the types described, it has been proved under quite general conditions that the error tends to zero as $h \to 0$. We now want to consider the error for finite h, and we shall sketch briefly three approaches to the problem, concentrating in this section on elliptic equations.

Let us write $U(h)$ for the approximate finite-difference solution, and u for the exact solution, of a given problem. For certain problems, strict upper bounds have been obtained for the error $|U(h)-u|$ over the region, generally in terms of some high-order derivatives of u (see Forsythe and Wasow 1960, §23).

For example, suppose that we have the elliptic equation

$$\nabla^2 u = g \tag{65}$$

over a closed region, with values of u specified on the boundary. The error of the simplest finite-difference approximation to $\nabla^2 u$ at an interior point satisfies

$$\left| (\delta_x^2 u + \delta_y^2 u) - h^2 \nabla^2 u \right| \leq \tfrac{1}{6} h^4 M_4, \tag{66}$$

where M_2 is an upper bound for $\left|\dfrac{\partial^4 u}{\partial x^4}\right|, \left|\dfrac{\partial^4 u}{\partial y^4}\right|$ over the region. We use this approximation to set up the linear equations for $U(h)$ at interior points, and assume that we can satisfy the boundary conditions exactly (i.e. that the boundary curve intersects the mesh-lines only at mesh-points). Then, provided the fourth derivatives of u are bounded in the *closed* region, we can show that

$$|u - U(h)| < \tfrac{1}{12} M_4 h^2 R^2, \tag{67}$$

at points where $U(h)$ is defined, where R is the radius of a circle which encloses the region.

For general regions we cannot satisfy the boundary conditions exactly, and we have to use interpolation at mesh-points near the boundary. The accuracy of $U(h)$ then depends on the order of the interpolating formula. For linear interpolation, (67) is replaced by

$$|u - U(h)| < \tfrac{1}{12} M_4 h^2 R^2 + M_2 h^2, \tag{68}$$

where M_2 is an upper bound for the second derivatives of u. Further results are given by Bramble and Hubbard (1962). The approximation of normal-gradient boundary conditions presents special difficulties, particularly on curved boundaries. It is always possible to devise formulae of high accuracy at the boundaries (Fox 1950), but they may be inconvenient in practice because they may destroy the symmetry of the finite-difference matrix, or cause it to lose Property A.

The main limitation of results of the above type is that they require the derivatives concerned to be bounded in the closed region. This condition is generally not fulfilled at points on the boundary where the direction of the tangent is discontinuous, i.e. at corners. Laasonen (1958) discusses the order of the approximation obtained at corners for the particular case of Laplace's equation. The problem of geometrical singularities will be mentioned again in §9.

Upper bounds for the error are generally obtained in terms of quantities such as M_2 and M_4, which are seldom known. However, these bounds show the relation between accuracy and mesh-size, and hence the improvement to be obtained by repeating the calculation on a finer mesh. This leads to the idea of the *deferred approach to the limit* (Richardson and Gaunt 1926). If we assume that $U(h)$ is a well-behaved function of h, at any point where it is defined, we can expand it in a series of the form

$$U(h) = u + A_1h + A_2h^2 + A_3h^3 + \ldots, \tag{69}$$

since $U(h) \to u$ as $h \to 0$. By considering the approximate equations satisfied by $U(h)$, and applying methods similar to those of Fox (1957, Chapter 10), we can find which of the coefficients $A_1, A_2, A_3, \ldots$ in (69) is the first that does not vanish identically. Suppose it is A_q; then we have, neglecting higher terms,

$$\left.\begin{aligned}
U(h) &\simeq u + A_qh^q \\
U(\tfrac{1}{2}h) &\simeq u + \frac{1}{2^q}A_qh^q
\end{aligned}\right\}. \tag{70}$$

We can eliminate the error term to the same approximation, and obtain

$$u \simeq \frac{2^qU(\tfrac{1}{2}h) - U(h)}{2^q - 1}, \tag{71}$$

at points where both $U(h)$ and $U(\tfrac{1}{2}h)$ are defined.

For a smooth function and a moderately small value of h, we would expect the formula (71) to give a result of better accuracy than $U(\tfrac{1}{2}h)$. The difficulties in applying this method of extrapolation lie in determining the correct value of q, and in estimating the accuracy of the final result. The value of q is affected by the order of the approximation on the boundary as well as at interior points, and also by singularities, which lead to a more complicated expression than (69) for $U(h)$.

Another method for correcting an approximate solution is the difference-correction method of Fox (1947), discussed more recently by Bickley, Michaelson and Osborne (1961). If we include higher terms in the finite-difference expressions for the derivatives in an equation such as (65), we have

$$h^2\nabla^2u = (\delta_x^2 + \delta_y^2)u - \tfrac{1}{12}(\delta_x^4 + \delta_y^4)u + \tfrac{1}{90}(\delta_x^6 + \delta_y^6)u - \ldots \tag{72}$$

We then set up the following iterative procedure for solving the equation

$$(\delta_x^2 + \delta_y^2)u^{(n+1)} = h^2g + \tfrac{1}{12}(\delta_x^4 + \delta_y^4)u^{(n)} - \tfrac{1}{90}(\delta_x^6 + \delta_y^6)u^{(n)} + \ldots \tag{73}$$

with $u^{(0)} = 0$. If this iteration converges, we gain the advantage of a high-order representation of the derivatives, without increasing the complexity of the matrix of the linear equations to be solved at each step. Bickley *et al.* (1961)

show that certain difficulties arise in the theory when the right-hand side of (73) is regarded as an infinite series, and the method is only used in practice when the finite-difference series (72) converges rapidly. Some numerical experiments are described by Volkov (1957).

The difference correction can be conveniently used as a check on accuracy. If we include only fourth-order differences on the right of (73), the calculation of the correction terms is quite simple, though the formulae have to be modified near the boundary. We take $u^{(0)} = 0$, and calculate $u^{(1)}$ and $u^{(2)}$; then if $|u^{(1)} - u^{(2)}|$ is negligible, we expect $u^{(2)}$ to be accurate to the same number of figures, provided it is a smooth function, i.e. without singularities.

9. Other Problems and Methods

Finite-difference approximation is not the only method for obtaining numerical solutions to problems of the type we are considering. Collatz (1960, Chapter 5) discusses methods for boundary-value problems in which the solution is represented as a series of analytical functions of suitable form, e.g. simple powers or orthogonal polynomials in x and y, or eigenfunctions of the differential operator. The problem is then reduced to that of finding the coefficients in the expansion. For example, the function $u(x, y)$ satisfying some elliptic problem may be approximated by the finite series

$$U(\mathbf{a}) = \sum_0^n a_i f_i(x, y), \tag{74}$$

where the functions $f_i(x, y)$ are chosen to satisfy either the differential equation or the boundary conditions. The values of a_i are then found from the boundary conditions or the differential equation respectively.

Various methods are available for obtaining the a_i; we can use collocation at certain interior or boundary points, or we can minimize the integral of some function of the error $|U(\mathbf{a}) - u|$ around the boundary with respect to $\mathbf{a}$. Davis gives some numerical examples of the use of orthogonal polynomial expansions for the Dirichlet problem (in Todd 1962, Chapter 10). He considers several regions with awkwardly-shaped boundaries, which would be difficult to handle by finite-difference methods.

Expansions such as (74) are often useful in solving problems with geometrical or other singularities. We may be able to find an analytical expression for the solution which is valid in the region of the singularity, and which can be fitted to the equation or boundary conditions elsewhere. For example, suppose that the function u satisfies Laplace's equation in the interior of a region with a re-entrant corner of internal angle α ($\alpha > \pi$), and that u is zero on two straight-line boundaries meeting at the corner. Then, taking the corner as pole, we can express the local solution in polar coordinates as

$$U(\mathbf{a}) = \sum_1^n a_i r^{\pi i/\alpha} \sin \frac{\pi i \theta}{\alpha}. \tag{75}$$

This function satisfies Laplace's equation over the region, and also the boundary conditions near the singularity. We choose some suitable value of n, and determine the values of a_i by fitting the expression (75) to the remaining boundary conditions.

Alternatively, in a problem with several singularities, it may be more convenient to use a singular solution such as (75) in the neighbourhood of each singularity, and match it to a finite-difference solution elsewhere. Such a method is rather elaborate, but it gives better accuracy than simple finite differences.

In the case of parabolic equations, singularities may occur in the initial and boundary conditions, giving rise to errors in the finite-difference solution, but these are usually smoothed out as the integration proceeds. However, Parker and Crank (1964) give some examples in which the error in the discrete solution persists indefinitely. Fox (1962, Chapter 20) describes a method for removing an initial singularity by transforming the independent variable.

All the methods which have been suggested for dealing with singularities involve a substantial amount of work, and there is a need for new ideas and developments.

REFERENCES

ARMS, R. J., GATES, L. D. AND ZONDEK, B. 1956. A method of block iteration. *J. Soc. Ind. App. Math.* **4**, 220–229.

BICKLEY, W. G., MICHAELSON, S. AND OSBORNE, M. R. 1961. On finite-difference methods for the numerical solution of boundary-value problems. *Proc. Roy. Soc. A* **262**, 219–236.

BIRKHOFF, G. AND VARGA, R. S. 1959. Implicit alternating direction methods. *Trans. Amer. Math. Soc.* **92**, 13–24.

BRAMBLE, J. H. AND HUBBARD, B. E. 1962. On the formulation of finite difference analogues of the Dirichlet problem for Poisson's equation. *Num. Math.* **4**, 313–327.

CARRÉ, B. A. 1961. The determination of the optimum accelerating factor for successive over-relaxation. *Comp. J.* **4**, 73–78.

COLLATZ, L. 1960. *The Numerical Treatment of Differential Equations.* 3rd ed. Springer, Berlin.

CRANK, J. AND NICOLSON, P. 1947. A practical method for numerical evaluation of solutions of partial differential equations of the heat-conduction type. *Proc. Camb. Phil. Soc.* **43**, 50–67.

CUTHILL, E. H. AND VARGA, R. S. 1959. A method of normalized block iteration. *J. Assoc. Comp. Mach.* **6**, 236–244.

DOUGLAS, J. 1962. Alternating direction methods for three space variables. *Num. Math.* **4**, 41–63.

DOUGLAS, J. AND RACHFORD, H. H. 1956. On the numerical solution of heat conduction problems in two or three space variables. *Trans. Amer. Math. Soc.* **82**, 421–439.

FORSYTHE, G. E. AND WASOW, W. R. 1960. *Finite-difference Methods for Partial Differential Equations.* Wiley, New York.

FOX, L. 1947. Some improvements in the use of relaxation methods for the solution of ordinary and partial differential equations. *Proc. Roy. Soc. A* **190**, 31–59.

FOX, L. 1950. The numerical solution of elliptic differential equations when the boundary conditions involve a derivative. *Phil. Trans. A* **242**, 345–378.

Fox, L. 1957. *The Numerical Solution of Two-point Boundary Problems.* Clarendon Press, Oxford.

Fox, L. (ed.) 1962. *Numerical Solution of Ordinary and Partial Differential Equations.* Pergamon, Oxford.

KELLER, H. B. 1958. On some iterative methods for solving elliptic difference equations. *Q. App. Math.* **16**, 209–226.

KULSRUD, H. E. 1961. A practical technique for the determination of the optimum relaxation factor of the successive over-relaxation method. *Comm. Assoc. Comp. Mach.* **4**, 184–187.

LAASONEN, P. 1958. On the truncation error of discrete approximations to the solutions of Dirichlet problems in a domain with corners. *J. Assoc. Comp. Mach.* **5**, 32–38.

PARKER, I. B. AND CRANK, J. 1964. Persistent discretization errors in partial differential equations of parabolic type. *Comp. J.* **7**, 163–167.

PEACEMAN, D. W. AND RACHFORD, H. H. 1955. The numerical solution of parabolic and elliptic differential equations. *J. Soc. Ind. App. Math.* **3**, 28–41.

RICHARDSON, L. F. AND GAUNT, J. A. 1926. The deferred approach to the limit. *Phil. Trans.* A **226**, 299–361.

SOUTHWELL, R. V. 1946. *Relaxation Methods in Theoretical Physics.* Clarendon Press, Oxford.

STIEFEL, E. L. 1958. Kernel polynomials in linear algebra and their numerical application. *App. Math. Series* **49**, 1–22. Nat. Bur. Standards, Washington.

TODD, J. (ed.). 1962. *Survey of Numerical Analysis.* McGraw-Hill, New York.

VARGA, R. S. 1957. A comparison of the successive overrelaxation method and semi-iterative methods using Chebyshev polynomials. *J. Soc. Ind. App. Math.* **5**, 39–46.

VARGA, R. S. 1962. *Matrix Iterative Analysis.* Prentice-Hall, New York.

VOLKOV, E. A. 1957. Investigation of a method for increasing the accuracy of the method of nets in the solution of the Poisson equation. *Vichisl. Math.* **1**, 62–80.

WACHSPRESS, E. L. 1957. CURE: A generalized two-space-dimension multi-group coding for the IBM-704. Report KAPL-1724, Knollys Atomis Power Lab., Schenectady, New York.

WACHSPRESS, E. L. 1962. Optimum alternating-direction-implicit iteration parameters for a model problem. *J. Soc. Ind. App. Math.* **10**, 339–350.

WADSWORTH, M. AND WRAGG, A. 1964. The numerical solution of the heat conduction equation in one dimension. *Proc. Camb. Phil. Soc.* **60**, 897–907.

WRIGLEY, H. E. 1963. Accelerating the Jacobi method for solving simultaneous equations by Chebyshev extrapolation when the eigenvalues of the iteration matrix are complex. *Comp. J.* **6**, 169–176.

YOUNG, D. M. 1954. Iterative methods for solving partial difference equations of elliptic type. *Trans. Amer. Math. Soc.* **76**, 92–111.

YOUNG, D. M. AND EHRLICH, L. 1960. Some numerical studies of iterative methods for solving elliptic difference equations. *Boundary Problems in Differential Equations.* Wisconsin, Madison.

Chapter 6

Hyperbolic Partial Differential Equations

H. H. M. PIKE

Atomic Weapons Research Establishment, Aldermaston, Berkshire

1. Introduction

We begin with a short description of the properties of hyperbolic partial differential equations, taking as examples some equations arising in fluid dynamics. Consider the case of one-dimensional plane-parallel unsteady flow, and let ρ and u be the fluid density and velocity respectively. If the rate of mass flow ρu across the plane X exceeds that across the plane $X + \delta X$ then the density between the two planes must be increasing, i.e.

$$\delta X \Delta \rho = -\delta X \Delta t \, \frac{\partial(\rho u)}{\partial X}. \tag{1}$$

In this equation and throughout the chapter we use δ to denote a difference in the space direction and Δ the difference over a time interval at a fixed point in space.

The above relation gives us the partial differential equation

$$\frac{\partial \rho}{\partial t} + u \frac{\partial \rho}{\partial X} + \rho \frac{\partial u}{\partial X} = 0, \tag{2}$$

and similarly if we consider the rate of change of momentum of a given mass of fluid which at some instant is bounded by our two planes we find

$$\frac{\partial u}{\partial t} + u \frac{\partial u}{\partial X} + \frac{1}{\rho} \frac{\partial p}{\partial X} = 0, \tag{3}$$

where p is the pressure. For uniform entropy, p is a function of ρ alone and hence we have only two dependent variables, ρ and u. Equations (2) and (3) are non-linear, but since the coefficients are functions of ρ and u alone we could linearize them by interchanging dependent and independent variables provided the Jacobian J of the transformation were non-zero. In practice J is zero almost everywhere.

We can express the equations in a different form by using potential theory. For a simple polytropic equation of state $p/\rho^\gamma = $ constant, the velocity of sound c is given by

$$c^2 = \frac{dp}{d\rho} = \frac{\gamma p}{\rho}. \tag{4}$$

If we define a potential ϕ such that

$$\left.\begin{aligned}
\frac{\partial \phi}{\partial X} &= u \\[2mm]
\frac{\partial \phi}{\partial t} &= -\left(\frac{u^2}{2} + \frac{c^2}{\gamma - 1}\right)
\end{aligned}\right\}, \tag{5}$$

then (3) becomes an identity. Substituting in (2) and using (3) we get

$$(u^2 - c^2)\frac{\partial^2 \phi}{\partial X^2} + 2u\frac{\partial^2 \phi}{\partial X \partial t} + \frac{\partial^2 \phi}{\partial t^2} = 0, \tag{6}$$

where the coefficients are those of a quadratic with real factors. For this reason an equation such as (6) is termed hyperbolic.

Equation (6) may be written in factorized form as

$$\left[(u+c)\frac{\partial}{\partial X} + \frac{\partial}{\partial t}\right]\left[(u-c)\frac{\partial}{\partial X} + \frac{\partial}{\partial t}\right]\phi -$$
$$\frac{\partial \phi}{\partial X}\left[(u+c)\frac{\partial}{\partial X} + \frac{\partial}{\partial t}\right](u-c) = 0. \tag{7}$$

Hence along the direction defined by

$$\delta X = (u+c)\delta w, \qquad \delta t = \delta w, \tag{8}$$

where w is a parameter, we have

$$(u-c)\frac{d}{dw}\left(\frac{\partial \phi}{\partial X}\right) + \frac{d}{dw}\left(\frac{\partial \phi}{\partial t}\right) = 0, \tag{9}$$

which becomes an ordinary differential equation when we eliminate ϕ. Another equation can be obtained by interchanging $(u+c)$ and $(u-c)$ in (7), (8) and (9). Using (5) the two equations simplify to

$$du = \pm 2\, dc/(\gamma - 1), \tag{10}$$

and these relations are satisfied along the curves defined by (8). These curves, called the characteristics, are in fact the paths of sound waves. They form two families with the property that one and only one curve of each family passes through any point in the (X, t) plane.

The relations (10) satisfied along the characteristics may be written in the equivalent form

$$dp = \pm \rho c\, du, \tag{11}$$

and this holds even for non-uniform entropy provided there is no heat conduction. We shall ignore entropy variations for the moment.

If we are given the values of u, ρ, and p at any number of points on one characteristic we can say very little about the solution elsewhere. We can find du/dp for the other characteristic direction, but we know nothing about $\partial p/\partial X$ or $\partial p/\partial t$. In almost every flow pattern of interest $\partial p/\partial X$ is discontinuous across some characteristics, which therefore require special treatment in numerical solution. However, p and u are never discontinuous across a characteristic. Discontinuities in p and hence in u occur across shocks, whose paths cut across characteristics and which also require special treatment. The quantity c is discontinuous across interfaces and may be discontinuous across some streamlines as well.

Given initial values at N points on some line L which is not a characteristic, we can find u and c at the $N(N-1)$ points in the (X, t) plane where the characteristics of one family through these points cut those of the other, but in principle we know nothing about the solution elsewhere. If we can assume that the solution is fairly smooth between the N given points, we can find the positions of the $N(N-1)$ intersections approximately, since we know the slopes $u \pm c$ of the characteristics at every intersection. We can similarly find the solution at MN points from given initial values at M and N points respectively on the two characteristics through one point, provided the initial values satisfy (10).

It should be noted that if an error from any source introduces a perturbation into the solution at some point, this will travel away from the point as two sound waves. These may be broken up into a number of smaller waves by reflections at discontinuities, but there is no diffusion mechanism to smooth them out.

In steady two-dimensional flow the analogue of (6) is

$$(u^2 - c^2) \frac{\partial^2 \phi}{\partial X^2} + 2uv \frac{\partial^2 \phi}{\partial X \partial Y} + (v^2 - c^2) \frac{\partial^2 \phi}{\partial Y^2} = 0, \qquad (12)$$

and this is only hyperbolic where $u^2 + v^2 > c^2$.

More detailed discussion of hyperbolic equations can be found in Courant and Friedrichs (1948).

With the exception of Eulerian finite differences, all the numerical methods described in this chapter have been developed for use at A.W.R.E. (Aldermaston). The emphasis has been on the equations of unsteady flow in one or two space dimensions and much less work has been done on steady flow. Characteristic methods are described first, followed by Eulerian and Lagrangian finite-difference methods and then by the particle-in-cell method, in a sequence giving increasing breadth of application.

Some of the methods are discussed by Fox (1962) but more detailed descriptions, especially of methods for two-dimensional unsteady problems, are given by Alder et al. (1964). A very readable account of gas dynamics from a physical standpoint is given by Liepmann and Roshko (1957).

2. Numerical Solution by Characteristics

Methods using characteristics are by far the best for calculations on desk machines since each point of the flow pattern can be plotted as soon as it is found. One can spread points thinly over uninteresting regions, and forecast special events such as shock collisions and deal with them directly. In other words this method makes maximum use of human intelligence and hence is not very suitable for automatic computers.

The equations for one-dimensional unsteady flow are derived in §1. The most useful form is

$$\begin{aligned} dp \pm \rho c\, du = 0, & \quad \text{along } dX = (u \pm c)\, dt \\ dS = 0, & \quad \text{along } dX = u\, dt \end{aligned} \Bigg\} , \qquad (13)$$

where S is the entropy. Simple approximations for the numerical solution of (13) are obtained by replacing the differentials by first-order differences. We can improve the accuracy by taking the mean of the values of the coefficients at the beginning and end of the arc, and repeating the calculation iteratively.

As stated earlier, $\partial p / \partial X$ will usually be discontinuous along certain characteristics, e.g. those which form the fore and aft boundaries of a rarefaction or compression wave. However, provided that all such limiting characteristics are used in the solution, we can find the lengths of our characteristic arcs with errors of $O(h^4)$, since we know the slope $u \pm c$ at each end of each arc. Hence errors in the X and t coordinates of each point will be $O(h^3)$, while for uniform entropy p and u can be calculated as accurately as we wish at the true point of intersection of the characteristics, and with errors $O(h^3)$ if we calculate a point whenever a characteristic crosses an interface or entropy discontinuity.

If entropy is non-uniform it is better to use a Lagrangian coordinate system moving with the fluid, in which the space coordinate x denotes the initial position of a particular particle of fluid. Entropy is now a given function of x, and the solution for each point requires iteration. For axial $(n = 1)$ or spherical $(n = 2)$ symmetry the characteristic relations have extra terms, and in Lagrangian coordinates they take the form

$$\begin{aligned} & dp \pm \rho c\, du \pm nuc\, dt/X = 0 \\ \text{along} \quad & dx = \pm \rho X^n c\, dt/(\rho_0 x^n) \end{aligned} \Bigg\} , \qquad (14)$$

where $x = X$ at $t = 0$. To find X for each point we integrate $(u \pm c)dt$ along the two characteristic arcs meeting at the point, and average the two values of X so obtained—the difference between them gives an estimate of the accuracy achieved.

Finally we may have to interpolate along all the characteristics to find the solution at a set of (irregularly spaced) points on the same time line. We can then integrate ρ as a function of X to find the mass of fluid in any region, and compare the result with that given by the two extreme values of x. This checks the overall accuracy of the calculation.

3. Treatment of Shocks and Other Special Points

Shocks travel at supersonic speed relative to fluid ahead but at subsonic speed relative to fluid behind. Hence each shock path separates two quite different flow patterns and on this path all dependent variables are double-valued. We shall use suffices 1 and 0 to refer to the high and low pressure sides of the shock respectively. Conditions on the low pressure side are computed from the two characteristics ahead of the shock in the usual way. Given the fluid velocity u_1 behind the shock (which is a measure of its strength), the complete solution behind the shock can be found from the Rankine-Hugoniot shock equations for conservation of mass and momentum. One characteristic runs into the shock from behind and this determines the rate of variation of shock strength, or equivalently of u_1. For a shock moving into unsteady fluid a double iteration is required. A procedure which usually converges quite well is as follows

(a) Extrapolate the shock velocity U to find the position of the next shock point.
(b) Use characteristics ahead of the shock to find the solution on the low pressure side.
(c) Extrapolate u_1 to the new point.
(d) Guess the specific volume V_1 and calculate

$$\left.\begin{array}{c} p_1 = p_0 + (u_1 - u_0)^2/(V_0 - V_1) \\ U = (V_0 u_1 - V_1 u_0)/(V_0 - V_1) \\ \text{Residual } R = E_1 - E_0 - \tfrac{1}{2}(p_0 + p_1)(V_0 - V_1) \end{array}\right\}. \tag{15}$$

(e) Calculate $(\partial R/\partial V_1)_{u_1}$ and hence improve V_1, p_1 and U.
(f) Recalculate the position of the point.

Repeat the steps from (b) to (f) iteratively until R is sufficiently small. Since the new point is the intersection of three characteristics with the shock path, at least two of these characteristic arcs must be obtained by interpolation.

A detonation front is treated in exactly the same way except that the heat of detonation Q is subtracted from the right-hand side of the equation for R in (15).

Special treatment is required for other types of special point, for example, at the interaction of a shock with a material interface or another shock, or at the birth of a new shock in a compression wave. Details are given by Alder *et al.* (1964). Each special point takes up to ten times as much computation as an ordinary point. In hand calculation one can see what special points one must compute, but on an automatic computer one has to apply a whole series of tests before computing any point to see whether it is about to have a special interaction. For this reason more than 90% of the computer program will be concerned with administrative matters.

An alternative method suggested by Hartree is to arrange the ordinary points on a rectangular lattice in the (x, t) plane. The two characteristic arcs from any such point are then projected back to the previous time line, and values of the dependent variables at the ends of the arcs are found by interpolation. Clearly iteration is needed. This method is in fact an explicit finite-difference method, and other forms of it are more convenient. As we said earlier, the errors in $\Delta p, \Delta x$, etc. along every small arc can be kept down to $O(h^4)$ if and only if all limiting characteristics are included in the calculation. This cannot be done if either the Hartree method or a finite-difference method is used.

The treatment for two-dimensional steady flow is very similar to that described above. An example is given by Ehlers (1959), who describes in detail a computer program for calculating the flow of an ideal gas from a Laval nozzle.

4. Unsteady Two-dimensional Problems

In two dimensions the Hartree method offers considerable advantage in simplifying the problem of keeping track of the points. Instead of two characteristic lines we now project a characteristic conoid back on to the previous time plane. There are two lines on this conoid along which ordinary differential equations hold, and a relation along the streamline provides the extra condition needed for the extra component of fluid velocity. Descriptions of the method are given by Fox (1962) and Alder et al. (1964).

This method only provides accurate solutions in very simple cases because many special lines, e.g. the interaction of two shock surfaces, cannot always be dealt with. Hence it is mainly of use in providing standard solutions to check more versatile methods.

5. Finite-difference Methods in Eulerian Coordinates

The use of Eulerian coordinates gives some very simple methods in one and two dimensions, but they have the disadvantage that only quite simple boundary conditions can be dealt with. The author has no personal experience of these methods.

If we consider the total energy content E of unit mass of fluid

$$E = e + \tfrac{1}{2}u^2, \tag{16}$$

where e is the internal energy, then in one space dimension our hydrodynamic equations may be written as

$$\left.\begin{aligned}
\frac{\partial \rho}{\partial t} &= -\frac{\partial}{\partial X}(\rho u) \\[2mm]
\frac{\partial}{\partial t}(\rho u) &= -\frac{\partial}{\partial X}(\rho u^2 + p) \\[2mm]
\frac{\partial}{\partial t}(\rho E) &= -\frac{\partial}{\partial X}(\rho E u + pu)
\end{aligned}\right\} , \tag{17}$$

which can be combined into the single vector equation

$$\frac{\partial \mathbf{w}}{\partial t} = -\frac{\partial \mathbf{f}}{\partial X}. \tag{18}$$

This form of the equations is said to be conservative because, when $\mathbf{f}$ is zero on two planes X_1 and X_2, the total mass, momentum, and energy of the fluid between X_1 and X_2 are constant.

The form (17) is particularly convenient for Eulerian calculations because we do not have to follow particle paths in order to find the entropy. Instead we calculate E and $\tfrac{1}{2}u^2$ directly, and find e from their difference. For problems with axial or spherical symmetry momentum is not conserved, but the method of solution is much the same.

There are many ways in which we can replace the differential equations by difference equations and most of these will give a fair description of large-scale flow patterns. However, many difference schemes are sensitive to short wavelength perturbations, arising for example from truncation errors, the shortest possible wavelength being twice the mesh spacing.

The usual treatment is to linearize the problem, giving a perturbation equivalent to superimposing a sound wave of small amplitude $\mathbf{d}$ on an otherwise uniform flow pattern. Then to first order we find that the amplitude $\mathbf{d}_k^{n+1}$ of the sound wave at the point X_k at time t^{n+1} is given by

$$\mathbf{d}_k^{n+1} = A\mathbf{d}_k^n, \tag{19}$$

where A is the amplification matrix. For many forms of difference equation, including the simple one

$$\mathbf{w}_k^{n+1} - \mathbf{w}_k^n = \frac{\Delta t}{2\delta X}(\mathbf{f}_{k-1}^n - \mathbf{f}_{k+1}^n), \tag{20}$$

at least one of the latent roots of A has a modulus exceeding unity, i.e. the amplitude of perturbations of the shortest possible wavelength grows without limit as the calculation proceeds, for any time step.

Lax showed that the simplest way to avoid instability is to replace the left-hand side of (20) by

$$\mathbf{w}_k^{n+1} - \tfrac{1}{2}(\mathbf{w}_{k-1}^n + \mathbf{w}_{k+1}^n), \tag{21}$$

and the calculation is then stable provided

$$\Delta t < \delta X/(|u| + c), \tag{22}$$

i.e. provided the time step is less than the time required for a sound wave to cross the mesh. This limitation on Δt is known as the Courant condition and always applies unless an implicit procedure is used.

Waves should travel at sonic speed. The Courant condition forces the edges of waves to travel faster, especially if Δt is chosen to be much less than its maximum permitted value, but the resultant error is trivial.

As an alternative to Lax's method one can achieve stability by using higher-order differences, but any hoped-for gain in accuracy may be illusory because, as stated earlier, first-order derivatives are discontinuous along every limiting characteristic.

We shall refer to Lax's method again in discussing the treatment of shocks. Replacing $\mathbf{w}_k^n$ by the mean of the values at the two neighbouring points on the same time line, as in (21), is equivalent to adding the term

$$\tfrac{1}{2}(\mathbf{w}_{k-1}^n - 2\mathbf{w}_k^n + \mathbf{w}_{k+1}^n) \simeq \tfrac{1}{2}(\delta X)^2 \, \partial^2\mathbf{w}/\partial X^2 \tag{23}$$

to the right-hand side of our difference equation, and therefore it introduces some diffusion of $\mathbf{w}$, i.e. of mass, momentum and energy. This has the effect of bringing in artificial viscosity and thermal conductivity as well as mass diffusion.

The extension of the explicit methods to two dimensions is very simple, and only obvious modifications have to be made to the equations above.

6. Lagrangian Finite-difference Methods in One Dimension

For any problem in which the motions of material interfaces have to be calculated the use of Lagrangian coordinates is a great help. The method we have found most satisfactory is an explicit, non-conservative one derived in part from work by Trulio and Trigger (1961). In this method the values of X, u and $\dot{u}$ are calculated for a set of mesh points x, but p, ρ and e are calculated for the material between two mesh points and hence are taken midway between pairs of mesh points. All variables are calculated on the same time lines.

The method of calculation is as follows. Given a complete solution for time t^n, values of X_k^{n+1} are calculated assuming constant acceleration. The "half-way" values of the density $\rho_{k+\frac{1}{2}}^{n+1}$ are then calculated, and the corresponding values $e_{k+\frac{1}{2}}^{n+1}$ are obtained from

$$\Delta e_{k+\frac{1}{2}}^n = p_{k+\frac{1}{2}}^n (V_{k+\frac{1}{2}}^n - V_{k+\frac{1}{2}}^{n+1}). \tag{24}$$

We can then find the pressures and hence the accelerations on the new time line. The averages of the accelerations at t^n and t^{n+1} are then used to obtain new values of u_k^{n+1}. This procedure gives second-order accuracy in the solution of *all* the difference equations.

For the new interface points only first-order accuracy is aimed at. This is obtained by placing such points midway between other mesh points and moving them with conservation of mass until the material pressures in the two half-meshes are equal.

7. Treatment of Strong Shocks

A strong shock may be treated by Hartree's characteristic method, which introduces one special point where the shock intersects each time line. Since the shock is subsonic relative to flow behind, and the Courant stability condition is satisfied, the special point advances less than one mesh interval per time step. When the shock strikes an interface a characteristic solution is built up until the transmitted shock has travelled about two meshes from the interface. Values of the dependent variables at the Lagrangian grid points are then obtained by interpolation, and the finite-difference method is resumed for all points except the transmitted shock. This re-zoning has the effect of smearing out the reflected shock (if any) over one mesh width, but since there is only a small increase in entropy across the reflected shock this introduces only a small error.

A shock point takes several times as long to calculate as an ordinary point, but if the shock is moving into stationary material the mesh points ahead of it need not be considered, so there is often a net saving of time.

A realistic treatment of strong shocks is necessary for an accurate solution, but a similar treatment of weak shocks would entail the usual bookkeeping problems. We therefore require a simpler method which gives sufficient accuracy when weak shocks are present, but which does not require the calculation of any special points.

8. Von Neumann's Treatment of Shocks

Von Neumann's method is useful in one dimension, and essential for two-dimensional calculations, and so we discuss it in some detail. The basic principle is that if a shock can be spread out over three or more meshes it can be treated as a simple wave, and no special treatment whatever is required. The simplest dissipative mechanism for smearing out a shock is viscosity, but we want to introduce this only in the region of the shock, so that the accuracy of the rest of the calculation is not affected.

The momentum and energy equations for viscous flow with axial symmetry are

$$\rho_0 \frac{\partial u}{\partial t} + \frac{X}{x}\frac{\partial p}{\partial x} = \frac{4X}{3x}\left\{ \mu \frac{\partial}{\partial x}\left(\frac{\partial u}{\partial X} + \frac{u}{X}\right) + \frac{\partial \mu}{\partial x}\left(\frac{\partial u}{\partial X} - \frac{u}{2X}\right)\right\}, \qquad (25)$$

$$\frac{\partial E}{\partial t} + p \frac{\partial V}{\partial t} = \frac{4\mu}{3} V\left(\frac{\partial u}{\partial X} - \frac{u}{2X}\right)^2, \qquad (26)$$

where μ is the coefficient of viscosity. If μ is very small, except where $\partial u/\partial X \gg u/X$, then to a sufficient approximation

$$\rho_0 \frac{\partial u}{\partial t} + \frac{X}{x}\frac{\partial p}{\partial x} = \frac{X}{x}\frac{\partial}{\partial x}\left(\frac{4\mu\rho}{3\rho_0}\frac{\partial u}{\partial x}\right), \qquad (27)$$

$$\frac{\partial E}{\partial t} + p \frac{\partial V}{\partial t} = \frac{\partial V}{\partial t}\left(\frac{4\mu\rho}{3\rho_0}\frac{\partial u}{\partial x}\right). \qquad (28)$$

Hence we can eliminate μ by writing

$$P = p+q, \qquad (29)$$

where

$$q = -\frac{4\mu}{3}\frac{\rho}{\rho_0}\frac{\partial u}{\partial x} \quad \text{or} \quad -\frac{4\mu}{3V}\frac{\partial V}{\partial t}. \qquad (30)$$

We take

$$\frac{4\mu}{3} = -\rho_0(b\delta x)^2 \frac{\partial u}{\partial x} \quad \text{when} \quad \frac{\partial u}{\partial x} < 0 \bigg\}, \qquad (31)$$
$$= 0 \quad \text{otherwise}$$

since we do not want viscosity to operate in a rarefaction wave.

The parameter b is chosen so as to spread the shock over the required distance; defining its width as amplitude/steepest slope, this is approximately $2b\delta x$, so we take $b \simeq 1\cdot 5$.

The right-hand side of (27) contains $\partial^2 u/\partial x^2$, and inside the shock this is one of the largest terms. Hence we have a truly parabolic equation posing its own stability problem for our explicit methods of solution. For the simple equation

$$\frac{\partial u}{\partial t} = \sigma \frac{\partial^2 u}{\partial x^2}, \qquad (32)$$

we know that the maximum time step for explicit solution is given by

$$\Delta t/(\delta x)^2 \le \sigma/2. \tag{33}$$

In our problem $\sigma \sim (u_1 - u_0)/b\delta x$ and hence we find a condition on $\Delta t/\delta x$ which limits the time step inside a strong shock to roughly half the Courant value. A more detailed but unpublished treatment by White of Los Alamos leads to a complicated condition of which the dominant terms give

$$W^2 \equiv \left(\frac{\rho c}{\rho_0} \frac{\Delta t}{\delta x}\right)^2 + 4b^2 \frac{\Delta V}{V} \le S^2 < 1. \tag{34}$$

W is known as the White number. S is a safety factor, equal to 0.9, say, to allow for the missing terms. To keep the calculation explicit, W is calculated for each mesh at the previous time step and the largest value W_{max} selected. The time step to be used is then calculated from

$$t^{n+1} - t^n = 0.8(t^n - t^{n-1})/W_{max}, \tag{35}$$

the factor 0.8 allowing both for S and for the error in W_{max}.

9. Other Forms of Viscosity

The following forms of viscous pressure q have been proposed

Von Neumann $q = \rho(b\delta x)^2 \left(\dfrac{\partial u}{\partial x}\right)^2$

Schulz $q = -K^2 \rho \left(\dfrac{\partial^2 u}{\partial x^2}\right)\dfrac{\partial u}{\partial x}$

Landshoff $q = -L\rho c\delta x \dfrac{\partial u}{\partial x}$

Lax $q = -\dfrac{\rho_0(\delta x)^2}{2\Delta t} \dfrac{\partial u}{\partial x}$

Lax also includes a thermal conduction term and a mass diffusion term; all three arise from his modification of the difference equations.

In all four cases q is taken to be zero for $\partial u/\partial x > 0$, and in the first three cases the parameter is adjusted to spread the shock over about three meshes (the parameter is unity in Lax's case). The first two forms are only important inside the shock and hence do not smooth the oscillations that appear in the solution following the shock. The other two forms smooth these oscillations much better at the cost of introducing a large viscosity everywhere. Lax's method is more convenient than Landshoff's in that it allows the full Courant time step to be used.

Figure 1 shows the pressure-distance curves obtained by a Lagrangian calculation for a steady strong shock using von Neumann's method instead of Hartree's method, for $b = 0$, 1 and 4. The calculation for $b = 0$ shows that we cannot just ignore the shock. On the other hand for $b = 4$ we get a very smooth shock at the cost of excessive width. In practice we have to compromise, using values of b between 1 and 2.

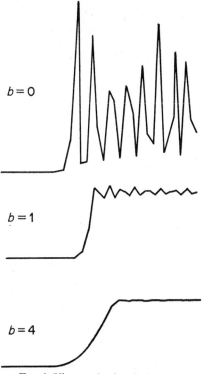

$b=0$

$b=1$

$b=4$

FIG. 1. Viscous shock calculations.

We always find that a viscous shock gives too large an entropy increase within a few mesh-lengths of an interface. One reason for this may be that the transmitted shock has the wrong shape; this factor can be very much reduced by choosing the mesh in the second material so that the transit time of the transmitted shock across a mesh is the same as for the incident shock. Unfortunately this needs to be done fairly accurately, and it can only be done for a limited range of incident shock strengths. It cannot be done at all for the reflected shock, so there will always be errors in the first material.

Another serious error arises if the second material is less than about three meshes thick, since the front of the wave reflected from the second interface interferes with the rear of the wave which has just got through the first interface. This error can usually be avoided in one dimension by reducing the mesh width, but this is not always possible in two-dimensional unsteady problems.

10. Conservative Equations in Lagrangian Coordinates

The conservative form of the equations is even simpler in Lagrangian than in Eulerian coordinates. Because of their suitability for mathematical analysis, the use of such equations for computing is often advocated in textbooks. They have the property that many forms of error in the computation are covered up. For example, an error in kinetic energy is immediately compensated by an error in internal energy so that the total energy is conserved. But the resultant disturbance produces two sound waves which transport energy away to other parts of the flow field. Hence the distribution of energy may be quite wrong.

The author much prefers the non-conservative form of equations given above, since an error then shows up immediately in the total energy of the system.

11. Lagrangian Finite-difference Methods for Two-dimensional Problems

Strictly speaking, a Lagrangian coordinate system is of no real use in two-dimensional unsteady problems, since the nearest neighbours of a point in real (Eulerian) space may be totally different from those in Lagrangian space. In fact we consider in this section methods of following, in Eulerian space, the motion of points fixed in the material. Problems of interest will involve shear, and we may start with coordinate axes along the principal axes of shear, but the latter will usually rotate. Hence the mesh in Eulerian space soon gets distorted and we are forced to consider generalized coordinates k, ℓ, say, taking lines of constant k or ℓ at unit intervals. If r and z are the corresponding Eulerian coordinates for axial symmetry then the mesh area is the Jacobian J where the suffixes refer to the four corners of the mesh (Fig. 2).

$$J = \frac{\partial(r, z)}{\partial(k, \ell)} = \tfrac{1}{2}(r_1 - r_3)(z_2 - z_4) - \tfrac{1}{2}(r_2 - r_4)(z_1 - z_3). \tag{36}$$

The procedure for the calculation is the same in principle as in the one-dimensional case. Given the positions and velocities of the mesh corners, and

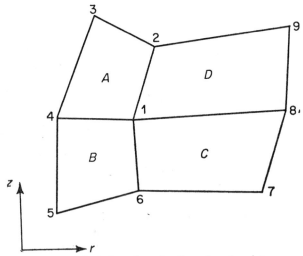

Fig. 2. Calculation of acceleration of mesh-point.

the internal energy of the mass M in the mesh, we calculate the density and hence the pressure, taken to be at the centroid of the mesh. We repeat this for every mesh, and then from the distribution of pressure points we calculate the accelerations of the mesh corners and hence their new positions and velocities at the end of the time step. The change in internal energy of the mass M during a time step is obtained by multiplying the change in volume by the initial pressure at the centroid. No attempt is made to iterate or to get second-order accuracy.

The acceleration of a material point is

$$\frac{1}{\rho}\nabla p = \left\{i\,\frac{\partial(z,\,p)}{\partial(\ell,\,k)} - j\,\frac{\partial(r,\,p)}{\partial(\ell,\,k)}\right\}\Big/ J, \tag{37}$$

where i and j are unit vectors in the r and z directions. In practice we calculate the acceleration of the mid-point of each mesh side. The acceleration of a mesh corner is then taken as the weighted mean of those of the mid-points of the four sides which meet at that point. Referring to Fig. 2, let s_{18} be the length of the side joining points 1 and 8, etc., and let n_{CD} be the length of the normal from the centroid of C to the boundary with D. Then the acceleration of the mid-point of s_{18} along its normal towards D is

$$(p_C - p_D)/(\rho_C n_{CD} + \rho_D n_{DC}).$$

For a nearly rectangular mesh

$$\rho_C n_{CD} s_{18} = M_C/\{2\pi(r_8 + r_1)\}, \tag{38}$$

and hence the mid-point of s_{18} has components of acceleration

$$\left.\begin{aligned}\ddot{r}_{18} &= -2\pi(p_C - p_D)(z_8 - z_1)(r_8 + r_1)/(M_C + M_D)\\ \ddot{z}_{18} &= 2\pi(p_C - p_D)(r_8 - r_1)(r_8 + r_1)/(M_C + M_D)\end{aligned}\right\}. \tag{39}$$

For a more distorted mesh we replace s_{18} by

$$s'_{18} = (s_{29} + 2s_{18} + s_{67})/4, \tag{40}$$

etc., so that

$$i\ddot{r}_{18} + j\ddot{z}_{18} = \frac{(p_C - p_D)}{2(\rho_C J_C + \rho_D J_D)}\left\{\begin{aligned}(z_9 - z_2 + 2z_8 - 2z_1 + z_7 - z_6)i\\ -(r_9 - r_2 + 2r_8 - 2r_1 + r_7 - r_6)j\end{aligned}\right\}. \tag{41}$$

The acceleration of point 1 has components

$$\ddot{r}_1 = \tfrac{1}{2}(\eta_{18}\ddot{r}_{18} + \eta_{12}\ddot{r}_{12} + \eta_{41}\ddot{r}_{41} + \eta_{61}\ddot{r}_{61}) \tag{42}$$

and similarly for $\ddot{z}_1$, where η_{18} is a weighting factor $\sim 1/s'_{18}$, etc.

This calculation is only correct to first order in the angle which measures the change in direction of a k or ℓ line at a mesh point. The kinetic energy is calculated exactly for a uniformly expanding mesh, e.g. for mesh C in Fig. 2,

$$\text{K.E.} = \frac{M_C}{48}\{(\dot{r}_1 + \dot{r}_6 + \dot{r}_7 + \dot{r}_8)^2 + (\dot{z}_1 + \dot{z}_6 + \dot{z}_7 + \dot{z}_8)^2\}$$

$$+ \frac{M_C}{24\bar{r}}\sum r_1(\dot{r}_1^2 + \dot{z}_1^2), \tag{43}$$

where $\bar{r}$ is the mean radius.

The von Neumann viscous pressure

$$q = \rho_0 b^2 J \Delta\rho/(\rho\Delta t) \quad \text{for } \Delta\rho > 0 \left.\right\}$$
$$= 0 \quad \text{otherwise} \qquad\qquad \tag{44}$$

is used with $\Delta\rho/\Delta t$ calculated from the previous time step to avoid iteration. The time step is limited by the White number as in (34).

Non-physical behaviour sometimes occurs with this method, in particular a strong shock striking one corner of a thin mesh may send that point over the opposite side during a time step so that the quadrilateral becomes two triangles, one of negative area. If the net area is negative the calculated pressure may be negative and an unstable situation may arise in which one mesh point shoots right across the whole field. But this fact is only known to its immediate Lagrangian neighbours so that calculation of the rest of the flow field is unaffected. This overlapping of two parts of the fluid is a peculiarity of Lagrangian calculations—to make them interact one must introduce a search procedure to locate neighbours in real (Eulerian) space.

The pressure gradient parallel to an interface must be the same on both sides. Hence materials of different densities must have different tangential accelerations and severe shearing of meshes may occur unless one material is allowed to slide over the other. This situation is met by the introduction of a slip line which is a double line of points, one in each material. The displacements of both sets of points are calculated during a time step, the tangential acceleration of each point being taken equal to that of the mid-point of the mesh side running from the point into its own material. At the end of the time step the two sides of the double line will have separated slightly, and this is remedied by moving the points on one line, usually in the less dense material, perpendicularly on to the other line, so producing meshes with more than four sides.

12. Non-ideal Fluid Properties

It is rather late to ask what problems involving two ideal fluids in contact one would wish to solve, but the answer is very few or none. Because of the density difference one would probably have Taylor instability and certainly Helmholtz instability of the interface, started off by the perturbation due to round-off errors. Most problems of interest have a damping mechanism, usually elastic strength or viscosity, either of which involves tensor forces, one dependent on strain and the other on rate of strain.

In problems of interest to the author, including solid materials driven by explosives, these materials behave as perfect fluids to a first approximation, but their motions are damped by shear stresses which, while much smaller than the total pressure, still suffice to damp out small-scale irregularities because of the large stress gradients produced. Hence the inclusion of elastic strength in our two-dimensional program enables us to solve more realistic problems and at the same time reduces mesh distortion. Very little extra programming is necessary since we already use two quite distinct equations of motion.

We introduce the stress deviators

$$s_a = \sigma_a + p, \quad \text{etc.} \tag{45}$$

where σ_a, σ_b, σ_c are the principal tensile stresses and $p = p(V, e)$. We treat s_a, s_b, s_c as the elastic part of the stress system. Clearly

$$s_a + s_b + s_c = 0, \tag{46}$$

and we use the von Mises yield criterion

$$s_a^2 + s_b^2 + s_c^2 \leq \tfrac{2}{3} Y_0^2, \tag{47}$$

where Y_0 is the yield strength in a simple tensile test.

If suffices 1, 2, 3 denote the r, z, ϕ components respectively, then in axial symmetry we have the strain components ε_1, ε_2, ε_3, ε_{12}. The corresponding stress deviator components are calculated from

$$\left. \begin{aligned} \dot{s}_1 &= 2\mu(\dot{\varepsilon}_1 - \dot{V}/3V) + \delta_1, \quad \text{etc.} \\ \dot{s}_{12} &= \mu\dot{\varepsilon}_{12} + \delta_{12} \end{aligned} \right\}, \tag{48}$$

where the dot denotes the time derivative and μ is the shear modulus. The δ terms are corrections to ensure that a simple rotation of the material leaves the stress distribution unchanged in a coordinate system rotating with the material. If an element rotates through an angle ω during a time step,

$$\sin \omega = \tfrac{1}{2}\left\{ \frac{\partial \dot{z}}{\partial r} - \frac{\partial \dot{r}}{\partial z} \right\}\Delta t, \tag{49}$$

$$\left. \begin{aligned} -\delta_2 = \delta_1 &= (s_2 - s_1)\sin^2 \omega + s_{12}\sin 2\omega \\ \delta_3 &= 0 \\ \delta_{12} &= -2s_{12}\sin^2 \omega + \tfrac{1}{2}(s_2 - s_1)\sin 2\omega \end{aligned} \right\}. \tag{50}$$

If at the end of a time step

$$s_1^2 + s_2^2 + s_3^2 + 2s_{12}^2 \equiv \tfrac{2}{3} Y^2 > \tfrac{2}{3} Y_0^2, \tag{51}$$

then all four components are reduced in the ratio Y_0/Y. This procedure keeps the elastic stress system at the yield point so long as the direction of shear remains unchanged, but permits elastic recovery if the direction of shear changes. Clearly one could generalize Y_0 to increase with increasing strain (work hardening) or decrease with increasing internal energy (temperature softening).

These elastic properties can give rise to interesting physical consequences since elastic waves travel substantially faster than comparable hydrodynamic ones. Also their amplitude may increase considerably as p increases. Such waves have been found experimentally by Al'tshuler et al. (1960).

13. Methods for Problems with Large Amounts of Shear

Suppose we have a dense, stiff material in contact with a less dense fluid which undergoes a great deal of shear, e.g. the air between a hammer and an anvil. We may be forced to treat the light fluid by a Eulerian method, but if we treat the dense material by the Lagrangian method we can retain the definition of the interfaces. Hence such a mixed method can be very useful, and two examples, of which the CEL code has wider application, are given in Alder *et al.* (1964).

At A.W.R.E. we have made a great deal of use of methods of the particle-in-cell type, which are also discussed in the above reference. These have the advantage that all materials can be allowed to undergo large amounts of shear while at the same time interfaces remain quite well defined.

14. The Particle-in-Cell Method

To simplify the algebra consider a one-dimensional case. Let us eliminate the problem of distortion of the Lagrangian mesh by re-zoning at every time step. The Lagrangian equation of motion is

$$\Delta u = \frac{\partial u}{\partial t}\,\Delta t = -\frac{1}{\rho_0}\frac{\partial p}{\partial x}\,\Delta t = -\frac{1}{\rho}\frac{\partial p}{\partial X}\,\Delta t. \tag{52}$$

If we transform back to the original mesh we have instead

$$\Delta u = -\frac{1}{\rho}\frac{\partial p}{\partial X}\,\Delta t - \frac{\partial u}{\partial X}\,u\Delta t, \tag{53}$$

which is, of course, the Eulerian equation. The crux of the matter is our treatment of the second term on the right of (53).

Suppose there is an interface between mesh k and mesh $k+1$. Then, for $u > 0$, re-zoning puts some of the material at k into mesh $k+1$. A simple Eulerian treatment must homogenize each mesh and hence some of the material at k diffuses forward one mesh every time step, so that the interface becomes very diffuse. To prevent this we must follow the path of the material that has been transferred from mesh k to mesh $k+1$. To keep the problem within bounds we divide the material in every cell into a finite number of particles each located at a point, and we record the (Eulerian) coordinates of every particle at every time step.

The calculation is carried out in two stages. Stage 1 is the "cell" or Lagrangian mesh calculation of momentum and internal energy. Since all dependent variables are calculated for the mid-point of each cell, they must be interpolated when required for the edges of cells. For example,

$$M_k\Delta u_k = \tfrac{1}{2}(p_{k-1}-p_k+p_k-p_{k+1})\Delta t. \tag{54}$$

This gives a set of provisional velocities u'_k at the centre of each cell at the end of the time step.

In stage 2 the velocity of every particle is calculated from its coordinates at the beginning of the time step by linear interpolation among the provisional velocities u'. Hence its position at the end of the time step is calculated and recorded. If it has moved into a new cell the momentum and energy it takes with it are $m\,u'$ and $\tfrac{1}{2}m\,u'^2$, i.e. the cell quantities, not calculated from interpolated velocities.

After all particles have been moved, the new cell velocity u_k is computed by dividing the total momentum by the total mass M_k, and hence the kinetic energy is calculated as $\tfrac{1}{2}M_k u_k^2$. This sharing of momentum inside a cell implies a drop in kinetic energy, and the lost energy is added to the internal energy of the cell.

This method introduces several errors. First, since the equations of state are non-linear, the transfer of a particle from one cell to the next leaves the mean density of the two unchanged but alters the mean pressure. Approximate corrections to the equation of state depending on the relative probabilities of various particle configurations have been devised; these increase in proportion to the second derivative $\partial^2 p/\partial \rho^2$ of the isentropic pressure-density relation, and decrease roughly in proportion to the square root of the number of particles per cell. A second error arises from the sharing of particle momenta at the end of a time step. This diffusion introduces an effective viscosity equal to $\frac{1}{2}\rho|u|\delta s$, where δs is the mean cell side. One can remove the gross effects of this term by extrapolating from the results of two calculations with different cell sizes. After doing this we have found quite good agreement with the corresponding Lagrangian mesh calculations. A third error arises from the fact that the difference form of the cell momentum equation (54) is unstable. This means that in stagnant regions oscillations in cell velocities may grow until damped by the $\frac{1}{2}\rho|u|\delta s$ viscosity term they generate. The most important consequence of this generation of random kinetic energy is a loss of internal energy, since total energy is conserved. This loss of entropy does not occur in regions where the mean fluid velocity is high.

Shocks or detonation waves can be dealt with by including the usual linear or quadratic artificial viscous pressure into the cell equations. Other non-ideal properties such as thermal conduction can also be introduced, and an approximate treatment of elastic properties has been devised by Riney (1962), but we have had no experience with this.

The particle-in-cell method provides a very versatile method for calculating quite complicated compressible flow patterns. For example, it can handle the penetration of a jet of one fluid through another quite well, provided surface tension is not important. Typically one can calculate the total momentum or energy of any substantial part of the flow field with an error of only a few per cent. One has to pay for this in computer time, of course, since the method takes about three times as long as the Lagrangian mesh method for a problem on which either method could be used. For example, if one has 50×100 cells initially containing 16 particles each, one uses 45,000 words of cell information plus 240,000 words of particle information per time step. On an IBM 7090 computer, the calculation takes about 15 secs. per 1000 cells per time step.

15. The Particle-and-Force Method

In a particle-in-cell calculation the particles play a subsidiary part. An alternative approach is to make the particle calculation of major importance and to use cells in a minor role. We then get a close analogy to the kinetic theory of gases. The particles are taken to be mutually repulsive and the potential energy of repulsion provides the internal energy. The type of repulsive-force law required to produce a given equation of state can in principle be derived from statistical mechanics. To make the problem manageable, forces are assumed to operate only between neighbours, and for each particle the number of neighbours is limited to twice the number of space dimensions of the problem. A dissipative mechanism analogous to artificial viscosity can be provided by mutual repulsive forces proportional to the relative velocity of approach (if positive) of a particle and its neighbour.

The main advantage claimed for this method over the particle-in-cell method is that destruction of entropy cannot occur. However, it is even more expensive in computing time, some 50% of this time being spent in locating the nearest neighbours of each particle. It is here that cells are used, to limit the area over which a search has to be made for the neighbours of any one particle.

The method is still in an early stage of development (Daly *et al.* 1965). One of the biggest difficulties is in finding force laws which will produce realistic equations of state for dense materials.

Acknowledgements

This chapter is based on the work, some of it unpublished, of many of the author's colleagues in the Mathematical Physics Division of A.W.R.E. Aldermaston, whose help the author gratefully acknowledges. Major contributions have been made by A. E. Glennie, N. E. Hoskin, B. W. Pearson, L. A. Elliott, and J. G. T. Jones. Thanks are also due to the Director, A.W.R.E., for permission to publish.

REFERENCES

ALDER, B., FERNBACH, S. AND ROTENBURG, M. 1964. *Methods in Computational Physics*, Vol. **3**. Academic Press, New York.

AL'TSHULER, L. V., KORMER, S. B., BRAZHNIK, M. I., VLADIMIROV, L. A., SPERANSKAYA, M. P. AND FUNTIKOV, A. I. 1960. The isentropic compressibility of aluminium, copper, lead and iron at high pressures. Soviet Physics J.E.T.P. **11**, 766–775.

COURANT, R. AND FRIEDRICHS, K. O. 1948. *Supersonic Flow and Shock Waves.* Interscience, New York.

DALY, B. J., HARLOW, F. H. AND WELCH, J. E. 1965. Numerical fluid dynamics using the particle-and-force method. Part I. The method and its applications. Part II. Some basic properties of particle dynamics. *Los Alamos Report LA-3144.*

EHLERS, F. E. 1959. The method of characteristics for isoenergetic supersonic flows adapted for high-speed digital computers. *J. Soc. Ind. App. Math.* **7**, 85–100.

FOX, L. 1962. *Numerical Solution of Ordinary and Partial Differential Equations.* Pergamon, Oxford.

LIEPMANN, H. W. AND ROSHKO, A. 1957. *Elements of Gasdynamics.* Wiley, New York.

RINEY, T. D. 1962. Solution of visco-plastic equations for axi-symmetric hypervelocity impact. *General Electric Space Sciences Laboratory Report No. R62SD95.*

TRULIO, J. G. AND TRIGGER, K. R. 1961. Numerical solution of the one-dimensional Lagrangian hydrodynamic equations. *University of California Radiation Laboratory Report UCRL-6267.*

Chapter 7

Polynomial and Rational Approximation to Functions of One Variable

A. R. CURTIS

*Atomic Energy Research Establishment,
Harwell, Didcot, Berkshire*

1. Introduction

Many functions required in numerical work are not expressible in terms of elementary functions such as e^x or $\sin x$, for which library routines are supplied with most computers, but are defined in more complicated ways. A function may be defined by a definite integral, for example the Bessel function

$$I_n(x) = \frac{1}{\pi} \int_0^\pi \exp(x \cos \theta) \cos n\theta \, d\theta, \tag{1}$$

or the error function

$$\mathrm{erf}(x) = 2\pi^{-\frac{1}{2}} \int_0^x e^{-t^2} \, dt. \tag{2}$$

Again, the most straightforward definition may be as the sum of a power series, for example

$$I_n(x) = \sum_{r=0}^\infty \frac{(\frac{1}{2}x)^{n+2r}}{r!(n+r)!}. \tag{3}$$

Generally, the direct use of such a definition to calculate function values for arbitrary arguments is prohibitively expensive in computing time, since often we may require evaluation for very many arguments, perhaps of the order of millions. There is thus a need for simpler methods of calculating such functions to given accuracies.

Generally, for numerical work the absolute error in any function value should not exceed a prescribed tolerance. However, for some functions it is more appropriate to set a limit on the relative error. An example is the exponential function itself. In order to get accuracy to nine significant figures in e^x for $x = -10$, say, an absolute error smaller than 3.10^{-14} is necessary; on most computers, this would be an impracticably small absolute error for $x = +10$, but a relative error of 5.10^{-10} would be acceptable over a very wide range. The two cases of absolute and relative error are special cases of weighted

135

error. Suppose that we use a function $\phi(x)$ as an approximation to a wanted function $f(x)$. We suppose that there is a positive weight function $g(x)$, and that we regard the error function as

$$\eta(x) = [f(x) - \phi(x)]/g(x). \tag{4}$$

Then if $g(x) = 1$ we are considering absolute error, while if $g(x) = f(x)$ (assumed positive) we are considering relative error.

Because most computers have arithmetic units providing hardware for addition, subtraction, multiplication and division, approximating functions which can be easily evaluated by combining such operations are usually preferred. Among such functions, polynomials are outstanding. The fact that they are linear functions of their coefficients is an advantage in some methods for finding approximations, but is not of great importance in using them. Rational functions, i.e. ratios of polynomials, are as convenient in use, and it turns out that they can often give much higher accuracy for a given evaluation time.

We may frequently be willing to use different approximating functions in different ranges of the independent variable. As an example, the following approximations to the Bessel function $I_0(x)$ can be obtained by truncating series given by Clenshaw (1962):

$$I_0(x) \simeq 127\cdot733440 + 190\cdot494320 T_2(x/8)$$
$$+ 82\cdot489033 T_4(x/8) + 22\cdot274819 T_6(x/8)$$
$$+ 4\cdot011674 T_8(x/8) + 0\cdot509493 T_{10}(x/8) + 0\cdot047719 T_{12}(x/8)$$
$$+ 0\cdot003416 T_{14}(x/8) + 0\cdot000192 T_{16}(x/8) \pm 1\cdot2.10^{-5}$$
$$(0 \le x \le 8), \tag{5}$$

$$I_0(x) \simeq x^{-\frac{1}{2}} e^{+x}[0\cdot39916585 + 0\cdot00627824 T_1(8/x)$$
$$+ 0\cdot00022511 T_2(8/x) + 0\cdot00001528 T_3(8/x) \pm 1\cdot8.10^{-6}]$$
$$(8 \le x \le \infty). \tag{6}$$

However, this may not be necessary even in the case of an infinite range, as shown by the example (Curtis and Osborne, 1966)

$$f(x) = \tfrac{1}{2}\pi^{\frac{1}{2}} e^{x^2}(1 - \mathrm{erf}\, x) = e^{x^2} \int_x^\infty e^{-t^2}\, dt$$

$$\simeq \frac{1\cdot69071595 + 1\cdot45117156x + 0\cdot50003230x^2}{1\cdot90764542 + 3\cdot79485940x + 2\cdot90845448x^2 + x^3} (1 \pm 6\cdot46.10^{-5})$$
$$(0 \le x \le \infty). \tag{7}$$

2. Methods for Polynomial Approximations

Perhaps the commonest method of finding polynomial approximations is truncation of a convergent Taylor series. For example, if x is near to zero we lose significance in computing $\sinh x$ from its definition

$$\sinh x = \tfrac{1}{2}(e^x - e^{-x}). \tag{8}$$

But if $|x| \le 0 \cdot 1$, the approximation

$$\sinh x \simeq x + \frac{x^3}{6} + \frac{x^5}{120} \tag{9}$$

is correct to nine significant figures, and can be used instead. This is a reasonable use of the method (although a "best" approximation of the same form but with different coefficients would probably have smaller error by an order of magnitude). However, this method is uneconomical when high accuracy is required over longer ranges.

An allied method is the use of an asymptotic expansion. For the function $f(x)$ of (7) we have

$$f(x) \simeq \frac{1}{2x}\left(1 - \frac{\frac{1}{2}}{x^2} + \frac{\frac{1}{2} \cdot \frac{3}{2}}{x^4} - \frac{\frac{1}{2} \cdot \frac{3}{2} \cdot \frac{5}{2}}{x^6} + \dots\right), \tag{10}$$

where the error is less than the first term neglected. If $x \ge 4$, the sum of the first five terms gives a relative error not greater than about 10^{-4}. Thus a truncation of the series to five terms gives an approximation of this accuracy, valid for $x \ge 4$, which is a polynomial in x^{-1}. But comparison with (7) shows this to be an uneconomic approximation.

The reason such approximations are uneconomic is easy to find in the case of convergent expansions. Truncation of the Taylor series for $f(x)$ after the term in x^n gives an error

$$\eta_T(x) = \frac{x^{n+1}}{(n+1)!} f^{(n+1)}(\theta x), \tag{11}$$

where $0 < \theta < 1$. But the Lagrangian interpolation polynomial based on points $x_1, x_2, \dots, x_{n+1}$ has an error

$$\eta_L(x) = \frac{f^{(n+1)}(u)}{(n+1)!} \prod_{r=1}^{n+1} (x - x_r) \tag{12}$$

where u is inside the interval I spanned by the x_r. If we wish to use the approximation over the range $0 \le x \le a$, then

$$|\eta_T(x)| \le \frac{a^{n+1}}{(n+1)!} \sup_{0 < x < a} |f^{(n+1)}(x)|, \tag{13}$$

while

$$|\eta_L(x)| \le \frac{a^{n+1}}{(n+1)!} \sup_{u \in I} |f^{(n+1)}(u)| \sup_{0 \le \xi \le 1} \left|\prod_{r=1}^{n+1} \left(\xi - \frac{x_r}{a}\right)\right|. \tag{14}$$

It is known that by the choice

$$\frac{x_r}{a} = \cos^2\left(\frac{(r - \frac{1}{2})\pi}{2(n+1)}\right) \tag{15}$$

the last factor in (14) can be made as small as $2^{-(2n+1)}$, while I is clearly contained in $(0, a)$. Thus the use of the interpolation polynomial to $f(x)$ at the collocation points given by (15) gives in general a much smaller error, for the same degree, than the truncated Taylor series. It is fair to point out that the interpolation polynomial may give a far larger error than the Taylor series at points outside the interval $[0, a]$ for which it is designed.

This raises the question, is there an approximating polynomial which, among all those of degree n, gives minimum error? This is easily answered in the affirmative, by using elementary ideas of function spaces.

For the choice (15) of the x_r, the last factor in (12) is related to a Chebyshev polynomial,

$$\prod_{r=1}^{n+1} (x-x_r) = a^{n+1} \cdot 2^{-(2n+1)} T_{n+1}\left(\frac{2x}{a} - 1\right). \tag{16}$$

where if $\zeta = \cos \theta$, $T_n(\zeta) = \cos n\theta$. This suggests that truncating an expansion in Chebyshev polynomials may be better than truncating an expansion in powers of x. Consider the exponential function

$$e^{\lambda x} = \sum_0^\infty \frac{(\lambda x)^n}{n!}. \tag{17}$$

In terms of Chebyshev polynomials

$$e^{\lambda x} = \sum_0^\infty{}' C_n(\lambda) T_n(2x-1), \qquad 0 \le x \le 1, \tag{18}$$

where

$$C_n(\lambda) = 2 \exp(\lambda/2) I_n(\lambda/2), \tag{19}$$

and the prime indicates that the term for $n = 0$ is to be halved. For $n \gg \lambda$, we have

$$I_n(\lambda/2) \sim (\tfrac{1}{4}\lambda)^n/n!, \tag{20}$$

so that the terms in (17) are ultimately $2^{2n-1} e^{-\lambda/2}$ times the corresponding terms in (18), for $|x| \le 1$. The convergence of the series (18) is thus much faster than that of (17) and this is the general state of affairs. In cases where the convergence is fast enough so that the error in truncation is approximately the first term neglected, this method gives substantially the same result as the above collocation method. However, they are useful in different situations. If it is practicable to compute function values at $(n+1)$ selected points in order to obtain the approximation, collocation can be used. If the coefficients in the Chebyshev expansion can be obtained analytically, truncation of this expansion can be used. The coefficients may be found approximately by collocation using a larger value of n and expressing the results in terms of Chebyshev polynomials. This can be conveniently done in general by using the discrete orthogonality property of these polynomials—see, for example, Clenshaw (1962).

It has been shown by Lebesgue (see, for example, Natanson 1964, p. 195, or Vitushkin 1961, p. 17) that the error obtained by truncation of Chebyshev series exceeds the error of the best nth degree approximation by a factor bounded by $(3+\log n)$. The least upper bound is certainly lower than this (Powell 1965; see also Clenshaw 1964). It would be interesting to know whether a similar result holds for the collocation method.

However, there is interest in methods of finding the best polynomial approximation, if only because they extend fairly easily to the problem of finding best rational approximations. Rational approximations can, as pointed out by Hastings (1955), be used successfully on a wider class of functions than can polynomials. Such methods make use of a basic theorem due to Chebyshev, quoted in the next section.

3. Methods for Best Approximations

The only methods available for finding best approximations are iterative ones based on Chebyshev's theorem. For the more general case of rational approximating functions, this theorem states (e.g. Achieser 1956, p. 55) that if $\phi(x)$ is any rational function of x whose degrees are not greater than ℓ in the numerator and m in the denominator, and if $f(x)$ is a given continuous function and $g(x)$ a given positive weight function on $[a, b]$, then there is in general a unique best approximation $\phi^*(x)$ characterized by the sign alternation properties of the error function

$$\eta^*(x) = \frac{f(x) - \phi^*(x)}{g(x)}. \tag{21}$$

These are that there is a set of $n+2 = \ell+m+2$ points x_r, $a \le x_0 < x_1 \ldots < x_{n+1} \le b$, (called a "reference") such that

$$\left.\begin{aligned} \eta^*(x_r) &= (-1)^r h^* \\ \sup_{a \le x \le b} |\eta^*(x)| &= |h^*| \end{aligned}\right\}. \tag{22}$$

An exceptional case arises when neither numerator nor denominator of ϕ^* is of maximum degree; this can happen only for special functions $f(x)$, and the effect is to reduce n by the smaller of the two defects. For polynomial approximation $m = 0$, $n = \ell$, and the exceptional case cannot arise.

The methods in general use are variants on one due to Maehly (1963). Let us write

$$\phi(x) = \frac{\sum_{j=0}^{\ell} a_j x^j}{\sum_{k=0}^{m} b_k x^k}. \tag{23}$$

Suppose we have a reference $\{x_r\}$, $r = 0, 1, \ldots, n+1$, and we choose h, $\phi(x)$ to satisfy the $(n+2)$ equations

$$[f(x_r) - (-1)^r g(x_r) h] \sum_0^m b_k x_r^k - \sum_0^\ell a_j x_r^j = 0. \tag{24}$$

These are linear and homogeneous in a_j, b_k, while h occurs only linearly as a multiplier of b_k. This is thus an eigenvalue problem in general, but if $m = 0$ we fix $b_0 = 1$ and we have a set of $(n+2)$ linear non-homogeneous equations for h and the $(n+1)$ a_j. Having found a solution of the equations giving a pole-free $\phi(x)$, we then locate the $(n+2)$ extrema of the resulting error function and take these as a new reference. The process has quadratic convergence.

At most one of the $(m+1)$ solutions of (24) can lead to a pole-free solution (Maehly 1963). All solutions are real (Werner 1963).

The methods differ mainly in the way they solve (24). Mattson (1960) linearises by using values of b_k from a previous iteration as multipliers of h. Stoer (1964) satisfies $(n+1)$ equations and uses Newton's method to adjust h so as to satisfy the last equation. Curtis and Osborne (1966) use inverse iteration to solve the eigenvalue problem (24). There is also scope for subtlety in the method used to search for the extrema of the error function.

These methods are in general successful in finding best approximations, but may differ in the number of evaluations of $f(x)$ and $g(x)$ required, and in their sensitivity to build-up of rounding errors. The method of Curtis and Osborne seems to be more robust than the others. Economy depends mainly on skill in searching for extrema.

Where economy in function evaluations is of vital importance, we may do well to consider minimizing the error on a fixed point set chosen in advance. Because of the normal crowding of reference points to one or both ends of the range, if this is to give a result close to a best approximation on the whole interval the points should be evenly spaced in θ, where $\cos \theta = (2x-b-a)/(b-a)$, rather than in x. The use of some $10(n+1)$ intervals should be adequate in most cases, but an *a posteriori* check should then be made to ensure that reference points are separated by at least five intervals.

This compares badly with the case of polynomial approximation, where collocation at $(n+1)$ points usually gives reasonable results. This is because of the lack of a general expression like (12) for the error function in the rational case. For polynomials, we were able to make a general choice of collocation points but, precisely because rational functions can approximate closely to a wider class of functions than can polynomials, the zeros or extrema of the error curves can be distributed in more general ways.

That the use of best rational approximations can be worth while is shown by the approximation (7). Other methods for finding rational approximations, such as the Padé table, are incapable of giving approximations valid over $0 \leq x < \infty$; while clearly polynomial approximations are unsuitable. Similar techniques could be used in approximating to other functions, e.g. for the exponential integral

$$E_1(x) = \int_1^\infty \frac{e^{-xt}\,dt}{t} \quad , \tag{25}$$

one might try

$$E_1(x) \simeq e^{-x} \ln\left(\frac{1+x}{x}\right)\phi(x), \qquad 0 \leq x < \infty, \tag{26}$$

where $\phi(x)$ is of the same degree in numerator and denominator.

REFERENCES

ACHIESER, N. I. 1956. *Theory of Approximation.* Ungar, New York.
CLENSHAW, C. W. 1962. Chebyshev series for mathematical functions. *Math. Tab. Nat. Phys. Lab.* **5**, H.M. Stationery Office, London.

CLENSHAW, C. W. 1964. A comparison of "best" polynomial approximations with truncated Chebyshev series expansions. *J. Soc. Ind. App. Math.* ser. B. **1**, 26–37.

CURTIS, A. R. AND OSBORNE, M. R. 1966. The construction of best rational approximations to functions. *Comp. J.* (to appear).

HASTINGS, C. 1955. *Approximations for Digital Computers.* Princeton University Press.

MAEHLY, H. J., 1963. Methods for fitting rational approximations. Part II. *J. Assoc. Comp. Mach.* **10**, 257–266.

MATTSON, H. F. 1960. An algorithm for finding rational approximations. Air Force Cambridge Research Lab., Bedford, Massachusetts.

NATANSON, L. P. 1964. *Constructive Theory of Functions.* Vol. 1. (trans.). Ungar, New York.

POWELL, M. J. D. 1965. Private communication.

STOER, J. 1964. A direct method for Chebyshev approximation by rational functions. *J. Assoc. Comp. Mach.* **11**, 59–69.

VITUSHKIN, A. G. 1961. *Theory of the Transmission and Processing of Information.* Pergamon, Oxford.

WERNER, H. 1963. Rationale Tschebyscheff Approximation, Eigenwerttheorie und Differenzenrechnung. *Arch. Rational Mech. Anal.* **13**, 330–347.

Chapter 8

Minimization of Functions of Several Variables

M. J. D. POWELL

Atomic Energy Research Establishment,
Harwell, Didcot, Berkshire

1. Introduction

The range of applications of minimization of functions of several variables includes such problems as

(i) The calculation of control parameters of a chemical plant, say, to minimize waste, minimize cost or maximize output.

(ii) Curve fitting and the determination of parameters from experiments.

(iii) The solution of non-linear equations.

(iv) The determining of parameters in numerical analysis formulae which minimize the resultant error, in some sense.

As well as a wide range of applications, there is a wide range of different types of minimization problem. In this chapter, the procedures I consider to be the most useful are discussed, and, in some cases, extensions to existing methods are proposed. Thus a compendium of algorithms is provided, and some research topics are suggested. If there is undue emphasis on unconstrained minimization, it is because my experience has been mainly in this field. In many applications constraints are essential.

The general problem is to minimize

$$F(x_1, x_2, \ldots, x_n)$$

subject to $h_i(x_1, \ldots, x_n) \geq 0; i = 1, 2, \ldots, m$.

The variables are real numbers, their values being restricted by the constraints. If a vector $\mathbf{x} = (x_1, x_2, \ldots, x_n)$ satisfies the constraints we call it *feasible*. It is assumed that $F(\mathbf{x})$ can be determined for all feasible choices of $(x_1, x_2, \ldots, x_n)$. The procedures to be described calculate local minima; the problem of finding global minima is discussed briefly in §12.

The wide range of minimization algorithms arises from consideration of the following questions

(i)   Are there constraints on the values the variables may take?

(ii) Are derivatives of $F(\mathbf{x})$ and/or the constraining functions available?

(iii) To what extent can $F(\mathbf{x})$ be regarded as a continuous function?

(iv) Are there special features, such as $F(\mathbf{x})$ being a sum of squares or the constraints being linear, that can be exploited?

Considerations (ii) and (iii) merit comment. Calculating formulae for derivatives and programming their evaluation requires effort, and is a possible source of error. Therefore for a small problem it may be economic to use a slower algorithm that does not require derivatives. Regarding (iii) it must be remembered that differentiable functions have zero derivatives at a minimum. Therefore near the solution a small change, of ε say, in a variable usually causes a change of order ε^2 in the function. Consequently many algorithms depend on accurate calculation of function values.

A further important consideration is the choice of variables. It is well known that in fitting a continuous function by a linear combination of specified functions it is advantageous if the specified functions are "orthogonal". Similar gains can arise from suitable changes of variables in the general minimization problem. If there are no constraints, one should strive to choose $(x_1, x_2, \ldots, x_n)$ so that the surfaces $F(\mathbf{x}) = $ constant are concentric hyperspheres.

We discuss first, in §§2–5, methods for the unconstrained minimization problem. §§6–9 deal with the constrained problem, and in the remaining sections we give some further techniques and general comments.

2. Generalized Newton-Raphson Method

We refer to a method as a Newton-Raphson method if it uses an iteration based on a Taylor series expansion about the current approximation to the required solution. We consider the generalized Newton-Raphson procedure first as it highlights the important features of unconstrained minimization problems.

We assume that the function to be minimized is differentiable, and suppose that at the start of an iteration the variables have the approximate values $\xi_1, \xi_2, \ldots, \xi_n$. If the required minimum is at $\xi_1 + \delta_1, \xi_2 + \delta_2, \ldots, \xi_n + \delta_n$, then

$$\left[\frac{\partial}{\partial x_i} F(\mathbf{x})\right]_{\mathbf{x}=\xi+\delta} = 0, \qquad i = 1, 2, \ldots, n. \tag{1}$$

From the Taylor series,

$$\left[\frac{\partial}{\partial x_i} F(\mathbf{x})\right]_{\mathbf{x}=\xi} + \sum_{j=1}^{n} \left[\frac{\partial^2}{\partial x_i \, \partial x_j} F(\mathbf{x})\right]_{\mathbf{x}=\xi} \delta_j + O(\delta^2) = 0. \tag{2}$$

We use the notation

$$g_i = \left[\frac{\partial}{\partial x_i} F(\mathbf{x})\right]_{\mathbf{x}=\xi}, \tag{3}$$

$$G_{ij} = \left[\frac{\partial^2}{\partial x_i \, \partial x_j} F(\mathbf{x})\right]_{\mathbf{x}=\xi}, \tag{4}$$

so that (2) gives

$$\delta = -G^{-1}[\mathbf{g} + O(\delta^2)]. \tag{5}$$

Therefore, using superscripts for the iteration number, the generalized Newton-Raphson procedure is

$$\xi^{(n+1)} = \xi^{(n)} - G^{-1}\mathbf{g}^{(n)}. \tag{6}$$

The disadvantages of this method are well known. First there is no device to force convergence from a poor approximation, secondly it is necessary that second derivatives exist and are available, and thirdly the procedure breaks down if G is singular. On the other hand, the method is invariant under linear transformations of the variables, and its ultimate convergence is quadratic.

Because of the first disadvantage, it is advisable not to use the predicted correction directly, but to use a multiple of it, so that equation (6) becomes

$$\xi^{(n+1)} = \xi^{(n)} - \lambda G^{-1} g^{(n)}. \tag{7}$$

λ is a number which is chosen so that $\xi^{(n+1)}$ is approximately the minimum in the direction $-G^{-1} g^{(n)}$ from $\xi^{(n)}$, so determining it is a one-dimensional minimization problem. Unfortunately, even (7) does not ensure convergence; consider, for example,

$$F(x_1, x_2) = x_1^4 + x_1 x_2 + (1 + x_2)^2, \tag{8}$$

and take $\xi_1 = \xi_2 = 0$. Clearly

$$g^T = (0, 2), \tag{9}$$

$$G = \begin{bmatrix} 0 & 1 \\ 1 & 2 \end{bmatrix}, \tag{10}$$

and therefore

$$(-G^{-1} g)^T = (-2, 0). \tag{11}$$

Thus the required value of λ is that which minimizes $F(2\lambda, 0)$, namely $\lambda = 0$, and no progress can be made from the starting approximation, although the first derivative vector is substantial.

The second disadvantage also merits discussion. Without knowledge of the second derivative terms, ultimate quadratic convergence cannot be achieved. In the next two sections we describe procedures that effectively obtain this knowledge from function values and first derivatives, but quadratic convergence is of prime importance only if the solution is required to high accuracy.

3. Minimization using First Derivatives

First we discuss the method of steepest descent. Applying the Newton-Raphson procedure to the function of equation (8) at $(0, 0)$ fails because the resultant direction of search $-G^{-1} g^{(n)}$ is orthogonal to the derivative vector $g^{(n)}$. This cannot happen if the matrix G^{-1} is positive definite. The steepest descent method is obtained by replacing G^{-1} by the unit matrix, the iteration being

$$\xi^{(n+1)} = \xi^{(n)} - \lambda g^{(n)}. \tag{12}$$

However, except for economizing on multiplications, there is no virtue in choosing the unit matrix. A fundamental objection to steepest descent in its simplest form is that it is dependent on the scaling of the variables, and an intelligent choice of a constant positive definite matrix to replace G^{-1} in (7) can be very rewarding. Having made this choice, we assume that the variables are transformed so that the iteration is given by (12), and consider the resulting procedure.

It has the advantages that only first derivatives are required, and that it will probably converge from a poor approximation. Unfortunately the convergence can be extremely slow, and this is usually due to a poor choice of metric. It often happens that the function to be minimized is such that *no* choice of metric will cause the iteration (12) to be efficient for all reasonable values of the variables, so one should be very critical before applying the steepest descent method.

An important advance in minimization algorithms was made by Davidon (1959), who worked out an automatic procedure for changing the metric. In Davidon's method the iteration corresponding to equation (7) is

$$\xi^{(n+1)} = \xi^{(n)} - \lambda H^{(n)} g^{(n)}, \tag{13}$$

where $H^{(n)}$ is a positive definite matrix which is changed from iteration to iteration. The basis of the change is that in a neighbourhood of the minimum

$$\xi^{(n+1)} - \xi^{(n)} \simeq G^{-1}[g^{(n+1)} - g^{(n)}], \tag{14}$$

so $H^{(n+1)}$ is chosen in such a way that

$$\xi^{(n+1)} - \xi^{(n)} = H^{(n+1)}[g^{(n+1)} - g^{(n)}]. \tag{15}$$

The initial $H^{(1)}$ may be taken to be any positive definite symmetric matrix. It has been proved (Fletcher and Powell 1963) that the matrix $H^{(n)}$ remains positive definite, and that it converges to the matrix G^{-1} evaluated at the minimum. Therefore fast ultimate convergence is obtained. Experience shows that, away from the minimum, Davidon's method is generally much superior to steepest descents, but there remains an unexplained difficulty. Examples have occurred in which some steps of Davidon's method cause small changes in the variables at points where a step of steepest descent would give a large improvement. This shows that the metric associated with $H^{(n)}$ can be temporarily bad, and further advances would probably be made if the cause of the trouble were recognized.

Fletcher and Reeves (1964) have discussed more generally the conditions under which fast ultimate convergence can be expected. They point out that if $F(x_1, x_2, \ldots, x_n)$ is an exact quadratic form, whose function values and first derivatives are available, it is possible to calculate, in a number of ways, n directions in the space of the variables such that searching along each one in turn yields the minimum. Davidon's method is one such procedure, and they describe another which does not require the storage of a matrix.

4. Minimization Using Function Values Only

This is a broader field than that of §3 because the problem often arises of minimizing functions which are not well defined, or which are continuous but not differentiable. Therefore sometimes heuristic approaches are most effective, and these must be considered. However we will discuss first procedures designed to have fast convergence if the second derivatives are continuous.

We will start with the method of Powell (1964), which is an extension of Smith's (1962) method. The basis of Smith's method is that fast ultimate convergence results from a procedure that would find the minimum of a quadratic function in a finite number of steps, so we consider this problem. If $F(x_1, x_2)$ is an exact quadratic having a minimum, the contours $F(x_1, x_2) =$ constant are as shown in Figure 1. The centre of the family of ellipses can be

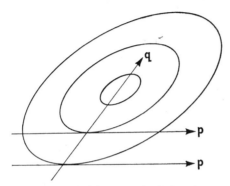

Fig. 1. Minimizing a quadratic function.

found by searching along two parallel directions for minima, and then searching along the line joining the resultant points. Clearly this technique can be applied to find the minimum in any two-dimensional subspace of the space of the variables in an n-dimensional problem. Then the minimum in a three-dimensional subspace is the minimum on a line joining the minima in two parallel two-dimensional subspaces. The construction may be extended to calculate the minimum in the full space of the variables, and this constitutes an iteration of Smith's method. An undesirable feature of this approach is that an approximate minimum has to be found in an $(n-1)$-dimensional subspace before the last variable is introduced, so that unequal emphasis is given to the different variables.

Powell's method gives equal emphasis to all the variables, and each iteration is much shorter, but it requires n iterations to minimize a quadratic. Each iteration depends on n directions in the parameter space, and the method causes these to become mutually conjugate (**p** and **q** are mutually conjugate directions in Figure 1). Because the method would break down if the directions became linearly dependent, there is a special modification to prevent this. It has repercussions which are serious when n exceeds about fifteen. These are not properly understood, and some insight might lead to significant improvements.

Fletcher (1965) has compared Smith's and Powell's conjugate direction methods, and he also considers a procedure described by Swann (1964). This last method is an extension of Rosenbrock's (1960), which searches for a minimum along n orthogonal directions in each iteration. The first of these directions is that of the total step made on the previous iteration, and this feature probably contributes most to the convergence. Again a theoretical investigation might lead to improvements, particularly as the method is dependent on the scaling of the variables.

We now turn to methods which are suitable for functions that are not well defined, for example observations subject to experimental error, so that we do not expect replication for the same values of the variables. The methods should not depend critically on the precise function values, and the simplex method of Spendley *et al.* (1962) is particularly useful.

In this it is assumed that the variables are scaled so that they are comparable in size, and that we have function values at the vertices of a regular simplex (a regular simplex in n-dimensional space has $(n+1)$ vertices, and edges of equal length, an example being a regular tetrahedron in three-dimensional space). In an iteration the vertex at which the function value is largest is found, and it is then replaced by its reflection in the opposite face of the simplex. Nelder and Mead (1965) have developed this procedure to such an extent that they find it more efficient than Powell's conjugate direction method for three particular functions. This is surprising because the only use they make of function values is to compare them.

5. Minimization of a Sum of Squares

In the case where $F(\mathbf{x})$ is a sum of squares,

$$F(x_1, x_2, \ldots, x_n) = \sum_{k=1}^{m} [f_k(x_1, x_2, \ldots, x_n)]^2, \ m \geq n, \tag{16}$$

and each $f_k(\mathbf{x})$ is relatively small at the minimum, procedures that are considerably more efficient than those already described have been worked out. One of the most useful comes from equation (2), the basis of Newton-Raphson iteration. Substituting (16) in (2) we have

$$\sum_{k=1}^{m} \frac{\partial f_k(\xi)}{\partial x_i} f_k(\xi) + \sum_{j=1}^{n} \left[\sum_{k=1}^{m} \frac{\partial f_k(\xi)}{\partial x_i} \frac{\partial f_k(\xi)}{\partial x_j} + f_k(\xi) \frac{\partial^2 f_k(\xi)}{\partial x_i \, \partial x_j} \right] \delta_j + 0(\delta^2) = 0. \tag{17}$$

If $f_k(\xi + \delta) = 0$, $f_k(\xi)$ is of order δ, and the term $f_k(\xi) \dfrac{\partial^2 f_k(\xi)}{\partial x_i \, \partial x_j} \delta_j$ may be absorbed in $0(\delta^2)$. If $f_k(\xi + \delta) \neq 0$ we lose quadratic convergence if we neglect this term and define δ by

$$\sum_{k=1}^{m} \frac{\partial f_k(\xi)}{\partial x_i} f_k(\xi) + \sum_{j=1}^{n} \left[\sum_{k=1}^{m} \frac{\partial f_k(\xi)}{\partial x_i} \frac{\partial f_k(\xi)}{\partial x_j} \right] \delta_j = 0, \tag{18}$$

but we gain substantially by having no explicit second derivative terms in the equation.

This iteration is sometimes called the Gauss method and, to demonstrate the analogy with Newton-Raphson, it is convenient to write it in the form of equation (6)

$$\xi^{(n+1)} = \xi^{(n)} - G^{-1}\mathbf{g}^{(n)}$$

where
$$G_{ij} = 2\sum_{k=1}^{m} \frac{\partial f_k(\xi)}{\partial x_i} \cdot \frac{\partial f_k(\xi)}{\partial x_j}. \tag{19}$$

Note that G is usually positive definite, so the predicted correction to $\xi^{(n)}$ is in a direction of descent in the space of the variables. The iteration (19) may diverge, so as before we search for a minimum along the predicted direction and take

$$\xi^{(n+1)} = \xi^{(n)} - \lambda G^{-1}\mathbf{g}^{(n)}. \tag{20}$$

Marquardt (1963) remarks that it is not uncommon for even the iteration (20) to fail to converge, but this has not been my experience.

Marquardt describes a variant in which (20) is modified to

$$\xi^{(n+1)} = \xi^{(n)} - (G + \lambda D)^{-1}\mathbf{g}^{(n)}, \tag{21}$$

where D is a diagonal matrix with positive diagonal elements that reflect the scaling of the variables. He proves that if λ is sufficiently large

$$F(\xi^{(n+1)}) < F(\xi^{(n)}), \tag{22}$$

unless, of course, $\|\mathbf{g}^{(n)}\|$ is zero. A definite advantage of (21) over (20) is that, for $\lambda > 0$, $(G + \lambda D)^{-1}$ is well defined, whereas G may be singular in some cases. On the other hand the introduction of λ in this way presents problems.

Powell (1965) has worked out a procedure for least-squares problems using only function values. The derivatives are approximated by differences, and the organization of the method is such that extra function evaluations are required only in initiating the iterations.

6. Linear Programming

Turning now to minimization with constraints, we begin by considering some features of linear programming which may be of value in solving a general constrained minimization problem. Space does not permit a detailed description of the methods, but it is indisputable that they are of great practical importance. In particular, acceptable answers to some non-linear minimizations may be obtained by approximating the functions so that they depend linearly on the variables.

The general linear programming problem is to minimize a linear function subject to linear inequality, and sometimes equality, constraints. We have

$$F(x_1, x_2, \ldots, x_n) = \sum_{i=1}^{n} c_i x_i, \tag{23}$$

with the following conditions on the variables

$$\left.\begin{array}{ll}
\displaystyle\sum_{j=1}^{n} a_{ij}x_j \geq b_i, & i = 1, 2, \ldots, m \\[3mm]
\displaystyle\sum_{j=1}^{n} \alpha_{ij}x_j = \beta_i, & i = 1, 2, \ldots, \mu
\end{array}\right\}. \tag{24}$$

As before, a point $(x_1, x_2, \ldots, x_n)$ in the space of the variables is called feasible if it satisfies the constraints and, disregarding $F(\mathbf{x})$, we first have to find a feasible point, or prove that none exists. If a feasible point exists the equality constraints may be used to eliminate some of the variables, so we can suppose that $\mu = 0$. Now let us try variables $\bar{x}_1, \bar{x}_2, \ldots, \bar{x}_n$. Suppose, for definiteness, that

$$\sum_{j=1}^{n} a_{ij}\bar{x}_j - b_i = -\bar{\xi}_i < 0 \text{ (say)}, \qquad i = 1, 2, \ldots, p \le m, \qquad (25)$$

the remaining inequality constraints of (24), if any, being satisfied. Consider the problem, similar to that above, of minimizing

$$F^*(x_1, x_2, \ldots, x_n, \xi_1, \xi_2, \ldots, \xi_p) = \sum_{i=1}^{p} \xi_i, \qquad (26)$$

subject to

$$\left.\begin{aligned}
\sum_{j=1}^{n} a_{ij}x_j &\ge b_i, && i = p+1, p+2, \ldots, m \\
\sum_{j=1}^{n} a_{ij}x_j &\ge b_i - \xi_i, && i = 1, 2, \ldots, p \\
\xi_i &\ge 0, && i = 1, 2, \ldots, p
\end{aligned}\right\}. \qquad (27)$$

Then $(\bar{x}_1, \bar{x}_2, \ldots, \bar{x}_n, \bar{\xi}_1, \bar{\xi}_2, \ldots, \bar{\xi}_p)$ is a feasible point of (27), and if (24) has feasible points, solving the second problem will find one. Generally the latter will not have a unique solution, but it is of interest to see that we can calculate feasible points by minimization.

Since $F(\mathbf{x})$ is linear in the variables, it is monotonic (not necessarily strictly) along all lines in the space of the variables. Therefore, if $F(\mathbf{x}) \not\equiv 0$, it is only the constraints that make it possible for $F(\mathbf{x})$ to take its minimum value at a finite point. If the position of the minimum is unique, it must therefore be at the intersection of at least n constraining hyperplanes, i.e. at a vertex of the feasible region. Therefore a method for calculating the minimum is to move from vertex to vertex, along edges of the feasible region, in such a way that $F(\mathbf{x})$ decreases at every stage. This is the basis of the simplex algorithm (see Gass 1958, for example), which is particularly elegant when the problem is formulated so that the inequality constraints impose non-negativity conditions on all the variables.

This last desideratum may be achieved by applying a duality theorem. By way of illustration we state a general one due to Wolfe (1961), and then quote a corollary for reformulating the problem of (23) and (24).

Given that $F(x_1, x_2, \ldots, x_n)$ is a convex differentiable function of $\mathbf{x}$, and that for $i = 1, 2, \ldots, m$ the functions $h_i(x_1, x_2, \ldots, x_n)$ are concave differentiable functions of $\mathbf{x}$, we define primal and dual problems as follows

Primal   Minimize $F(\mathbf{x})$ subject to

$$h_i(\mathbf{x}) \ge 0, \qquad i = 1, 2, \ldots, m. \qquad (28)$$

Dual   Maximize $\phi(\mathbf{x}, \mathbf{u}) = F(\mathbf{x}) - \sum_{i=1}^{m} u_i h_i(\mathbf{x})$ subject to

$$u_i \ge 0, \qquad i = 1, 2, \ldots, m, \qquad (29)$$

and

$$\frac{\partial}{\partial x_j} \phi(\mathbf{x}, \mathbf{u}) = 0, \qquad j = 1, 2, \ldots, n.$$

The theorem states that if $\mathbf{x}_0$ solves the primal problem, there exists a vector $\mathbf{u}_0$ such that $(\mathbf{x}_0, \mathbf{u}_0)$ solves the dual problem and $F(\mathbf{x}_0) = \phi(\mathbf{x}_0, \mathbf{u}_0)$.

If all functions are linear, the corollary is that the problems become

Primal   Minimize $F(\mathbf{x}) = \sum\limits_{j=1}^{n} c_j x_j$ subject to

$$\left. \begin{array}{l} \\ \sum\limits_{j=1}^{n} a_{ij} x_j - b_i \geq 0, \qquad i = 1, 2, \ldots, m \end{array} \right\}. \tag{30}$$

Dual   Maximize $\phi(\mathbf{u}) = \sum\limits_{i=1}^{m} u_i b_i$ subject to

$$\left. \begin{array}{ll} u_i \geq 0, & i = 1, 2, \ldots, m \\ \end{array} \right\}. \tag{31}$$

and $$\sum\limits_{i=1}^{m} u_i a_{ij} = c_j, \qquad j = 1, 2, \ldots, n$$

An algorithm to be described in §9 is also suitable for solving the linear programming problem.

7. Conditions for a Local Minimum

The basic difference between users of unconstrained minimization methods and those who apply linear programming techniques is that the former regard constraints as a nuisance, while for the latter they are essential in obtaining a solution. Consequently the general problem in which both $F(\mathbf{x})$ and the constraints are non-linear is regarded differently by the two schools and, at the present time, neither has profited much from the experiences of the other. Consequently considerable advances should be made in the next few years, and the next three sections underline this point of view.

If the objective and constraint functions are differentiable, a local minimum is reached when a move in any direction not of ascent would take one outside the feasible region. This may be stated as a theorem.

We define $\boldsymbol{\xi}$ to be the current vector of variables, $\mathbf{g}$ to be the direction of steepest descent for $F(\mathbf{x})$ at $\boldsymbol{\xi}$, and $\mathbf{n}_1, \mathbf{n}_2, \ldots, \mathbf{n}_p$ to be vectors normal to those constraining surfaces that are effective at $\boldsymbol{\xi}$. The signs of the normal vectors are such that they point outwards from the feasible region. If $F(\mathbf{x})$ is convex and the constraining functions are concave in a neighbourhood of $\boldsymbol{\xi}$, a sufficient condition that $F(\boldsymbol{\xi})$ be a local minimum of $F(\mathbf{x})$ is that we may express $\mathbf{g}$ as

$$\mathbf{g} = \sum_{i=1}^{p} \lambda_i \mathbf{n}_i, \tag{32}$$

where the scalars $\lambda_1, \lambda_2, \ldots, \lambda_p$ are all non-negative.

A valid criticism of the theorem is that one is assuming convexity and concavity in order to avoid detailed consideration of directions which are orthogonal to **g**. That there is a need for more general theorems is illustrated by the example of Figure 2. The contours $F(\mathbf{x})$ = constant are concentric circles, their centre being in the unfeasible region. The feasible region is

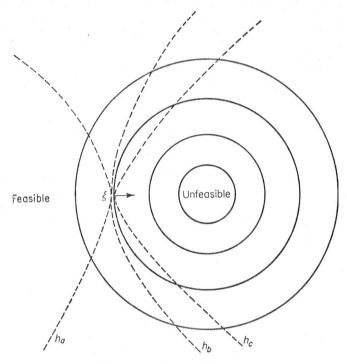

Feasible

Unfeasible

ξ

h_a

h_b

h_c

FIG. 2. The limitations of convexity/concavity theorems.

bounded by one of the three constraints h_a, h_b or h_c. The theorem applies if the boundary is h_a, but it does not differentiate between h_b and h_c. It is apparent that

(i) ξ is a local minimum even if the constraint is h_b, and
(ii) more useful theorems must take curvature into account.

8. Minimization without Violating Constraints

Algorithms for minimization subject to constraints divide into two classes, depending on whether or not they require function values outside the feasible region. The classes have little in common, so we allow them distinct sections.

Methods that insist that constraints are not violated ensure this either by modifying the function to be minimized so that it becomes large at the boundary of the feasible region, or by automatically choosing new values of the variables if a point outside the region is indicated. Box (1965) has described a procedure of the latter type, but I favour the former because of the successful experience of Fiacco and McCormick (1964), who have developed Carroll's (1961) response surface technique.

They regard the problem as a succession of unconstrained minimizations, each depending on a positive parameter r. The function that is minimized is

$$P(\mathbf{x}, r) = F(\mathbf{x}) + r \sum_{i=1}^{m} \frac{1}{h_i(\mathbf{x})}, \tag{33}$$

starting from a feasible point. The reciprocal terms can ensure that feasible minima are found. Let $\xi(r)$ be the vector of variables yielding the lowest value of $P(\mathbf{x}, r)$ in the feasible region.

Theorem. If $F(\mathbf{x})$ is continuous, and its minimum value in the feasible region occurs at a unique point ξ, and if ξ is adjacent to the interior of the feasible region, then

$$\lim_{r \to 0} \xi(r) = \xi. \tag{34}$$

Proof. For any $\varepsilon > 0$ there exists an interior point ξ_ε such that

$$F(\xi_\varepsilon) - F(\xi) < \tfrac{1}{2}\varepsilon. \tag{35}$$

Therefore if

$$r < \tfrac{1}{2}\varepsilon \Big/ \sum_{i=1}^{m} \frac{1}{h_i(\xi_\varepsilon)} \tag{36}$$

it follows that

$$P(\xi(r), r) \le P(\xi_\varepsilon, r) < F(\xi) + \varepsilon, \tag{37}$$

and

$$\lim_{r \to 0} P(\xi(r), r) = F(\xi). \tag{38}$$

The theorem follows from the uniqueness of ξ.

Fiacco and McCormick emphasize a duality theorem that is applicable when $F(\mathbf{x})$ is convex and $h_i(\mathbf{x})$, $i = 1, 2, \ldots, m$, is concave. It states that

$$F(\xi(r)) - r \sum_{i=1}^{m} \frac{1}{h_i(\xi(r))} < F(\xi), \tag{39}$$

the left-hand side tending to the right as $r \to 0$. Therefore in some cases we have upper and lower bounds on the functions we are minimizing.

Under the conditions required to prove (39), they have shown that the components of $\xi(r)$ have an asymptotic expansion in powers of $r^{\frac{1}{2}}$. Therefore the convergence to ξ may be accelerated.

In my opinion an extension to their algorithm could be outstandingly efficient. At present they use Davidon's method for each minimization of (33), but this could be improved because of the unusual form of the function, owing to the singularity imposed by the constraints. All the data about the singularity are available, and perhaps this information should be used explicitly. In particular the effect of altering r on the best choice of $H^{(n)}$ in equation (13) should be calculable.

9. Projection Methods of Constrained Minimization

First we consider the relatively easy problem of minimization subject to linear constraints. This discussion could have been included in the last section because, except for rounding errors, the constraints are not violated. However, the difficulties that arise are more appropriate to this section.

We know that finding a feasible point is a linear programming problem, but when a general non-linear function $F(\mathbf{x})$ is considered, we have the important difference that fewer than n of the constraints may be effective at the minimum. The essence of a projection method is that when constraints become effective the path of descent follows them, but it is important to be able to leave constraining surfaces when necessary. Rosen (1960) describes how the effective constraints may be recognized, and he suggests following them by applying a projection operator to the steepest descent vector. However, because of the problem of the metric considered in §3, this approach will not necessarily give fast ultimate convergence. Obviously it would be better to have a variable metric in which to define the steepest descent vector, but as far as I know this has not been investigated.

Rosen (1961) has generalized his algorithm to take account of non-linear constraints. At the current approximation, $\mathbf{y}$ say, to the position of the minimum, he represents the effective constraints by their supporting hyperplanes (these can be derived from the first-order terms in the Taylor series expansion of $h_i(\mathbf{x})$ about $\mathbf{y}$), and he then applies the projection operator of his earlier method to the steepest descent vector. A move along the resultant direction of descent probably leads to unfeasible points, owing to the curvature of the constraints, so he includes an elegant procedure for projection back into the feasible region. However his method is not as useful as it might be because it is based on restrictive assumptions in order to guarantee convergence. Solutions are required for many problems not satisfying convexity and concavity conditions, and it would be of interest to know something about the difficulties of applying projection techniques to these.

In concluding this section I should point out that obtaining second-order convergence in solving the general minimization problem by using a projection technique is particularly arduous. From Figure 2 we appreciated the importance of the curvature of the constraints $h_i(\mathbf{x}) \geq 0$, and this is emphasized further by the following example

$$\left. \begin{array}{l} \text{Minimize } x+y \\ \text{subject to} \qquad x^2 + y^2 \leq 1 \end{array} \right\}. \tag{40}$$

This problem has a unique solution only because of the curvature of the constraint, so it appears that to obtain fast ultimate convergence, second derivatives of all the constraints as well as of the function to be minimized must be taken into account.

10. The Minimum of a Function of One Variable

As we have seen, a number of minimization methods reduce the many-variable problem to that of repeatedly finding minima along certain lines in the space of the variables. Therefore the choice of procedure for minimizing a function of one variable is of great importance. There are two fundamentally different approaches to this problem.

The first is the "Fibonacci search" (see Spang 1962, for instance), which has achieved popularity as it has been proved, in a sense, to be "optimal". It is a technique for bracketing a local minimum of a function $f(x)$ in a given range $a \leq x \leq b$ by using only function values. The points at which $f(x)$ is calculated are determined by the procedure, and the optimum property is that, in the worst case, after a certain number of evaluations of $f(x)$, the length of the interval within which a local minimum must lie is least. A criticism of this procedure is that it uses function values only in comparisons, whereas it is usually advantageous to use calculated values of $f(x)$ explicitly.

The second approach is to interpolate using a low-order polynomial. Most of the methods of §4 use the parabola defined by three function values, while Davidon's method fits a cubic polynomial to the function and the first derivative at two points. Further details are given in the papers describing the methods.

It is not sufficient to have a good method for one-dimensional minimization, because special problems can still arise in applications. Consider, for example, the minimization of

$$F(x_1, x_2) = [1 - x_1 \, e^{-x_2}]^2 + [2 - x_1 \, e^{-2x_2}]^2. \tag{41}$$

Suppose that x_1 is fixed and the value of x_2 that minimizes $F(x_1, x_2)$ is required. This value of x_2 is infinite if $x_1 < 0$, although the minimum of $F(x_1, x_2)$ in the full space of the variables is well defined.

11. Reducing the Number of Variables or Constraints

In a number of minimization problems the function is such that if the values of $x_1, x_2, \ldots, x_p$, say, are given, the "best" values of the remaining variables may be calculated analytically. In this case $F(x_1, x_2, \ldots, x_n)$ may be regarded as a function of the first p variables only, the dependence on the remainder being defined by the analytic formula.

As an example of this technique, consider the problem of calculating a function of the form

$$\phi(t) = \sum_{j=1}^{p} a_j \, e^{\lambda_j t} \tag{42}$$

which best fits observed values of $\phi(t)$ in a least-squares sense. If the given observations of $\phi(t_i)$ are d_i, $i = 1, 2, \ldots, k$, we require the values of $a_1, a_2, \ldots, a_p$ and $\lambda_1, \lambda_2, \ldots, \lambda_p$ which minimize

$$\sum_{i=1}^{k} [\phi(t_i) - d_i]^2. \tag{43}$$

We define

$$(x_1, x_2, \ldots, x_p) = (\lambda_1, \lambda_2, \ldots, \lambda_p \tag{44}$$

6*

and

$$(x_{p+1}, x_{p+2}, \ldots, x_n) = (a_1, a_2, \ldots, a_p). \tag{45}$$

For any choice of $\lambda_1, \lambda_2, \ldots, \lambda_p$, the best choice of the remaining variables is defined by linear least-squares equations.

Alternatively, direct elimination of $a_1, a_2, \ldots, a_p$ leads to the problem of determining $\lambda_1, \lambda_2, \ldots, \lambda_p$ such that the Euclidean distance of the vector

$$(d_1, d_2, \ldots, d_k)$$

from the space spanned by the p vectors

$$(e^{\lambda_j t_1}, e^{\lambda_j t_2}, \ldots, e^{\lambda_j t_k}), \qquad j = 1, 2, \ldots, p,$$

is a minimum.

Sometimes the number of constraints may be reduced by transforming the variables (Halton 1965). This device is best explained by an example. The problem of minimizing $F(x_1, x_2)$ subject to

$$x_1 \geq 0, \qquad -1 \leq x_2 \leq 1 \tag{46}$$

is equivalent to the unconstrained minimization of

$$\phi(t_1, t_2) = F(t_1^2, \sin t_2). \tag{47}$$

12. Finding the Global Minimum

The objective of the minimization methods so far described is to follow a line of descent through the space of the variables to a local minimum. Frequently the number of evaluations of $F(x_1, x_2, \ldots, x_n)$ is of order n^2, so (except for $n = 1$ and perhaps 2), information about $F(\mathbf{x})$ is acquired over a very small part of the space of the variables. To calculate the global minimum the entire feasible region has to be investigated, which appears to be a task of much greater magnitude. At present the usual recourse is to find local minima from a number of different starting approximations, and this has been apparently successful on a number of problems. It would be of value to devise procedures which would ensure finding a global minimum if $F(x_1, x_2, \ldots, x_n)$ satisfied a reasonable criterion, such as a Lipschitz condition. I would expect such procedures to be too laborious for $n \geq 5$, but they would certainly be useful for $n = 1, 2$, and 3.

13. Conclusion

The discussion of the different methods shows that much useful work remains to be done in the field of minimization. In addition I could have stressed the great demand for efficient practical algorithms, but my interest is more in theory than in applications. Therefore, in conclusion, I will summarize my opinion of the present state of the art in minimization.

(i) Insufficient consideration is given to the choice and scaling of variables.

(ii) The reason why even the better methods for unconstrained minimization sometimes make little progress is not understood, and the understanding could lead to substantial improvements.

(iii) For problems with linear constraints, a projection method works well, but there is an outstanding need for such a method with a variable metric.

(iv) For problems with non-linear constraints, the type of approach used in the response surface technique appears to be most promising.

(v) In view of the large number of problems that fail to conform, too much effort is directed towards proving theorems and developing procedures for functions satisfying convexity and concavity conditions.

REFERENCES

BOX, M. J. 1965. A new method of constrained optimization and a comparison with other methods. *Comp. J.* **8**, 42–52.

CARROLL, C. W. 1961. The created response surface technique for optimizing nonlinear restrained systems. *Operations Research,* **9**, 169–184.

DAVIDON, W. C. 1959. Variable metric method for minimization. A.E.C. Research and Development Report, ANL–5990 (Rev.).

FIACCO, A. V. AND McCORMICK, G. P. 1964. Computational algorithm for the sequential unconstrained minimization technique for nonlinear programming. *Management Science,* **10**, 601–617.

FLETCHER, R. 1965. Function minimization without evaluating derivatives—a review. *Comp. J.* **8**, 33–41.

FLETCHER, R. AND POWELL, M. J. D. 1963. A rapidly convergent descent method for minimization. *Comp. J.* **6**, 163–168.

FLETCHER, R. AND REEVES, C. M. 1964. Function minimization by conjugate gradients. *Comp. J.* **7**, 149–154.

GASS, S. I. 1958. *Linear Programming.* McGraw-Hill, New York.

HALTON, J. H. 1965. Private communication.

MARQUARDT, D. W. 1963. An algorithm for least-squares estimation of nonlinear parameters. *J. Soc. Ind. App. Math.* **11**, 431–441.

NELDER, J. A. AND MEAD, R. 1965. A simplex method for function minimization. *Comp. J.* **7**, 308–313.

POWELL, M. J. D. 1964. An efficient method for finding the minimum of a function of several variables without calculating derivatives. *Comp. J.* **7**, 155–162.

POWELL, M. J. D. 1965. A method for minimizing the sum of squares of nonlinear function without calculating derivatives. *Comp. J.* **7**, 303–307.

ROSEN, J. B. 1960. The gradient projection method for nonlinear programming. Part I. Linear constraints. *J. Soc. Ind. App. Math.* **8**, 181–217.

ROSEN, J. B. 1961. The gradient projection method for nonlinear programming. Part II. Nonlinear constraints. *J. Soc. Ind. App. Math.* **9**, 514–532.

ROSENBROCK, H. H. 1960. An automatic method for finding the greatest or least value of a function. *Comp. J.* **3**, 175–184.

SMITH, C. S. 1962. The automatic computation of maximum likelihood estimates. N.C.B. Scientific Dept. Report No. S.C. 846/MR/40.

SPANG, H. A., III. 1962. A review of minimization techniques for nonlinear functions. *S.I.A.M. Review* **4**, 343–365.

SPENDLEY, W., HEXT, G. R. AND HIMSWORTH, F. R. 1962. Sequential application of simplex designs in optimization and evolutionary operation. *Technometrics,* **4**, 441–461.

SWANN, W. H. 1964. Report on the development of a new direct search method of optimization. I.C.I. Ltd. Central Instrument Laboratory. Research Note 64/3.

WOLFE, P. 1961. A duality theorem for nonlinear programming. *Q. App. Math.* **19**, 239–244.

Chapter 9

Applications of Computers to Pure Mathematics

H. P. F. Swinnerton-Dyer

Mathematical Laboratory, Corn Exchange Street, Cambridge

1. Introduction

An applied mathematician spends his time solving problems, and often other people's problems; so he feels bound to give the best answer he can to any question, even though he knows that the answer is not absolutely complete and may not be absolutely correct. If a problem cannot be solved in general terms, then it is worth while to solve it numerically in what he hopes are typical special cases; if his judgment is good, he can then give at least a rough description of the way the solution behaves in general. For an applied mathematician, therefore, a computer is a valuable tool.

A pure mathematician's concern, however, is to give rigorous proofs of statements whose truth he is already confident of, and further information about special cases is not much use to him. Numerical results are things on which one bases conjectures, and in pure mathematics a conjecture is only important if it sheds new light on the structure of a subject—that is, if it reveals connections between things which were previously thought to be unrelated. The opportunities for this are very limited. I shall discuss two such cases—one in which this programme has been carried through by Birch and me, and has led to conjectures of a very unexpected sort (Birch and Swinnerton-Dyer 1963, 1965), and another in which we do not understand the structure of the subject and there is a rich field for intelligently directed calculation. (Of course, calculation must be intelligently directed—listing another ten thousand prime numbers or digits of π in the hope that they will some day be useful to somebody is a wholly futile activity.)

2. An Application in Number Theory

Let $f(x, y) = 0$ be an inhomogeneous cubic equation with rational coefficients; can we find rational solutions of this equation, and if so, what can we say about the set of all rational solutions? This is a model for an important unsolved question; in contrast, the theory for a quadratic equation has been known for two centuries, and the theory for quartic or higher equations is likely not to be very interesting when it is discovered. The principal reason why this is important is that, if we regard $f(x, y) = 0$ as the equation of a curve, its points can be given the structure of a commutative group in a natural way. To simplify the description, suppose that the curve has the

159

special form $y^2 = x^3 - ax - b$, with a, b integers (which is quite typical of the general case). If we denote the law of composition by an asterisk, then for points P, Q on the curve we define $P*Q$ to be the point A in Fig. 1, where ZA is vertical. It can be shown† that this does give a group law, with the point at infinity on the curve as the identity of the group. Obviously if P and Q are rational, so is $A = P*Q$; thus the rational points on the curve themselves form a group under this law. Mordell proved that this group is finitely generated— that is, there are rational points $P_1, \ldots, P_g$ such that *every* rational point on the curve has the form $P_{i_1}*\ldots*P_{i_r}$ for some $i_1, \ldots, i_r$ (Mordell 1922; see also Weil 1928, 1930). His proof gives an upper bound for g in terms of a and b;

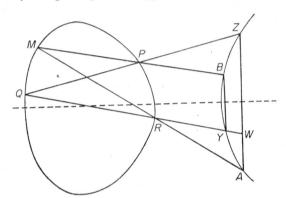

FIG. 1. Group relation on a cubic curve.

but it gives no way of finding the least value of g, still less the points $P_1, \ldots, P_g$ in any particular case. In practice, one can usually find these with enough hard work, but there is no sure-fire method of doing so, or even of deciding whether there are rational points on the curve at all. Indeed, it was generally thought that these were matters of chance, unconnected with anything else in the theory.

What can we hope to connect g with? It should be something that ought to be large when there ought to be a lot of rational points on the curve, and the known theory for the quadratic case provides a clue. Clearly we can only solve $f(x, y) = 0$ if we can solve every congruence $f(x, y) \equiv 0 \bmod p^m$, where p is prime and $m > 0$. If f is quadratic, this necessary condition is also sufficient. If f is cubic this is no longer so; indeed for the equation $y^2 = x^3 - ax - b$ to which I have restricted myself, the corresponding congruences

† The only difficulty lies in proving the associative law $(P*Q)*R = P*(Q*R)$, which is equivalent to saying that the points M, P, B in Fig. 1 are collinear. To show this, let V be the point at infinity on the curve, and W the intersection of AZ and QR, and let $g(x, y) = 0$ be the equation of the degenerate cubic consisting of the lines PQZ, AMR and BVY. For a suitable choice of λ, the curve $f - \lambda g = 0$ passes through W and hence through all ten named points. It is a cubic having four points in common with each of the lines $QRWY$ and $AVWZ$, and therefore must contain each of them; hence it breaks up into three lines, and the third one must contain the remaining points, M, P and B.

are always all soluble. But finding a rational solution of the equation is the same as finding a compatible set of solutions of the congruences; taking a very naive attitude, one can hope that this will be unusually easy (that is, g will be large) if the congruences have on the average unexpectedly many solutions, and unusually hard if they have unexpectedly few. If we exclude the finitely many primes which divide $6(4a^3 - 27b^2)$, then each integral solution of $y^2 \equiv x^3 - ax - b \bmod p$ gives rise to just p^{m-1} solutions $\bmod p^m$, one for each of the possible values of $y \bmod p^m$ which arise from the given value of $y \bmod p$. Moreover, we expect the congruence $\bmod p^m$ to have on the average p^m solutions, for there are p^{2m} possible pairs $(x, y) \bmod p^m$ and p^m possible values for $y^2 - (x^3 - ax - b) \bmod p^m$. Hence the ratio

(actual number of solutions)/(expected number of solutions)

depends only on p and not on m; and it is equal to N_p/p, where N_p is the number of solutions of $y^2 \equiv x^3 - ax - b \bmod p$. This seems to suggest that we should examine the product $\Pi(N_p/p)$; but this is an oversimplification because we have failed to allow for the fractional solutions of the congruence. The revised argument needs no new ideas, but its details are tedious; it turns out that we should consider

$$\prod\{(N_p + 1)/p\}.$$

The extra "1" can be thought of as corresponding to the point at infinity on the curve.

The individual terms of this product are quite easy to calculate—to find N_p, one forms the possible values of $x^3 - ax - b$ and the possible values of y^2, and looks for coincidences; this takes of order p operations. Experiment showed that the partial product of the first thousand or so terms was large when g was large, so that we were on the right lines; but it also showed that the product could behave quite badly. It is known that

$$|N_p/p - 1| < 2p^{-\frac{1}{2}} \tag{1}$$

and that no stronger result need hold; and it is also known that

$$\prod_{p<P}\left(1 + \frac{1}{p}\right) \sim C \log P \tag{2}$$

for a certain constant C whose value is unimportant. This and certain other reasons suggested that the right form for the conjecture was

$$\prod_{p<P}\left(\frac{N_p + 1}{p}\right) \sim C (\log P)^g, \tag{3}$$

where C is a constant depending in some way on the particular equation. To the already half-converted, the numerical evidence appeared to fit this quite well; Birch and I found that we were able to guess the value of g correctly from the behaviour of the product at least nine times out of ten. (For the range of values of a, b that we considered, $g = 0, 1, 2,$ or occasionally 3.) To our sceptical friends, the evidence was less decisive.

Unfortunately, the fit is unlikely to be very close for the range of values of P which are within the range of the computer. By analogy with known simpler problems, if the conjecture is true, it is an approximation to an exact formula which at best will have the form

$$\prod_{p<P}\left(\frac{N_p+1}{p}\right) = C\,(\log P)^g\{1+P^{-\frac{1}{4}}\sum a_i\cos\,(b_i\log P+c_i)\} \qquad (4)$$

for some a_i, b_i, c_i. Here the error term oscillates too slowly to be averaged out, and it decreases only slowly compared to the main term. We have spent a great deal of effort in looking for a satisfactory objective way of estimating g from the numerical data available, and have had no success at all. It seems that further progress in general requires a new idea.

Fortunately there is a particular type of equation which is more amenable than the general one; this is the case $y^2 = x^3 - ax$, with $b = 0$. It is trivial that $N_p = p$ for $p \equiv 3 \bmod 4$; if $p \equiv 1 \bmod 4$ we can write $p = u^2 + v^2$ with u, v integers, and it is known that $N_p = p + 2u$. (The choice among the four values of u is governed by known rules into which I need not enter in detail.) Thus

$$\frac{N_p+1}{p} = \left(1+\frac{1}{p}\right) \quad\text{or}\quad \left(1+\frac{1}{u+iv}\right)\left(1+\frac{1}{u-iv}\right). \qquad (5)$$

After some manipulation one can obtain the formal identity

$$\left\{\prod\left(\frac{N_p+1}{p}\right)\right\}^{-1} = \sum_{m,n}{}'\frac{\chi_a(m+in)}{m+in} \qquad (6)$$

in which the sum is over all integers m, n not both zero; here χ_a is the quartic residue symbol, whose essential properties are that it is a fourth root of unity which depends only on a and the residue classes of m and n mod $4a$. (I describe the identity as formal because the right-hand side is not absolutely convergent, while I cannot prove that the left-hand side converges at all.) We can now express the right-hand side in finite terms, by writing $m = 4au+\mu$, $n = 4av+\nu$, where u, v run over all integers and μ, ν each run through a set of residue classes mod $4a$. Formally we have

$$\sum_{m,n}{}'\frac{\chi_a(m+in)}{(m+in)} = \sum_{\mu,\nu}{}'\frac{\chi_a(\mu+i\nu)}{4a}\sum_{u,v}\left\{u+iv+\frac{\mu+i\nu}{4a}\right\}^{-1}; \qquad (7)$$

here the inner sum is known from the theory of Weierstrass elliptic functions, and the outer sum is finite.

In this way we have an easily calculable expression, which according to the previous conjecture should vanish if and only if $g > 0$. We have been able to prove that this expression is the product of an integer and a straightforward factor, and hence we have been able to calculate it exactly in several hundred cases. The results confirm the conjecture in every case. Of course this is not the end of the story. The integer which has just appeared in the case $g = 0$ can be provisionally identified in the theory, and we have some very suggestive results for the case $g = 1$; but I shall say no more about this.

What I have described above is a topic in which computation has had all the success that it can hope for; it has drastically changed the way in which one expects the subject to develop, and we now have to wait for the proofs to catch up with the conjectures. This will probably be a slow business; but it is dangerous to push experiment too far ahead of proof, for fear of losing one's feel for a subject.

3. Non-linear Ordinary Differential Equations

The branch of pure mathematics which seems to me to offer the greatest rewards for intelligent computation at the moment is the theory of ordinary differential equations. All the equations that can be solved exactly were solved in the nineteenth century; so the aim of the modern theory is to describe qualitatively the behaviour of the solutions of an equation, and in particular how this varies with the parameters of the equation†. Unfortunately we have no more than a collection of sub-theories to deal with particular types of problem, and we have no idea how these should link up. Consider for example the equation

$$\ddot{x} + x = \lambda f(x, \dot{x}), \tag{8}$$

where λ is a parameter. If λ is small, we have a quite adequate and straightforward theory; in the $(x, \dot{x})$ plane there are a certain number of periodic trajectories, which are approximately circles of the form $x^2 + \dot{x}^2 = $ constant and which we know how to find for given f; any other trajectory spirals slowly inwards or outwards, and tends to one of the periodic trajectories (or possibly to the origin or to infinity). If λ is large, we have a reasonably satisfactory theory, though it is not so complete, and is a good deal more difficult to apply. Again we have some periodic trajectories—this time made up of almost vertical and almost horizontal pieces—and all other trajectories tend to these. But of course there need not be the same number of periodic trajectories in the small parameter and the large parameter cases, and we know very little about how these periodic solutions can appear and disappear as λ increases. If we take a higher order equation—say the linked system

$$\left.\begin{aligned} \ddot{x} + x &= \lambda f(x, \dot{x}, y, \dot{y}) \\ \ddot{y} + c^2 y &= \lambda g(x, \dot{x}, y, \dot{y}) \end{aligned}\right\} \tag{9}$$

—the situation becomes much worse. If λ is small, we can describe the behaviour of the trajectories of this system in terms of the solution of a single second-order equation, and hence we can still give a reasonably complete qualitative description. In general some of the limiting trajectories will, to a first approximation, represent independent oscillations of x and y with fixed amplitudes; but in others there will be a slow transfer of energy from x to y and back, taking a time comparable with λ^{-1}. When λ is large there are some approximate methods available, though it would be going too far to call them a theory. In a few particular cases they have been pushed through to give a qualitative description of the solutions, and this differs fundamentally from

† The classical theory hoped to produce explicit formulae, and could produce nothing if these did not exist; the modern theory hopes to produce statements like "This equation has one stable periodic solution, to which all others tend".

that of the small-parameter theory. Only by numerical means can we hope to know how the transition from one to the other is accomplished.

I have given these merely as examples. There are other situations in which we know that even more curious things must occur—notably for periodic equations which have stable subharmonics of several different orders—and there are undoubtedly equations about which we know too little to realize how interesting they are. As far as I know, the only person who has put in any serious numerical work on these problems is Hayashi (1964 and references). (Extensive numerical work has been done on the three body problem, but this seems to me unlikely to illuminate the rest of the subject.) Hayashi has done enough to show that there are rich rewards to be gained, and a plentiful supply of problems to attack; there is some doubt how far his results are completely accurate†, but they are certainly highly suggestive.

† For reasons of speed he has been forced to rely very substantially on analogue rather than on digital computing. This means that one cannot always be sure that the equation he is solving is quite what he claims it to be; it also means that he must lay most of his emphasis on stable solutions, whereas it seems that one cannot give a comprehensive description of the behaviour of an equation unless one knows a lot about its unstable periodic solutions as well.

REFERENCES

BIRCH, B. J. AND SWINNERTON-DYER, H. P. F. 1963. Notes on elliptic curves. I. *J. f.d. reine u. angew. Math.* **212**, 7–25.

BIRCH, B. J. AND SWINNERTON-DYER, H. P. F. 1965. Notes on elliptic curves. II. *J. f.d. reine u. angew. Math.* **218**, 79–108.

HAYASHI, C. 1964. *Non-linear Oscillations in Physical Systems.* McGraw-Hill, New York, Toronto, London.

MORDELL, L. J. 1922. On the rational solutions of the indeterminate equations of the third and fourth degrees. *Proc. Camb. Phil. Soc.* **21**, 179–192.

WEIL, A. 1928. L'arithmétique sur les courbes algébriques. *Act. Math. (Stockholm)* **52**, 281–315.

WEIL, A. 1930. Sur un théorème de Mordell. *Bull. Sc. Math.* (2) **54**, 182–191.

Chapter 10

Techniques of Operational Research

S. Vajda

University of Birmingham, Edgbaston, Birmingham

1. The Basic Problem of Linear Programming

I shall consider in this chapter the branch of Applied Mathematics called Operational Research, and I shall restrict myself to mathematical techniques within Operational Research. There are quite a number of these techniques, and the best way to start is to describe just one of them, namely, Linear Programming.

In its mathematical form, linear programming is concerned with the following problem: we have a number of linear inequalities

$$\sum_{i=1}^{n} a_{ij} x_i \geq b_j, \qquad j = 1, 2, \ldots, m, \tag{1}$$

and we are looking for those values of the variables x_i which satisfy the inequalities, with the further condition that they must not be negative, $x_i \geq 0$, $i = 1, 2, \ldots, n$. We are interested to learn whether these inequalities have solutions at all, and if they have, how many. If a solution exists, then we would like to find at least one set of values of the x_i which minimizes the expression $\sum_{i=1}^{n} c_i x_i$. If the inequalities (1) were equations, then from matrix algebra we would know the relation between the rank of certain matrices and the number of solutions. In the case of inequalities, the matter is not so simple, and in fact a somewhat complicated procedure is needed to tell us whether there is a solution at all. It is quite obvious that not all sets have solutions; for example, if we have $x_i \geq 2$ and $-x_i \geq -1$, it is plain that no solutions exist, since the second inequality is the same as $x_i \leq 1$, which contradicts the first inequality.

Let us now consider a larger example, to show where the problems about the existence of solutions for these inequalities lie. In order to get some idea of the problems involved, we can, if we are dealing with only two variables, represent the inequalities on a diagram with x_1 and x_2 as coordinates: we are only interested in points in the first quadrant because in any other part of the plane either x_1 or x_2 will be negative. We take first the images of the corresponding equations, which are just straight lines, and then each inequality is satisfied in the half-plane on one side of the corresponding line.

Consider the example

$$\text{Maximize} \quad x_1 + x_2 \left.\begin{array}{l} \\ \end{array}\right\}$$
$$\text{subject to} \quad 2x_1 + x_2 \leq 1 \left.\begin{array}{l} \\ \end{array}\right\}$$
$$x_1 + 2x_2 \leq 1 \left.\begin{array}{l} \\ \end{array}\right\} \qquad (2)$$
$$x_1, x_2 \geq 0 \left.\begin{array}{l} \\ \end{array}\right\}$$

The points satisfying the inequalities lie within the rectangle $ABCD$ (Fig. 1), which is called the *feasible region*. To maximize the given linear expression, we want to take, out of the pencil of parallel straight lines $x_1 + x_2 = $ constant, the one which is as far away from the origin as possible without leaving the feasible region, and we see that in this particular case we can go just as far as

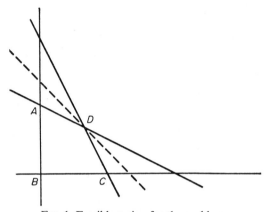

FIG. 1. Feasible region for the problem.

the dotted line in Fig. 1. Therefore it is plain that the point D, whose co-ordinates are $x_1 = \frac{1}{3}$, $x_2 = \frac{1}{3}$, gives us the extreme value of $x_1 + x_2$, so that these values solve our linear programming problem.

This is all very trivial, but note that the diagram suggests that the answer is given by just one point, i.e. that there is just one solution. There are exceptions to this, but one can see that in general the solution is represented by some vertex of the feasible region. We are therefore particularly interested in the number of these vertices in the general case. In two dimensions the answer is very simple, but I want to show where the problem lies. If we have for instance the two inequalities

$$x_1 + 3x_2 \leq 5 \left.\begin{array}{l} \\ \end{array}\right\}$$
$$x_1 + 4x_2 \leq 8 \left.\begin{array}{l} \\ \end{array}\right\} \qquad (3)$$

then there are only three vertices, because the second inequality adds nothing to the determination of the feasible region. In the previous example there are four, while if we have m inequalities in two dimensions, it is easily seen that the feasible region can never have more than $m + 2$ vertices. The question arises naturally: what is the maximum number in more than two dimensions?

This is a problem which has not been fully solved. Some formulae have been given which are generally accepted as correct, but they have not yet been proved.

Why should we want to find the number of vertices? Apart from the interesting geometry of the matter, it is also interesting from the point of view of numerical analysis, when we consider a method of finding that vertex of the feasible region which is furthest away from the origin in a preferred direction. The procedure is as follows: we start at any vertex, and then move to some adjacent vertex, unless we are convinced that we are already at the point furthest away in the direction we want to go. So we creep along the edges of the region until we cannot improve any further, and we have then solved the problem. Now since our procedure consists in starting with some vertex and creeping along the edges of the feasible region, we are, of course, interested to find out how long it might take us to get to the answer. In two dimensions it cannot take more than $m+2$ steps, but in the general case in n dimensions, the question, as I said, has not yet been definitely answered.

I should point out that although our procedure may be called iterative, it is not iterative in the sense of Chapter 2, (§8). A procedure there is described as iterative when it is asymptotic, that is, when it requires an infinite number of steps to give the exact answer. Our procedure gives the final answer in a finite number of steps. The method just described is called the Simplex method, for no particular reason except a historical accident, which has no mathematical interest in itself.

2. Application of Linear Programming to Matrix Inversion

This method of solving linear inequalities by Linear Programming is useful also in connection with the familiar problem of the inversion of a matrix. Suppose that you have a computer, and for some curious reason you have a program to solve linear programming problems, but not to invert a matrix. In that case the linear programming technique can be used to invert the matrix.

To show this, let us first rewrite the inequalities (1) in the form

$$\sum_{i=1}^{n} a_{ij}x_i - x_{n+j} = b_j, \qquad j = 1, 2, \ldots, m, \tag{4}$$

where it is understood that the x_{n+j} are also non-negative. We see that the linear programming problem can be defined in terms of m equations in $n+m$ variables, instead of m inequalities in n variables. Now let us write these equations in matrix notation

$$A\mathbf{x} - I\bar{\mathbf{x}} = \mathbf{b}, \tag{5}$$

where $\mathbf{x} = (x_1, x_2, \ldots, x_n)$, $\bar{\mathbf{x}} = (x_{n+1}, \ldots, x_{n+m})$. Then the fact that the solution of any linear programming problem is generally given by a vertex means that, of the $n+m$ components of $\mathbf{x}$ and $\bar{\mathbf{x}}$, m will be positive (or zero) and the remaining n will be zero. In particular, take $m = n$, and suppose that A is non-singular. Then

$$\mathbf{x} = A^{-1}\bar{\mathbf{x}} + A^{-1}\mathbf{b}. \tag{6}$$

If in the solution the components of **x** are positive, and those of $\bar{\mathbf{x}}$ are zero, then the solution effectively gives A^{-1}, because it gives the components of **x** in terms of the other variables. So in order to invert A, I have to ensure that the answer which I get when $\bar{\mathbf{x}} = \mathbf{O}$ has a non-negative **x**. This I can easily do by considering the following system

$$\left.\begin{array}{l} a_{11}x_1+a_{21}x_2+\ldots+a_{n1}x_n-x_{n+1} = a_{11}+a_{21}+\ldots+a_{n1} \\ \cdot \\ a_{1n}x_1+a_{2n}x_2+\ldots+a_{nn}x_n-x_{n+n} = a_{1n}+a_{2n}+\ldots+a_{nn} \end{array}\right\}. \qquad (7)$$

For this system of equations, it is clear that $x_1 = x_2 = \ldots = x_n = 1$, with all the other x_i zero, gives a solution, because of the form of the right-hand side. To make sure that this is the final answer obtained, I minimize a suitable expression, say $x_{n+1}+\ldots+x_{2n}$. Then the answer will be that all these x_{n+i} are zero, because that gives the smallest possible value.

I suggest that this is quite a reasonable way of inverting a matrix. Many years ago I tried this method on the matrix mentioned in Chapter 1, (§3), a segment of the Hilbert matrix. I compared my results with those given by Todd (1954), and found that my solutions were on the whole better than his. In this same book a paper by Fox describes a number of methods for the inversion of matrices, which in effect are all distinguished by the choice of the pivot, i.e. of the particular coefficient which tells you what variable to eliminate next in what is essentially Gauss-Jordan elimination. The method I have just described is simply an additional method for finding the pivot, and could be considered as another variant of Gauss-Jordan elimination.

3. Integer Linear Programming

So much about linear programming in its original form. But in some cases we are faced with problems of linear programming type for which the conditions so far described are not really sufficient. We may have problems where it is not sufficient to say that the variables must be non-negative, they must also be integers. In the oldest Linear Programming problem, the so-called Trans-portation Problem, we have, say, 3, 4 and 5 ships in certain ports, and we want to bring these 12 ships to some other ports, so that there are 6 in one place, 2 in another and 4 in a third. If we want to do this in the most efficient way, we must first define what we mean by efficient. If we say that the total sailing time of all the ships must be as small as possible, we need to know how long it takes to sail from any of the ports of departure to any of the ports of arrival, and we can then work out by a very simple method the best redistribution of the 3, 4 and 5 ships into 6, 2 and 4.

Once the procedure is explained (I shall not describe it here), it is obvious. But it cannot be completely obvious, because many mathematicians worked on this particular problem and did not solve it. They only thought of approximation methods, which seemed to be plausible. It is rather surprising, now that we know how to do it, that these mathematicians did not think of the method, but perhaps it is a general fact that mathematicians do not think of the simplest way of doing numerical calculations. In this particular problem, it would not help at all if somebody said that the most efficient way was to send one and a half ships here, and one and a half there; this does not solve the problem. The method we use now is such that the answer is automatically given in integers. Some optimistic people therefore thought that whenever we want an answer in integers, we automatically get it in integers. However, it is not as simple as that, as the following very trivial example will show.

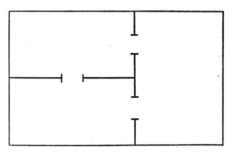

FIG. 2. The picture gallery problem.

Figure 2 is the plan of a picture gallery, and we want to find the smallest number of attendants who can be placed in such a way that every one of the three rooms is watched by at least one of the attendants. This is a linear programming problem, and the answer is that you put half an attendant at every door. Every room is then being watched by $\frac{1}{2}+\frac{1}{2} = 1$ attendant, but the result is of course nonsense. Therefore we want a method which solves the linear programming problem with the further condition that certain of the variables must be integers. Such a method does exist, and it is now being actively investigated to find out some of its intricacies, and to make improvements for practical purposes. The techniques so far devised lead to very large problems, and if we use a computer we may find that they exceed the capacity of the machine, because additional variables have to be introduced repeatedly. Therefore I would not say that we have yet reached the final answer to integer linear programming problems, although we know how to solve them in theory. And we can use our knowledge to solve some rather interesting cases.

For illustration, I will just mention some combinatorial problems. Suppose that you have a box which contains, if I may give a very homely example, separate compartments for one orange, one apple, one pear and one cucumber. Assume that you cannot buy an orange, an apple, a pear or a cucumber singly, but only in pre-packed parcels. One such parcel contains an orange and a cucumber, another contains an orange and an apple, a third contains a cucumber and a pear, and so on. The question is, how many of these parcels can be accommodated in the box. The first two parcels cannot be combined, because you would have to accommodate two oranges and the box can only contain one. This is called the packing problem, for obvious reasons. The problem which is in a way converse to this is the so-called covering problem. In this you want at least one orange, at least one apple, at least one pear and at least one cucumber. How many of these parcels at least must you buy so that you will have one of each of your categories? This is again a problem of integer linear programming.

I will just add that there is a very interesting algebraic problem to find what conditions on the pattern of the coefficients a_{ij} of the inequalities (1) make the answer appear automatically in integers. This problem has been solved inasmuch as certain sufficient conditions are known, but we do not yet know sufficient and necessary conditions for the answer to come out in integers.

4. Non-linear Problems

Investigations in Operational Research have not, of course, stopped at linear problems. We are interested also in non-linear problems, where either the constraints or the expression to be minimized is non-linear. Of course, if there were no constraints, we would apply the steepest descent method, or something similar (see Chapter 8). Problems in mathematical programming are complicated by the fact that we want to minimize with some additional side conditions. We know from differential calculus that to minimize a function subject to side conditions which are equations, we can use the well-known technique of Lagrange multipliers. But in our case the side conditions are *in*equalities. Therefore we cannot use the Lagrange technique; we can, however, use something very similar. To state this in a vague, not quite rigorous way, we may say that while in the usual Lagrange multiplier method we are looking for extrema, i.e. maxima or minima, of an expression like

$$f(x) + \sum \lambda_i g_i(x),$$

where the side conditions are $g_i(x) = 0$, in the case where the side conditions are inequalities we are looking not for maxima or minima, but for a saddle-point.

From a purely algebraic point of view, the nucleus of linear programming theory is contained in the following consideration. If we want to minimize $\mathbf{c}^T\mathbf{x}$ subject to $A\mathbf{x} \geq \mathbf{b}$, $\mathbf{x} \geq \mathbf{O}$, then we can associate with this problem another problem, namely to maximize $\mathbf{b}^T\mathbf{y}$, subject to $A^T\mathbf{y} \leq \mathbf{c}$, $\mathbf{y} \geq \mathbf{O}$. These two problems are closely connected, and if a finite minimum exists for the first, then a finite maximum exists for the second, and the two values are equal. This is the so-called duality theorem, which was conjectured by von Neumann and proved by him in a special case, viz. the case where both $\mathbf{b}$ and $\mathbf{c}$ are vectors having all components unity. With these conditions, the result stated is the main theorem of the Theory of Games, and therefore if we want to solve a game we use linear programming. A modified form of the duality theorem exists in non-linear programming, but it is much more complicated and I will not give the details.

5. The Problem of Flow in a Network

I will now describe a problem which at first sight seems unconnected with the duality theorem, but which has in fact a connection with it. A current problem of Operational Research, which is of interest to many other people such as civil and electrical engineers, is the problem of flow in a network. Let us consider a graph consisting of points which we call vertices or nodes, and of connections between certain pairs of nodes; these connections are called links, or edges, or arcs. Let us assume that these links are pipes with various cross-sections, through which we can send a liquid in one direction only. We attach numbers to the arcs, to represent the capacities of the pipes, and we ask how much liquid can be sent from a source at one vertex to a sink at another without over-saturating the capacities of the intermediate arcs.

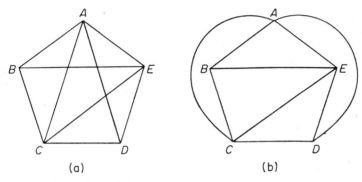

Fig. 3. A graph drawn in (a) non-planar (b) planar form.

There exist very simple methods of finding the maximum flow through a planar network, by which I mean one in which the arcs do not intersect—the arcs only meet in points which are nodes. For example, Fig. 3a shows a network with intersections; however, these are quite unnecessary, because the same connections can be shown on a planar graph without any intersections, as in Fig. 3b. Some people might suppose that every graph can be drawn as a planar network, but this is not true, as we can see by considering the well-known problem illustrated in Fig. 4. In this we want to connect the houses to the utilities so that no intersections occur, and we quickly find that this is impossible.

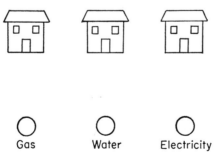

Fig. 4. The domestic supply problem.

A theorem due to Kuratowski states that any graph is planar, i.e. it can be drawn without intersections, unless it contains either this pattern or another pattern which is simply a pentagon with all its diagonals, which again cannot be drawn as a planar graph. (The statement about the pentagon is also connected with the four-colour problem. If it were possible to draw the pentagon with all its diagonals in a planar form, that is without intersections, we could construct a map which needs five colours if all pairs of adjacent countries are to be coloured differently. Suppose the countries start as small areas at each vertex, and expand along the edges meeting at the vertex until they reach another country, then each of the five countries would eventually meet all the other countries. But if this were possible, then the corresponding map would need five colours, while we know from the four-colour theorem that such a map cannot exist.)

Returning to the problem of finding the maximum flow in a planar network, this is easily solved if we know how to find the shortest distance between two points of a graph. The latter problem is very simple—essentially one does it by systematic trial and error. In order to show the connection between these two problems, I shall take the network of Fig. 5, and construct another network which I shall call its dual in the following way. I draw first lines to infinity from the source and sink (points A and B), and put a point into every mesh of the resulting figure. Then I connect the points in adjacent meshes by lines

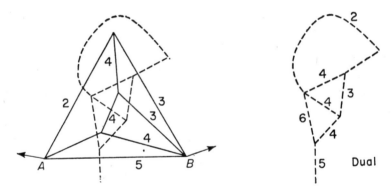

Fig. 5. A planar network and its dual.

(dotted in Fig. 5) which must clearly cross the lines of the original network. These new lines are numbered to correspond with the original lines which they cross.

Now let me introduce a new concept, that of a cut. This is defined in the following way. I partition the vertices of the original network into two aggregates such that one contains the source and the other the sink. A cut is then the set of all arcs which connect any node of one aggregate to a node of the other (e.g. the dotted lines in Fig. 6 form a cut). It is clear that if I omit the arcs of the cut I get two disconnected graphs. Since the source belongs to one

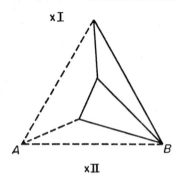

FIG. 6. A cut in the planar network.

and the sink to the other, there will be no path by which I can go from the source to the sink. But I can find a path from point I in Fig. 6 to point II which passes between the two graphs. Now if the numbers in the dual network are taken to be lengths, then the length of this path is the same as the total capacity of the cut, because the lines of the second network have the same numbers attached to them as those of the first network which they cross. To find the shortest way from I to II is equivalent to finding the cut with the smallest total capacity, and so the shortest path of the dual equals the minimum cut of the original.

Now consider another aspect of the cut. If I leave out the arcs of the cut, there is no way from the source to the sink. Therefore any flow from source to sink must use at least one of the arcs of the cut. From this it follows fairly easily that no flow can be larger than the capacity of any cut. Thus if I can find a cut whose capacity is equal to some flow, then this must be the minimum cut, and the flow must be the maximum flow. (It can be shown that such a cut always exists.) Since the minimum cut is equal to the shortest path in the dual, it follows that the maximum flow in one graph is equal to the shortest path in the dual graph. Thus if I want to find the maximum flow through a network, I work out the dual of it, find the shortest path through the dual and that gives me the capacity of the cut, and hence the maximum flow. This does not tell me where the maximum flow goes, but a fairly simple method exists for completing the problem.

REFERENCES

BERGE, C. AND GHOUILA-HOURI, A. 1965. *Programming, Games and Transportation Networks.* Methuen, London.

DANTZIG, G. B. 1963. *Linear Programming and Extensions.* Princeton.

TODD, J. 1954. The condition of finite segments of the Hilbert matrix. App. Math. Series **39**, 109–116. Nat. Bur. Standards, Washington.

VAJDA, S. 1956. *The Theory of Games and Linear Programming.* Methuen, London.

VAJDA, S. 1961. *Mathematical Programming.* Addison-Wesley, Reading, Mass.

Chapter 11

Some Industrial Applications

1. Introduction

The problems which arise in industrial computing groups cover so wide a field that it is impossible to summarize here the full extent of the applications of numerical analysis. This chapter gives a few examples of current work, which illustrate the value of mathematical analysis of particular problems, as well as the use of general methods, and also indicate the scope for further research.

The first part gives a brief survey of the types of problems encountered in an aircraft firm, and the methods which have been found useful in solving them. Part II discusses in more detail some numerical techniques for problems involving systems of ordinary differential equations, arising in the study of chemical reactions. The final part describes a method for calculating the flow through a turbine, for use in design and performance studies, where the problem involves the solution of a complicated system of non-linear partial differential equations.

Part I. Engineering Applications in an Aircraft Firm

H. P. Y. Hitch

British Aircraft Corporation (Operating) Ltd., Weybridge, Surrey

2. Types of Problem Encountered

The British Aircraft Corporation (Weybridge) has been operating a computing service for all its technical branches since 1956. The equipment has steadily increased from one Pegasus computer without magnetic tape to three Pegasus machines, two of them with magnetic tapes. Because of the heavy work load there has been little opportunity for investigations outside the immediate problems, but these have been many and various.

The broadest class is that of boundary-value problems. These occur in aerodynamics, where the partial differential equation is often converted into an integral equation, which is then solved by collocation. The standard techniques were derived in the pre-computer era, and the choice of collocation points and solving functions is more suited to analysis than computation. They also occur in structural analysis, where the problem is that of finding the internal loads in redundant structures, and in dynamics, in the problem of finding the natural modes and frequencies of vibration of a structure, and the critical speeds of aircraft flutter. All these problems are non-linear, but the classical solutions for the linearized cases are meaningful and of great value.

The next main class covers the solution of ordinary differential equations of the initial-value kind. These occur in problems in dynamics in its widest sense, ranging from estimating the motion of a vehicle following a disturbance to the flow in a jet pump.

The next class is that of data processing work. Some problems, such as Weight Accounting, are simply matters of file maintenance, but certain purely technical problems involve a substantial amount of data processing, because of the vast quantity of numerical information which has to be handled.

Of marked absence in our work have been statistical problems, problems of management simulation, and partial differential equations as such. Most of our problems are of some size, and methods designed for a single differential equation, or for small matrices, are not of much interest.

3. Summary of Techniques and Applications

The main techniques used in the solution of these problems are the classical analytical methods of the turn of the century, and foremost comes matrix theory and linear algebra. On average 20% of our work is covered by these techniques and the availability of a good matrix interpretative scheme for Pegasus has simplified many of our problems. The only difficulty has been to dissuade people from creating matrix operations for doing simple jobs like collapsing a matrix. The need for powerful methods of finding the roots of matrices, both in the symmetric positive definite case, and in the general case, has always been felt. At first large matrices were set up by considering the structure as a whole, but these were difficult to solve, so the problem is often broken up into several matrices of smaller order. We have not much experience yet with the newer methods of Givens and Householder. Over all jobs the typical matrix size is still around 40. The aircraft flutter problem, considered as a complex eigenvalue problem of a complex matrix, still needs attention. In this problem a parameter representing speed is systematically varied, and at present the roots for each choice are found *ab initio*. Some method of accelerating the whole process should be obtainable, in view of this systematic variation. There is also interest in the inverse process, namely, the determination of the changes that need to be made to the matrix so that it has specified eigenvalues and vectors.

Next we have the integration methods for ordinary differential equations. Because of their availability and ease of programming, the Runge-Kutta procedures are almost invariably used. The facts that no special starting procedures are required, and that we know something about stability in simple cases, are helpful. Difficulties nonetheless exist concerning step-lengths and accuracy, especially, of course, in non-linear equations. The size of problems is increasing, and we may require the solution of up to 30 simultaneous second-order equations. The computing time is considerable, and it is made longer by the need to experiment with step-length and accuracy. Special interest attaches to linear systems, for which we have made special provision; here the overall solution times can be reduced by making use of the Duhamel integral. The techniques of the classic Laplace transform and the calculus of residues have been built into useful programs—one of the few cases where the old hand methods still survive.

Non-linear terms are handled quite easily by including them in the auxiliary routine used by the Runge-Kutta or other method. There is a noticeable inclination to use the simplest possible integration routine, including only two terms of the Taylor series, for problems involving discontinuous behaviour (for example, the jerking motion caused by friction, or the bouncing of a valve on a valve seat), and to take small step-lengths. In the fourth-order Runge-Kutta process it is not correct to handle these discontinuities anywhere but at the end of a complete step, but we sometimes do it, and where the step length is small enough this has not caused any difficulty in practice.

The structural problem deserves special mention. It is now possible to analyse the structure of large sections of the aircraft at once, sometimes almost all of it. This leads to large sets of sparse linear equations of band form. Typically, these are of order 300, but the order may go up to 1000, and even exceed this. The problem now becomes one of data processing, and we have to consider such things as intermediate dumping, file maintenance, file interrogation, and the like. Often the major problem is the setting up of the equations from the fundamental data and not their solution, which seems to be tolerably satisfactory with the classic methods, using matrix partitioning. Checking the accuracy of the results is another difficulty.

Problems in curve fitting, interpolation, and smoothing are continually arising. They have much in common, but require different approaches. Interpolation in multi-entry tables occurs, for example, in reading engine performance data, and may be complicated by discontinuities of slope, representing physical discontinuities in behaviour. It is also difficult to deal with data with "ragged edges". But these difficulties are in the programming rather than in the mathematics. The position is different in curve fitting, used for example to define the geometry of curved surfaces such as ship hulls or aircraft wings and fuselages. Here the mathematics of the conventional spline curve and its three-dimensional analogue the membrane is valuable. The spline has advantages in formalizing the concept of "smoothness", as a property of the curve with the least variance of curvature. Finding a criterion of success in curve-fitting problems, other than visual inspection of the result, is sometimes difficult.

Another type of problem occurs in the solution of simultaneous non-linear algebraic equations. The classical methods of applied mathematics give no guidance, and on the whole the simplest approaches have been best. Simple "cut-and-try" techniques have often been satisfactory; these fall into three categories

(a) For equations of the form $x = F(x)$, if x_n is the nth estimate, and we compute $x_n^* = F(x_n)$, we take

$$x_{n+1} = \alpha x_n + \beta x_n^*,$$

α, β being at choice.

(b) From an initial guess x_1 we step x on progressively by Δx until some suitable error measure changes sign, when we replace Δx by $-\Delta x/k$ (k being some small integer), and repeat the process until the step-length falls below the desired accuracy.

(c) From two previous trials, we fit a straight line to the results to predict the new trial value of x. (This is, of course, the Newton-Raphson method, with the gradient estimated from the slope of a chord.)

Method (a) suffers from not knowing how to choose α, β. If the system oscillates, we can take $\alpha = \beta = \frac{1}{2}$, giving the arithmetic mean. If it converges monotonically, we can use the simplest choice $\alpha = 0$, $\beta = 1$. Method (b) is safe, in the sense that if Δx has the correct sign initially, a solution will always be found, but it may take a very long time. Method (c) has the well-known fault that the extrapolated value may be very far away from the old, and may lie in a totally invalid region.

It is usual in these problems to depend very heavily on the physics in looking for a solution, which is probably the best approach. An example is given by the simulation of air-conditioning in an aircraft, where the problem is essentially the determination of steady-state solutions of sets of differential equations. These have proved very difficult, and they might be made easier if we considered the differential equations more directly.

On the whole the classical mathematical techniques which have been known for many years have served us well; our concern now is to make proper use of more recent developments.

Part II. The Solution of a Set of Reaction Rate Equations

H. H. ROBERTSON

Imperial Chemical Industries Ltd., Wilton Works,
Middlesbrough, Yorkshire

4. Form of the Equations and Basic Methods

The concentrations of the reactants in a chemical reaction system are given by a set of first-order differential equations defining the rates of change of concentration with time as functions of the concentration. Thus, a typical set may be written

$$\frac{dy_i}{dx} = f_i(y_j), \qquad i = 1, 2, \ldots, k, \tag{1}$$

or in vector form $\dfrac{d\mathbf{y}}{dx} = \mathbf{f}(\mathbf{y})$.

For second-order reactions, the functions f_i are quadratic in the variables. In many cases each right-hand side contains a few such terms which may also appear with opposite sign in other equations. The set of equations is heavily structured and often strongly coupled and non-linear. Details of these equations may be found in the book by Frost and Pearson (1961). When the equations represent the behaviour of a system containing a number of fast and slow reactions, a forward integration of these equations becomes difficult.

The problem is simply illustrated by a set of first-order linear equations

$$\frac{dy}{dx} = Ay, \tag{2}$$

where $\mathbf{y}$ is a vector, and A a matrix. When the matrix A has eigenvalues with negative real parts the solution decays to zero for large x and is given explicitly by

$$\mathbf{y} = \sum b_i\, e^{\lambda_i x} \mathbf{v}_i, \tag{3}$$

where λ_i, $\mathbf{v}_i$ are the eigenvalues and vectors of A, and the b_i are arbitrary constants. These equations involve much labour to integrate when the eigenvalues are widely distributed along the negative real axis. The function itself may vary smoothly for quite small x, but the interval of integration required is often disproportionately small.

This phenomenon has been extensively studied, and references to recent work are given by Henrici (1962). Briefly, it is known that explicit linear multistep methods cannot be stable for all values of the integration interval h, and that some formulae of this type are unstable for any positive value of h. A number of integration formulae have been derived by Robertson (1960) which are stable for moderately large values of h, but these are only effective in dealing with this problem for restricted values of the condition number of the matrix A (i.e. the ratio of the largest to the smallest eigenvalue). The trapezoidal rule is stable for all values of the interval, and Dahlquist (1963) has shown that this procedure has equally satisfactory stability properties for non-linear equations.

If the Runge-Kutta method of integration is used, it is not possible to increase the interval of integration beyond the value

$$h = 2 \cdot 8/(|\lambda|_{max}), \tag{4}$$

approximately, and in many problems this is a severe restriction.

If we use the trapezoidal rule to integrate equations (1), and write $\mathbf{y}_n = \mathbf{y}(x_0 + nh)$, $\mathbf{f}_n = \mathbf{f}(\mathbf{y}_n)$, we have

$$\mathbf{y}_{n+1} = \mathbf{y}_n + \frac{h}{2}\,(\mathbf{f}_{n+1} + \mathbf{f}_n). \tag{5}$$

There is now no difficulty with instability of the numerical procedure, but another sort of trouble arises. The equations (5) are implicit for $\mathbf{y}_{n+1}$ and may be solved by repeated substitution according to

$$\mathbf{y}_{n+1}^{(s+1)} = \mathbf{y}_n + \frac{h}{2}\,(\mathbf{f}_{n+1}^{(s)} + \mathbf{f}_n), \tag{6}$$

where s is the iteration index. This iteration converges if

$$\frac{h}{2}\|F\| < 1, \tag{7}$$

where F is the Jacobian matrix $F = \left[\frac{\partial f_i}{\partial y_j}\right]$, and $\|F\|$ is the maximum modulus of its eigenvalues. This is just as severe a limitation as the stability restriction (4).

When the forward iteration (6) diverges, we may use the reverse iteration given by

$$\mathbf{y}_{n+1}^{(s)} = \mathbf{y}_n + \frac{h}{2}(\mathbf{f}_{n+1}^{(s+1)} + \mathbf{f}_n), \tag{8}$$

which still involves the solution of implicit equations, but is more stable. For reaction-rate equations with heavily structured right-hand sides this may be a feasible method, and an example is discussed below.

Another method of solving the equations (5) is to apply the Newton-Raphson algorithm, which gives the following equations for the corrections to an approximate solution $\mathbf{y}_{n+1}^{(s)}$

$$(I - F)\delta\mathbf{y}_{n+1}^{(s)} = \mathbf{y}_n - \mathbf{y}_{n+1}^{(s)} + \tfrac{1}{2}h(\mathbf{f}_n + \mathbf{f}_{n+1}^{(s)}). \tag{9}$$

For reaction-rate equations the matrix of coefficients is sparse, and a direct solution taking account of the zero elements of the matrix is a practical proposition.

5. An Example

Suppose the equations are defined by

$$\begin{aligned} f_1 &= -0\cdot04y_1 + 10^4 y_2 y_3 \\ f_2 &= 0\cdot04y_1 - 10^4 y_2 y_3 - 3.10^7 y_2^2 \\ f_3 &= \qquad\qquad 3.10^7 y_2^2 \end{aligned} \Bigg\}, \tag{10}$$

with initial conditions $y_1(0) = 1$, $y_2(0)$, $y_3(0) = 0$. These equations satisfy $\Sigma f_i = 0$, so we clearly have $\Sigma y_i = 1$. The Jacobian F has zero determinant.

We find that the Runge-Kutta method is limited by stability considerations to an interval of integration of 10^{-4}. For the trapezoidal rule, solution by repeated substitution in the forward direction, as in (6), is limited to a similar interval; the Newton-Raphson algorithm converges for any interval less than $0\cdot25$, but h must be small enough to give the accuracy required; but the reverse iteration of (8) converges rapidly at each step for $h > 10^{-4}$, and the interval is limited only by the accuracy required. The range of integration for this example is $0 \le x \le 40$ and we can use an integration step with (8) of $h = 1\cdot0$, so there is a factor of 1000 in computing time between the worst and the best methods of integration.

6. Transformation of the Variable

It can readily be shown that for the equation

$$\frac{dy}{dx} = f(y) + g(x) \tag{11}$$

the transformation

$$y = z(u), \tag{12}$$

giving the equation

$$\frac{du}{dx} = \frac{f(z(u))}{z'(u)} + \frac{g(x)}{z'(u)}, \tag{13}$$

gives no improvement of the convergence condition (7).

The transformation

$$y = e^{-\mu x} u, \tag{14}$$

on the other hand, does improve the convergence for positive μ but the variable u is now a rapidly increasing function and we can expect the truncation error to limit the interval.

7. Approximate Methods of Solution

The point at which the numerical difficulty becomes apparent in problems of this type is when the rapidly decaying terms have decreased to negligible proportions and the solution is slowly varying. At this point it would be desirable to increase the interval of integration but we are prevented from doing so either by instability of the integration procedure or by lack of convergence.

For the single equation

$$\frac{dy}{dx} = f(y) + g(x), \tag{15}$$

an approximate solution may be obtained when we are approaching the steady state by replacing the differential equation by the algebraic relation

$$f(y) + g(x) = 0. \tag{16}$$

This has the correct asymptotic behaviour for stable solutions, but a discontinuity is introduced in the function at the point x_1 say, where this replacement is made.

A second method is to replace the differential equation (15) by the equation

$$\frac{dy}{dx} = k(f(y) + g(x)) \tag{17}$$

with $k < 1$. The function is taken to be continuous at x_1. The equilibrium values are still preserved, but the slope of the function is now discontinuous at the point x_1 and, for a linear equation, it can be shown that a multiple of the complementary function of the new equation has been introduced.

7*

A third method is to introduce two constants k_1 and k_2, and take

$$\frac{dy}{dx} = k_1 f(y) + k_2 g(x). \tag{18}$$

k_1 is chosen to be less than unity and k_2 is determined so as to preserve the continuity of the derivative at x_1. For a linear equation with an exponential forcing function, it can be shown that the relative error of the solution at subsequent points is of the same order as our initial approximation, when we assumed that at x_1 the complementary function of the original equation was zero. In other words, the particular integrals of the equations (15) and (18) are equal.

For non-linear problems it is necessary to construct the equations satisfied by the difference between the current solution and the equilibrium solution, and to ensure that both $f(y)$ and $g(x)$ are separately zero as $x \to \infty$.

This device is not generally applicable to sets of equations, but for certain types of coupling it can be successfully applied to selected equations of the set, corresponding in our case to the fast reactions. The algorithm for repeated substitution with the trapezoidal rule may be readily adapted to this procedure. Whenever the convergence of the iterations is a limiting factor of the integration step, the value of k_1 is reduced and a new value of k_2 calculated.

Experimental work with this method is proceeding for sets of non-linear equations of the type described here. The method may also be applicable to particular problems in the theory of control of physical systems.

Part III. Three-dimensional Compressible Flow through Axial Flow Turbomachines

M. E. Silvester and R. Hetherington

Aero Engine Division, Rolls-Royce Ltd., Derby

8. Outline of the Problem

Traditional methods of compressor and turbine design have always involved a number of assumptions which avoided the need to compute the distribution of fluid velocities through the machine. However, in recent years the use of large computers and numerical methods has allowed us to solve fairly detailed mathematical models of the flow processes in the machine. From the point of view of workers in the field of rotating machinery this subject is very much alive, and work is continuing to improve the description of the physical processes involved, and to devise adequate methods for design and performance prediction within the framework of the numerical technique described below.

The basis of the method was first proposed by Wu and Wolfenstein (1950). These authors avoided the problem of numerical solution by considering only simple cases. More recently the method appears to have been developed independently in several places. Examples showing the application of similar techniques are given by Swan (1961), and Wright and Novak (1960). The present paper gives an account of the numerical procedures required for the successful use of the method.

An exact description of the flow through the complex system of rotating and stationary blades in a turbine would involve the solution in three space dimensions and time of the compressible, viscous, non-isentropic flow equations. Such a solution would be difficult conceptually and probably impossible to obtain on today's generation of computers. It is also doubtful whether such a solution would be desirable.

The simplest realistic model we can choose is that of axisymmetric swirling flow through an annulus. This neglects the time-dependent variations and assumes that the solution is independent of θ, the angular direction. Physically this implies that the wakes from upstream blade rows mix before they are incident on the following row, and that the blade row consists of an infinite number of infinitesimally thin blades. For the purpose of this paper we confine our attention to the equilibrium gas flow in the planes between the blade rows, where there are no blade forces. With these assumptions we may write down the equations of axisymmetric non-isentropic flow.

9. Basic Equations

(A summary of the notation used is given in §11.)

The mass continuity equation is

$$\frac{\partial}{\partial r}(\rho r u) + \frac{\partial}{\partial x}(\rho r w) = 0, \tag{1}$$

and conservation of momentum gives the three equations

$$u\frac{\partial u}{\partial r} + w\frac{\partial u}{\partial x} - \frac{v^2}{r} = -\frac{1}{\rho}\frac{\partial p}{\partial r}, \tag{2}$$

$$u\frac{\partial v}{\partial r} + w\frac{\partial v}{\partial x} + \frac{uv}{r} = 0, \tag{3}$$

$$u\frac{\partial w}{\partial r} + w\frac{\partial w}{\partial x} = -\frac{1}{\rho}\frac{\partial p}{\partial x}. \tag{4}$$

The equation for the conservation of energy may be written in the form

$$\mathrm{d}\{H - \tfrac{1}{2}(u^2 + v^2 + w^2)\} = T\,\mathrm{d}S + \frac{\mathrm{d}p}{\rho}. \tag{5}$$

Work is done on a particle of fluid as it crosses a rotor row producing an increase in the total enthalpy of that particle given by

$$\Delta H = \Omega(r_2 v_2 - r_1 v_1). \tag{6}$$

The temperature ratio along a stream surface is then

$$\frac{T_2}{T_1} = \frac{H_2 - \frac{1}{2}(u_2^2 + v_2^2 + w_2^2)}{H_1 - \frac{1}{2}(u_1^2 + v_1^2 + w_1^2)}. \tag{7}$$

A simple model for calculating the pressure losses caused by viscous and secondary flow effects is to assume that, while crossing a blade row, a particle of fluid does not obey the usual adiabatic law, but instead satisfies

$$p \propto \rho^n, \tag{8}$$

where

$$\frac{n}{n-1} = \eta_p \frac{\gamma}{\gamma-1} \tag{9}$$

and η_p is the polytropic efficiency.

The entropy increase of the particle may then be written

$$(S_2 - S_1)/R = (1 - \eta_p)\left(\frac{\gamma}{\gamma-1}\right)\log\left(\frac{T_2}{T_1}\right). \tag{10}$$

10. Method of Solution

Introducing the sonic velocity c by means of the equation

$$c^2 = \frac{dp}{d\rho}, \tag{11}$$

we may eliminate p and ρ between equations (1)—(5) and (11). It is also convenient to eliminate u and v as dependent variables and work in terms of α and λ defined by

$$u = w \tan \lambda, \tag{12}$$

$$v = w \tan \alpha. \tag{13}$$

We then have finally

$$\frac{\partial \phi}{\partial r} = T \frac{\partial S}{\partial r} + \psi, \tag{14}$$

where

$$\phi = H - \frac{1}{2}w^2\{1 + \tan^2 \alpha + \tan^2 \lambda\}, \tag{15}$$

$$\psi = \frac{w^2}{1 - (w^2/c^2)\sec^2 \lambda}\left\{\left(1 - \frac{w^2}{c^2}\right)\left(\frac{\tan^2 \alpha}{r} - \ddot{r}_s\right) + \frac{1}{2r^2}\frac{\partial}{\partial r}(r^2 \tan^2 \lambda)\right\}, \tag{16}$$

$$\ddot{r}_s = \left(\frac{d^2 r}{dx^2}\right) \text{ along a stream surface.} \tag{17}$$

Given a complete knowledge of the streamline trajectories, the upstream flow conditions, and the polytropic efficiency, equations (14)—(17) may be treated as a non-linear first-order ordinary differential equation for w: the angles α and λ are known, and along stream surfaces H and S may be expressed in terms of w by using equations (6), (10), (12) and (13). The condition that the flow across each plane between blade rows must equal the inlet mass flow provides the boundary condition required for the solution of (14) in each plane, so that by marching downstream from plane to plane from the uniform inlet conditions the flow field may be computed. The computation is performed on the mesh obtained by dividing the radius at each axial station x_i into equal increments, so that a general point is $(x_i, r_{i,j})$, as shown in Figure 1.

However, in general the streamline trajectories are not known, but we do know that the whirl angle relative to a blade row at exit from the row is closely determined by the blade geometry and spacing, so that we may assume a knowledge of the relative whirl angle β, which is related to α by the equation

$$\tan \beta = \tan \alpha - \frac{r\Omega}{w}. \tag{18}$$

We can evaluate the terms $\ddot{r}_s$ and $\tan \lambda$ at each point if we know the mass flow

$$m_{i,j} = 2\pi \int_{r_{i,1}}^{r_{i,j}} \rho w r \, dr \tag{19}$$

at each point, for a stream surface is a surface of constant mass flow. Thus the stream surface through $(x_i, r_{i,j})$ contains a mass flow $m_{i,j}$. By interpolation in the mass flows, we may determine the points of intersection of the stream surface with the planes x_{i-2}, x_{i-1}, x_{i+1}, and x_{i+2}, and fit the resulting five points to a smooth curve. General physical considerations suggest that a suitable curve is that taken up by a thin flexible spline. We approximate this curve with four cubics, each joining two adjacent points, which are matched in slope and curvature at common points and determined in such a way that the integral

$$I = \int_{x_{i-2}}^{x_{i+2}} \left(\frac{d^2 r}{dx^2}\right)^2 dx \tag{20}$$

is minimized. Initially, the right-hand member of (19) is not known and we start with the guess

$$m_{i,j} = M \frac{(r_{i,j}^2 - r_{i,1}^2)}{(r_{i,jmax}^2 - r_{i,1}^2)}. \tag{21}$$

Equation (14) is written in finite-difference form as

$$\phi_{i,j+1} = \phi_{i,j} + \tfrac{1}{2}\{(T_{i,j+1} + T_{i,j})(S_{i,j+1} - S_{i,j}) + (\psi_{i,j+1} + \psi_{i,j})(r_{i,j+1} - r_{i,j})\}. \tag{22}$$

If we denote by a single suffix j the values of the variables on the intersection of the plane at axial distance x_{i-1} and the stream surface passing through the point $(x_i, r_{i,j})$, then equations (6), (7), (10) and (18) may be written

$$H_{i,j} = H_j + \Omega(r_{i,j} w_{i,j} \tan \alpha_{i,j} - r_j w_j \tan \alpha_j), \tag{23}$$

$$T_{i,j} = T_j \left\{ \frac{H_{i,j} - \frac{1}{2} w_{i,j}(1 + \tan^2 \lambda_{i,j} + \tan^2 \alpha_{i,j})}{H_j - \frac{1}{2} w_j(1 + \tan^2 \lambda_j + \tan^2 \alpha_j)} \right\}, \tag{24}$$

$$S_{i,j} = S_j + R(1 - \eta_p) \frac{\gamma}{\gamma - 1} \log \left(\frac{T_{i,j}}{T_j} \right), \tag{25}$$

$$\tan \beta_{i,j} = \tan \alpha_{i,j} - r_{i,j} \Omega / w_{i,j}. \tag{26}$$

The variables with single suffix j are found by interpolation in the corresponding variables at the previous axial station x_{i-1}. When the flow is known at the point $(x_i, r_{i,j})$, equations (22) to (26), together with the known angle $\beta_{i,j+1}$ and the estimated values of $\tan \lambda$ and $\ddot{r}_s$ at $(x_i, r_{i,j+1})$, can be solved iteratively for $w_{i,j+1}$ and hence for the flow at the point $(x_i, r_{i,j+1})$. Because this iterative routine is used many times and in a wide variety of situations, we require an iteration method which is simple and rapidly convergent. We obtain this by using Aitken's extrapolation, whenever the number of iterations exceeds three.

The process described above permits us to integrate equation (14) in the plane x_i when the boundary condition is known. We suppose there exists a single-valued relation between the axial velocity at mid-stream and the total mass flow obtained from the solution corresponding to that velocity. From two successive solutions, obtained from two estimates of the mid-stream axial velocity, we extrapolate linearly to the desired mass flow to obtain a new estimate of the velocity. Iterating in this manner we determine a mid-stream axial velocity as boundary condition to equation (14), with the property that the corresponding solution passes the inlet mass flow. Passing downstream from plane to plane we thus compute the entire flow field. Downstream of the final blade row, we replace our assumption that β is known by the law of conservation of angular momentum of a particle of fluid, as expressed by equation (3). Far downstream of the last blade row, we make the flow parallel so that we may terminate the marching process.

After each complete sweep through the flow field, we can re-estimate the slopes and curvatures of the stream surfaces, for we can use the new solution to evaluate the corresponding mass flows $\bar{m}_{i,j}$. We do not use these values directly to find the curvature terms, but we form a weighted mean with the previous values, so that, if superscripts denote the number of the iteration, we take

$$m_{i,j}^{(n+1)} = \mu \bar{m}_{i,j}^{(n)} + (1 - \mu) m_{i,j}^{(n)}. \tag{27}$$

This outermost iteration is highly sensitive to the relaxation factor μ. For turbomachinery so far investigated, convergence has been obtained using values of μ less than 0·2. For larger values of μ, the procedure generally diverges in an oscillatory manner. Figure 2 shows the effect of a small change in μ on the progress of the iterations at an axial station in the middle of a three-stage compressor.

The procedure described here was developed without too much regard for mathematical rigour; each difficulty was treated as it arose, and the validity was finally judged by the success in predicting experimental results. In conclusion it may be remarked that the method uses numerical mathematics to a far greater extent than methods traditionally employed in the field of turbomachinery research, and it is only the first step towards more detailed studies. Already some progress has been made towards the introduction of stations within blade rows, and the calculation of losses by laws obtained empirically from cascade tests.

11. Notation

x Distance measured along axis of turbomachine.
r Distance measured normal to axis of turbomachine.
u Radial component of velocity.
v Whirl component of velocity.
w Axial component of velocity.
p Static pressure.
ρ Gas density.
T Static temperature.
S Entropy.
H Total enthalpy.
γ Ratio of specific heats of gas.
Ω Angular velocity of rotation of machine.
λ Radial angle.
α Absolute whirl angle.
β Relative whirl angle.
M Inlet mass flow.

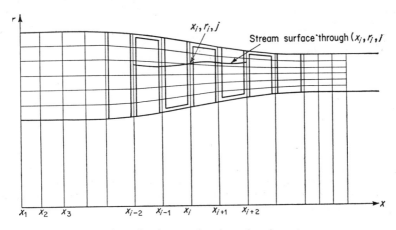

FIG. 1. Representation of a plane section through a three-stage compressor.

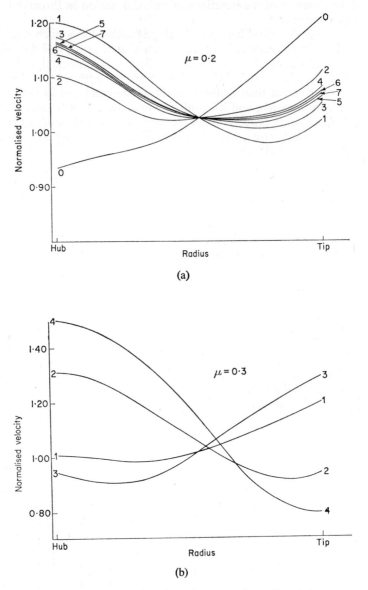

FIG. 2. Comparison of outermost iterations for two values of μ. (Diagrams show the normalized axial velocity distribution for each iteration at a blade row within a three-stage compressor. The iteration index zero refers to the result obtained by neglecting the curvature of stream surfaces.)

REFERENCES

Part II

DAHLQUIST, G. G. 1963. A special stability problem for linear multistep methods. *Nordisk Tidskr. Informations-Behandling*. **3**, 27–43.

FROST, A. A. AND PEARSON, R. G. 1961. *Kinetics and Mechanism*. Wiley, New York.

HENRICI, P. 1962. *Discrete Variable Methods in Ordinary Differential Equations*. Wiley, New York.

ROBERTSON, H. H. 1960. Some new formulae for the numerical integration of ordinary differential equations. *Information Processing*, UNESCO, Paris. 106–108.

Part III

SWAN, W. C. 1961. A practical method of predicting transonic compressor design. *Trans. Amer. Soc. Mech. Eng*. **83**, series A, 322–330.

WRIGHT, L. C. AND NOVAK, R. A. 1960. Aerodynamic design and development of the General Electric C.J. 805–23 Aft Fan Component. *Amer. Soc. Mech. Eng. Paper No. 60*. WA–270.

WU, C. H. AND WOLFENSTEIN, L. 1950. Application of radial equilibrium condition to axial flow compressor and turbine design. *Nat. Advisory Council on Aeronautics, Washington*. (*Report No. 1950*).

Chapter 12

Computation in School and University Teaching

Part I: Numerical Analysis in the Schools

A. J. Moakes

St Paul's School, London, W.14.

1. Recent Developments

I must begin by saying something about the revolution which has struck school mathematics in the last few years. Those who have visited French or American schools recently will have observed the tendency towards greater abstraction in mathematical teaching, and the early introduction of general mathematical ideas, for example of set theory and group structures, which were formerly reserved for study at university level. In this country, alongside the abstract structural work which is a feature of all the new school syllabuses, there is another element which I can best describe as computational in the broadest sense of the word. We owe this to the strong British tradition of practical application, which many of us would wish to maintain.

Cross-fertilization between the two strains, the abstract and the computational, is easier than might appear, especially in the British climate. In this country traditional algebra is introduced first as a generalization of the intuitive ideas of arithmetic, and only at a later stage is it regarded as an example of a structural system. Thus we have managed not only to avoid a pedagogic pitfall, but also to avoid throwing emphasis in the direction less concerned with applications.

The fact that desk-machines are coming into use more widely in schools is not in itself evidence that we are teaching numerical analysis. (It may be indeed that we are giving way to the blandishments of the distributors, who no longer find a sufficient market for their wares in university departments.) In fact, in the lower classes we use desk-machines, as we use slide-rules, tables, and on occasion nomograms, partly to accustom boys to the idea of choosing the appropriate aid for any particular task, and partly for a reason which belongs specifically to our educational level, namely, for the light which the aids themselves shed on the nature of numerical processes.

It is only at the sixth-form level (i.e. in the last two years before University entrance) that we can be said to start numerical analysis as a recognizable subject. It is worthy of comment that until the late 1950s the school calculus text-books had followed one another for generations with stereotyped references to Newton's formula, Simpson's rule, and the numerical use of Taylor series. (With regard to layout and checking procedures, the late Victorian books were better on the whole than their successors.) A new note was struck in the last text-book which appeared under the name of Siddons (written, in fact, by a new generation of Harrow masters). Here for the first time numerical methods were given thorough treatment, though only in the final volume which most pupils do not reach at the school stage, and with scant reference to the relation of the methods to desk-machine or computer practice.

With such an obvious gap between school treatment and the computer world, great credit is due to a thoroughgoing attempt to bridge it by a grammar school (Hele's, Exeter), which had some desk-machines, and staff with the requisite knowledge. They launched out into a course linked with an examination syllabus (covering half a subject at "Advanced", i.e. pre-university, level) which had been designed by the examining board for technical colleges but was also available to schools. This experiment has not been widely followed, perhaps partly because of technical difficulties. I do not myself favour a solution on these lines, which requires a boy to choose at the age of 16 to do an exacting course in computation *instead* of some other branch of mathematics.

The problem of suitable work at school level was taken up by the committee for Mathematics in Education and Industry (M.E.I.) formed by the Mathematical Association and a number of industrial firms. My own school and a number of others have been working with the M.E.I. committee on practical steps to be taken. The solution we favour is that, up to Advanced level, an introduction to Numerical Analysis should be an integral part of the mathematics course; that it should be introduced point by point with the related analytical mathematics; and that it should be practised with machines wherever possible, but not examined with machines in the standard pass papers at present. However, in the additional "special papers" (formerly called scholarship level), we suggest that there should be provision for a limited amount of numerical analysis with machines, as one of three options: it is felt that in schools with the right attitude to A-level work, this may be a popular alternative. In our scheme, for candidates offering both applied mathematics (which can be either mechanics or statistics) and pure mathematics, the numerical analysis forms part of the *pure* mathematics course upon which it depends, rather than of the applied mathematics which may make use of it in practice. However, to provide encouragement for boys with a bent for hardware, there is provision in the "special" paper in applied mathematics for some questions on basic logic, NOR-logic, the functions of different parts of a computer, and so on.

The appropriate parts of two of the draft syllabuses, which have been submitted to the Oxford and Cambridge School Examination Board, are given in §3. The omissions will perhaps be the most notable feature; naturally we started with a longer list of topics, but they were reduced to the final version by a desire not to overload the syllabus, and by the need for preserving a balance with other parts of pure mathematics. We have a number of additional topics in mind, which might be part of the teaching syllabus without appearing in the examination.

2. Practical Work

In preparing pupils for the special paper, which involves the use of machines, our problems are similar to those of teachers in technical colleges or universities which run such courses. Where our situation is quite different is in the ordinary sixth-form course, in which numerical work is only one aspect of the mathematical teaching. At this stage, when the characteristic ideas and techniques of computational work are being developed, it is educationally desirable, and efficient in terms of the time spent, to plan the work as far as possible around co-operative class projects. In such projects, of which the tabulation of the values of a polynomial is a simple example, the blackboard is used as the "store", into which results are fed without checking, and checking procedures form the second phase of the enterprise. It should be remembered that the purpose of the work is not to acquire great technical efficiency, but to encourage interest, and to help mathematical understanding of methods.

At present very few schools are in a position to consider using an automatic computer for class-work. Experiments with small classes have been tried by a number of schools situated near Colleges which were willing to provide facilities for punching and running programs. It is likely that in the future, with the development of computers and their applications, there will be a move to teach programming to sixth-formers. It will then be important to make arrangements for testing their programs on a machine, to enable them to understand better the uses and limitations of computers.

3. Examples of Proposed Syllabuses

The following syllabuses are those proposed by the M.E.I. group for the General Certificate of Education at Advanced level, in Pure Mathematics. Only the topics concerned with numerical work are given, which constitute about one-quarter of the total in the basic syllabus, and up to three-sevenths (depending on the candidates' choice) in the special paper.

Basic Syllabus for the Advanced Level Examination

(It is hoped that candidates will have had opportunity to carry out these processes on machines but questions will, until notice is given to the contrary, be framed so as not to require them and their use in the examination will not be permitted at present.)

The idea of a program of calculation. The preparation and interpretation of a simple flow diagram.

Estimation of maximum error by the method of small changes. Adaptation of formulae to obtain greater accuracy, e.g. evaluation of the numerically smaller root of the quadratic equation $ax^2 + bx + c = 0$ in terms of the other, using $x_1 x_2 = c/a$.

Approximate evaluation of a function from an expansion, either given (e.g. Binomial expansion for n not a positive integer) or obtained by Taylor's method. An appreciation of rounding and truncation errors.

Simple examples of iterative methods e.g. for $\sqrt{N}$; for the sum of a convergent geometric series using $S_{n+1} = rS_n + a$; or for a root of a polynomial by Newton's method.

Numerical integration by Trapezium Rule and by Simpson's Rule. (Candidates should understand how these processes can be carried out to any degree of accuracy.)

Special Paper

The solution of not more than three simultaneous equations by pivotal condensation, using a sum-check. Appreciation of the nature of ill-conditioning.

Evaluation of a polynomial by nested multiplication. The properties of polynomial differences and their use as a checking or calculating procedure.

The nature of linear interpolation and its use, e.g. to find a starting value for iterative solution of $f(x) = 0$.

The approximations $(dy/dx)_0 \simeq (y_1 - y_{-1})/2h$ and $(d^2y/dx^2)_0 \simeq (y_1 - 2y_0 + y_{-1})/h^2$, where y_{-1}, y_0, y_1 are the ordinates at $x-h$, x, $x+h$ respectively. Application to the approximate step-by-step solution of $y'' = f(y)$ over a short range with suitable starting conditions.

Part II. Computation in University Teaching

J. Crank

Brunel University, London

4. Courses in Numerical Analysis

The term university is taken to include ancient and modern seats of learning of traditional style and also the Colleges of Advanced Technology, by virtue of their impending university status. Computation comprises the subject of Numerical Analysis and the use of desk-calculating machines, digital computers and analogue computers for numerical work.

Some universities have been organizing courses involving lectures in numerical methods and practical work with desk machines for many years, e.g. London, Edinburgh, Liverpool, to name only a few. Other university courses have included lectures in numerical analysis which have been mainly confined to the finite-difference calculus and conducted in essentially the same way as lectures on the infinitesimal or integral calculus, with no attempt to provide practice in the use of the methods. Numerical analysis received a considerable impetus with the advent of high-speed electronic computers around 1945, and the last few years have seen great developments in the teaching of the subject at undergraduate level. Much of the credit for launching systematic courses in numerical analysis, in which theory and practice are rightly combined, must, in my opinion, be given to the staff of the Colleges of Advanced Technology and to the National Council for Technological Awards, now superseded by the Council for National Academic Awards. Teaching staff have had to teach themselves numerical analysis and keep abreast of developments in the subject, while simultaneously giving out their newly-acquired knowledge in a form acceptable to undergraduates. Mention must be made here of the contribution made by the National Physical Laboratory and the Royal Aircraft Establishment, some of whose staff round about 1956-58 gave courses of evening lectures at Northampton College of Advanced Technology from which many teachers in technical education in the London area received their first inspiration.

Under the provision for the Diplomas in Technology the syllabuses for courses were written by the staff of the college which submitted them, and considered by the Mathematics Panel of the N.C.T.A. Colleges soon came to realize what the Panel regarded as an acceptable form of syllabus, so it is not altogether surprising that a fairly standard syllabus has emerged over the last few years. Details are given in §10.

Virtually all courses leading to the Diploma in Technology in Mathematics have included certain aspects of Pure and Applied Mathematics, Numerical Analysis and Statistics more or less on an equal footing. Difficulties are foreseeable now that the title of Diploma in Technology is being superseded by B.Sc. for all degrees awarded by the C.N.A.A.; the description Honours Degree *Mathematics* will cover courses in which the emphasis is almost entirely on algebra and analysis and the more abstract branches of the subject as well as others with a broader, more practical, base. However, in time the name of the university or college at which the degree is obtained will identify its nature and content.

It is worth remarking here that we are, with few exceptions, in the first generation of teachers of Numerical Analysis. Very few of them have taken a systematic course in the subject themselves, certainly not at undergraduate level. What is needed now is for those who have practical experience of using numerical methods and of teaching them to give us the benefit of their double experience by writing textbooks at undergraduate level. These need to be written in a lucid, expository, style and to include a large number of exercises, some with solutions incorporated in the text and others for the students to attempt.

5. The Changing Pattern of Syllabuses

Syllabuses in Numerical Analysis are continually being modified in the light of teaching experience, the influence of computers, and developments in the subject itself. Some of the factors which contribute to change are the following.

1) If all schools taught numerical analysis up to the standard of the syllabus used by the Associated Examining Board, for example, much of the work now done in the first year at the university would have been covered by

students before they left school. Universities need to watch developments in the schools and modify their own syllabuses in computation accordingly.

2) Formulae for interpolation, differentiation and integration in terms of high-order differences occupy a less important place in numerical work now than they did a few years ago, because computers handle more easily formulae of Lagrangian type in which function values are used directly instead of differences. Syllabuses are coming to reflect this change of emphasis and less time is being devoted to the teaching of the finite-difference calculus. Techniques such as the relaxation method, which calls for human judgment in the reduction of residuals, have given way to more systematic methods of successive approximation, though it is always possible that relaxation may return to favour as computers become larger and faster, and capable of exercising a more sophisticated judgment.

3) Taylor's series has occupied pride of place among mathematical expansions for years. Recently it has been realized that expanding in terms of Chebyshev polynomials leads to economy in the number of terms in a series, and hence in the computer storage needed to define a function to a prescribed accuracy. No syllabus is respectable nowadays unless the name Chebyshev appears prominently, and orthogonal polynomials generally are basking in reflected glory.

4) Step-by-step procedures, for solving differential equations for example, are prone to an accumulation of errors which can sometimes grow so rapidly as to swamp entirely the solution which is sought, and to give results which are not even qualitatively correct. Computers prefer methods in which a given cycle of operations is continually repeated, and because of their speeds of operation they are able to handle far more steps than a human being operating a desk machine. The consequences of accumulated errors are therefore much more apparent and devastating. This is the problem of instability. The diagnosis of instability by pure mathematical analysis and the invention of stable algorithms is a subject which is probably engaging the attention of more workers in numerical analysis than any other single topic; it is a matter of which undergraduates must be made aware. However, while the analysis and even precise definitions of instability are still being actively discussed by research workers, it is important to maintain a sense of perspective in undergraduate teaching.

5) There is a shift of emphasis today away from the application of numerical methods in practical problems to the mathematical analysis of the algorithms themselves. The question of stability is one important problem; others are convergence and consistency, and error analysis. These are vital matters, and help to make the subject more respectable in the eyes of the pure mathematicians, but in the writer's view it would be a pity if too high a price were paid for this respectability. For most students, certainly for non-mathematicians, the justification for studying numerical analysis is their need to solve real practical problems. A balance must be maintained between a blind application of numerical methods, and an excessively detailed analysis of methods which are never used. There is a tendency for mathematical analysts

to concentrate on linear systems, although systems of practical interest are frequently non-linear. In such cases a numerical investigation undoubtedly requires great caution, but it would inhibit the development of computing if no work were to be attempted in non-linear problems until a detailed analysis of convergence had been completed. Historically, the application of a method often comes first and its analysis and justification follow later.

A sense of balance is necessary in all teaching but it is particularly difficult to achieve in such a rapidly growing field as numerical analysis, where methods come into prominence and are forgotten again within two or three years. In the writer's view it is important that undergraduate teaching should concern itself, for the most part, with basic principles and reasonably well-established techniques, with a hint only of what is happening in the front line of research. Experience of teaching numerical analysis is confirming this opinion as year by year it becomes clear that some topics which previously excited the lecturer's interest, and were included in the syllabus, are either too fleeting or too sophisticated for the average undergraduate to comprehend. The place for such topics is in post-graduate work, and in this connection the setting up of M.Sc. courses and postgraduate diplomas is to be welcomed.

6. Courses for Scientists and Engineers

The syllabus given in §10 is intended for mathematicians taking a specialist option in Numerical Analysis in the final year of their course. For other students, including scientists and engineers as well as mathematicians, some of the more advanced topics are omitted. An international conference organized by O.E.C.D. in January 1965 on "Mathematics for Engineers" strongly emphasized the need for all undergraduates studying engineering to learn about computing and numerical methods. A core syllabus in mathematics, which was recommended for all undergraduate engineers, includes 25 hours for computation and 40 hours each for Numerical Analysis and Statistics. This is out of a total of 325 hours which the conference suggested should be devoted to mathematics in the first two years of the undergraduate course. It was thought very important that computing and numerical analysis should be included as early as possible, so that the teaching in mathematics and engineering subjects could have this background in mind.

The increasing demand for engineers and other staff by the computer industry itself is leading to the emergence of cross-disciplines, in which parts of two or more existing courses are combined to form a new subject for a first degree, with the title "Computer Science". A precise definition of the scope of such a course is still a matter for debate, but certainly numerical analysis and computer programming will be included. In addition, some courses will contain electrical engineering, i.e. computer "hardware", while others will concentrate more on the theory of programming and communication, i.e. developments in "soft-ware". Some people feel that computer science should also embrace the much wider field of computer applications in engineering and management. Certainly the computer manufacturers and other industrial firms need graduates trained in all these fields, and several combinations of subjects could provide courses of sufficient intellectual content to rank as honours degree courses.

7. Computers in Undergraduate Courses

As recently as 1963, the Ministry of Education, as it then was, held the view that perhaps three or four computers strategically placed in the North of England, the Midlands, the South and possibly the West Country would provide adequately for the needs of technical education. At the time when my own college (Brunel) was equipped with a comparatively small Elliott 803 computer, this was thought to be generous provision for the educational needs of the whole of Middlesex. However, the number of computers in education, as well as their size and speed, has increased very considerably since then. Large powerful machines, like the I.C.T. Atlas, the English Electric KDF9, and the IBM 7090, are to be found as second-generation computers in universities and major colleges, and modest computers like the Elliott 803 with 8000 word store are almost commonplace. We may soon enter an era of multiple-access computing and conversational facilities.

In undergraduate courses, the emphasis is shifting towards the teaching of numerical methods which are more suitable for computers than for desk machines. Widely differing opinions are held about the value of preliminary instruction on desk machines before computer programming is taught. Extremists are to be found on both sides, and the best solution probably lies somewhere in the middle. The use of computers by undergraduates and others has been greatly facilitated by the development of procedure-oriented languages such as Fortran and Algol, and by the subroutines and procedures available for standard numerical algorithms. A number of books are now appearing in which numerical methods are described, for example, in the Algol language. Such a description permits the algorithm to be formulated without the ambiguity which can arise in a statement using only the mathematical equations.

It is possible to teach students to write programs and then to have them run by full-time operators, so that the student never sees or handles computer equipment himself. Colleges of Technology are often more inclined to let their undergraduates and research students handle the computer and its ancillary equipment than the universities, and thus to supplement their programming work with practical experience of computer operation. The following table shows how computer time has been allocated on the Brunel College computer (Elliott 803) during the session 1964/65

Teaching (all departments)	36%
Undergraduate projects	17%
Research (Mathematics)	16%
Research (other departments)	17%
Outside users	14%

The O.E.C.D. conference, referred to above, strongly urged that a high priority should be given to the use of computers for undergraduate teaching, and envisaged that additional equipment might need to be set aside for this purpose.

The question of access to the computer may look different as the size of computers increases, and as time-sharing and multiple-access facilities become more widely available. It is worth mentioning that students taking sandwich courses frequently have opportunities to use larger and faster computers during their periods in industry or government establishments than they have in college or university, and this can influence the time needed for computer instruction in the academic period. It is likely, however, that some systematic instruction will always be desirable in the college courses. As regards the form of this instruction, there is growing evidence to suggest that the normal lecture period of 45 to 60 minutes repeated at weekly intervals is not a suitable arrangement, but that longer half-day or full-day sessions provide a more efficient scheme. Wherever possible timetables should be re-arranged to allow a block of three or four complete days to be devoted to computer instruction

8. Practical Examinations and Course Work

There are many different views on the best way of examining the practical ability of students in computing. Some insist on the need for a practical examination, probably lasting six hours, into which the students may take textbooks, mathematical tables, and sometimes their own lecture notes. Usually desk machines are used, but in some cases students are asked to write a program and test it on a digital computer. Others feel that examinations of this kind are too chancy, and so far removed from normal working conditions as to be valueless. Instead they prefer to judge the student on course work, which may include one or more fairly large problems, together with practical examples of parts of the numerical analysis syllabus, for example, the solution of a differential equation by a deferred-correction method, or the evaluation of the eigenvalues and vectors of a matrix. In these projects, students may sometimes be asked to formulate the mathematical equations which represent a physical problem before solving them, and to present a written account of the work in which conclusions are drawn about the results. Somewhat more ambitious projects have always been a feature of courses for the Diploma in Technology. A student is expected to spend some six hours a week in the last year of the course on his project which will have, for him, some element of research.

For those who have to assess the candidates' work, there are pitfalls both in a formal practical examination which is apt to produce low marks because candidates go "off the rails" in ways the examiner had not foreseen, and in course work where the marks tend to be uniformly so high that examiners may wish to discard them. On balance, course work and projects which include formulation of equations, together with a written account of what has been accomplished, have many advantages over practical examinations of a few hours duration.

9. The Computer—a Focal Point

Finally, one very important aspect of computing in universities must be mentioned. Experience is showing that a computer installation can provide a common meeting-ground for staff and students of all departments, and can also strengthen industrial contacts. The computer acts as a focal point for discussion and collaboration. It encourages non-mathematicians to think more about mathematics, and mathematicians find themselves learning the languages of their colleagues in other disciplines, and helping to formulate their problems. In the long run this could be the most significant of the contributions which computers will make to education.

10. An Undergraduate Syllabus in Numerical Analysis

The following is an example of a syllabus for undergraduates which occupies about 400 hours of teaching time, including lectures and practical work, over four years.

Introductory ideas: Simple error analysis.

Iterative methods: order of convergence; solution of non-linear equations and sets of equations; Newton-Raphson formula; Aitken's δ^2-process.

Polynomial equations: method of Ferrari for a quartic; Bairstow's method; method of Aitken-Bernoulli; root-squaring.

Finite differences: checking; operators; Newton, Bessel and Everett formulae for interpolation; inverse interpolation; formulae for differentiation and integration; modified and divided differences; Euler-Maclaurin formula; Lagrangian formulae; Neville-Aitken interpolation; bivariate interpolation; subtabulation; summation of series, Euler's and Wijngaarden's transformations.

Linear algebra: solution of simultaneous equations; elimination and triangular decomposition; matrix inversion; latent roots and vectors; iterative methods including successive over-relaxation and methods for large sets of equations; spectral radii; iterative methods for dominant latent roots and vectors with acceleration of convergence; root removal for symmetric and unsymmetric matrices; the Rayleigh quotient; the LR and QR methods for unsymmetric matrices; special methods for symmetric matrices; error analysis.

Orthogonal polynomials: economization of power series; curve fitting by series of Chebyshev polynomials; Lanczos' τ-method; summation, differentiation and integration of Chebyshev series; Gaussian integration.

Ordinary differential equations: Taylor series; predictor-corrector methods; Runge-Kutta method; deferred correction; two-point boundary value problem; convergence and stability; methods of Clenshaw and Lanczos for solution in Chebyshev series.

Partial differential equations: Classification: parabolic, elliptic, hyperbolic. Reduction of elliptic type to sets of algebraic equations and solution by direct and iterative methods. Solution of parabolic equations by explicit and implicit finite-difference methods; alternating-direction methods; moving boundaries. Hyperbolic equations by methods of characteristics and by finite-difference methods. Different co-ordinate systems. Singularities; analysis of stability, convergence, compatibility.

Part III. Further Comments on University Work

L. Fox and J. Walsh

11. Numerical Analysis and Pure Mathematics

The last section has dealt with the general field of university work in computation. However, some further points arise when we consider the more purely mathematical side of Numerical Analysis. The theme of many contributors to this symposium has been the gradual systematization and analysis of numerical methods, so that we are developing a coherent theory of parts of the subject which before were matters for intuition and experience. This "scientific" approach calls upon resources in many branches of mathematics; for example, Varga's work on iterative methods for linear equations has drawn upon the work of Frobenius. Some writers, particularly Collatz and Kantorovich, have shown that a unified view of many results in numerical analysis can be obtained by using the ideas of functional analysis. This may or may not lead to practical advances, but it certainly leads to greater understanding. The aim of such work is far more fundamental than merely to make the subject respectable; it is the characteristically mathematical activity of generalizing from particular cases, and abstracting the common features of whole classes of methods.

For this reason alone, it seems unwise to make a division between numerical analysis as a practical subject on the one hand, and pure analysis and more abstract mathematics on the other. It is true that many students are primarily attracted by practical applications, but it is still desirable to encourage them to learn as much as possible of the more rigorous and fundamental parts of the subject. Even on the practical level this is likely to be a good investment for their future professional work in mathematics, which will extend over perhaps 40 years of continually changing applications. (We are speaking here of mathematics specialists, not of scientists and engineers, who cannot be expected to have a taste for the more abstract work.) In numerical analysis it is probably necessary at present to describe and use techniques whose theory is incomplete, but the ideal of theoretical justification should remain.

Another important reason for maintaining the closest links with pure mathematics is the urgent need to attract more able mathematicians into the field. Outstanding contributions to Numerical Analysis in the past have often been made by leading pure or applied mathematicians, for whom numerical work was only part of their problem. Our aim nowadays should be to present the subject as genuinely mathematical in itself, and as a source of methods for problems in Applied Mathematics (not the *only* methods nor always the best) which should be part of the equipment of any well-trained mathematician. Thus more experts in pure and applied mathematics may be encouraged to make contributions, using their special knowledge of other branches. Further, competent mathematicians may be led to specialize in the subject, and to help fill the many vacancies for university teachers and research workers in industry.

12. Programming for Undergraduates

As regards training in programming, the actual learning of a computer language such as Algol is a fairly simple matter. However, the running of programs tends to involve the student in a number of details, such as the precise form of program tapes or card-decks, the operation of punching equipment and even of the computer, which are not an essential part of a mathematics course. (Few Universities have enough ancillary staff to do all necessary tape-punching.) Some students enjoy this work, and it helps to make the subject of Numerical Analysis come alive for them, but others, perhaps more theoretically-minded, find that it quickly becomes tedious. The time spent on tape-editing may be very large, and it cannot be regarded as of great educational value. So while extensive programming courses may be suitable for the more practically-minded students, they should perhaps be an optional addition to the more advanced theoretical courses. Obviously all students in Numerical Analysis should appreciate the characteristics and capabilities of computers, but they need not necessarily spend time on detailed programming. (This aspect of computation may change radically with the introduction of Project MAC-type systems, where the communication with the machine is direct. However, at present few Universities can hope to obtain enough equipment to run large undergraduate classes with on-line access.)

Another point is that programming systems have been changing rather rapidly, and techniques which may be superseded within two or three years should not absorb too much of an undergraduate's time. Many of us can remember the generation of programmers which had acquired a high degree of skill in machine coding, and consequently was rather inclined to resist the introduction of autocodes, in spite of their many advantages.

It is true that industrial firms would prefer to take on new graduates who were fully trained in the current techniques, but it is difficult to provide such training anyway, because of the great variety of machines and programming systems in use in industry. Universities need to consider long-term training as well as immediate demands. There has been a tendency in some firms to regard programming as the only necessary skill in a computing department, and mathematics as relatively unimportant. This is reasonable for many types of commercial work, of the data-processing variety, but for scientific work it is very far from the truth. We can safely assume that firms which recruit graduates for computing will teach them programming, but it is considerably less certain that they will train them in basic mathematics if the universities do not.

One way of meeting the industrial demand is through one-year post-graduate Diploma or M.Sc. courses, of which a number are now running in British universities. These are for students who intend to make their career in computing, and it is reasonable at this level to provide a more specialized training than in the first degree course, and to cover the latest developments in techniques, together with practical work.

Our remarks here apply to mathematical specialists who are studying numerical analysis as a part of mathematics. For specialists in Computer Science different considerations apply, and they will obviously have extensive training in techniques of programming, in order to develop the fundamental principles of computer languages and compilers, which are now beginning to take shape.

Author Index

A

Achieser, N. I., 139, *140*
Alder, B., 119, 121, 122, 132, *134*
Al'tshuler, L. V., 131, *134*
Alway, G. G., 20, *26*
Arms, R. J., 105, *115*

B

Bauer, F. L., 37, 42, *60*
Bennett, J. M., 25, *26*
Berge, C., *173*
Bickley, W. G., 113, *115*
Birch, B. J., 159, *164*
Birkhoff, G., 111, *115*
Box, M. J., 152, *157*
Bramble, J. H., 112, *115*
Brazhnik, M. I., 131, *134*
Butcher, J. C., 82, *97*

C

Carré, B. A., 23, *26*, 104, *115*
Carroll, C. W., 153, *157*
Clenshaw, C. W., 8, *9*, 67, 68, 70, *97*, 136, 138, *140, 141*
Collatz, L., 114, *115*
Courant, R., 29, *60*, 119, *134*
Crank, J., 108, 109, 115, *115, 116*
Curtis, A. R., 136, 140, *141*
Cuthill, E. H., 105, *115*

D

Dahlquist, G., 7, *9*, 66, 74, 78, 79, 85, 86, 87, 90, 91, *97*, 179, *189*
Daly, B. J., 134, *134*
Dantzig, G. B., *173*
Davidon, W. C., 146, 153, 155, *157*
Douglas, J., 110, *115*

E

Eberlein, P. J., 53, 59, *60*

E (continued)

Ehlers, F. E., 121, *134*
Ehrlich, L., 111, *116*
Engeli, M., 25, *26*

F

Fernbach, S., 119, 121, 122, 132, *134*
Fiacco, A. V., 153, *157*
Fletcher, R., 146, 147, *157*
Forsythe, G. E., 104, 112, *115*
Fox, L., *60*, 67, 79, 81, 82, 84, 85, 86, 90, 92, 93, 94, 97, *97*, 101, 109, 112, 113, 115, *115, 116*, 119, 122, *134*, 168
Francis, J. G. F., 47, 49, 51, 52, 59, *60*, 61
Friedrichs, K. O., 119, *134*
Frost, A. A., 179, *189*
Funtikov, A. I., 131, *134*

G

Gass, S. I., 150, *157*
Gates, L. D., 105, *115*
Gaunt, J. A., 113, *116*
Ghouila-Houri, A., *173*
Gibbons, A., 83, 84, *97*
Gill, S., 72, *97*
Ginsburg, T., 25, *26*
Givens, W., 37, 38, 39, 42, 57, 59, *60*
Goldstine, H. H., 5, *9*
Goodwin, E. T., 67, 82, 84, 85, 86, 90, 92, *97*
Gragg, W. B., 82, *97*

H

Halton, J. H., 156, *157*
Harlow, F. H., 134, *134*
Haselgrove, C. B., 94, *98*
Hastings, C., 139, *141*
Hayashi, C., 164, *164*
Henrici, P., 36, *60*, 79, *98*, 179, *189*
Hestenes, M. R., 25, *26*
Hext, G. R., 148, *157*

205

Subject Index

A

Accuracy of finite-difference solutions
of elliptic equations, 8, 111–114
hyperbolic equations, 120, 124
Adams-Bashforth method, 68, 70, 96
stability of, 81
Alternating-direction methods, 109–111
Approximation of functions, 8, 135
by Chebyshev polynomials, 8, 136,
138, 196
rational functions, 136, 139
spline curve, 185
Asymptotic expansion, 137

B

Band matrix, 19–21
and elliptic equations, 104
Bessel function, approximation of, 8, 136
Block iteration, 22–23, 104–106
Boundary conditions
for elliptic equations, 100, 112
ordinary differential equations,
64, 73, 75, 86, 94
parabolic equations, 100
Boundary-value problem, 64, 73, 93–95,
97, 175

C

Characteristic polynomial of a matrix,
27–29
Characteristics, 118–120, 121, 124
Chebyshev polynomials, use of,
in approximation of functions, 8, 136,
138, 196
iterative solution of linear equations, 23, 25, 106–107
ordinary differential equations,
69–71, 95–96
Chebyshev's theorem, 139
Cholesky's method, 19, 21
Collocation
for elliptic equations, 114–115
polynomial approximation, 138,
140

Compressible flow, equations of, 117–
118, 183
Computers, effect of, on numerical
methods, 2, 3, 27, 67, 72, 82, 101, 104,
136, 196
Condition,
general, 2–3
of eigenvalue problem, 29–31
eigenvector problem, 31
linear equations, 16
ordinary differential systems, 65
See also Ill-conditioning
Conjugate directions in minimization,
147
Conjugate gradient method, 24–25
Convergence
of Chebyshev series, 69–70, 96, 138
deferred-correction method, 85
finite-difference series, 68, 70, 114
finite-difference solution, 7, 8, 73,
76, 78–79, 112–113
predictor-corrector methods, 68,
81, 179–180
Taylor series, 69, 70, 96, 137
of iterative methods
for eigenvalue problem:
direct and inverse iteration, 54–
55
Hyman's method, 43
Jacobi's method, 36–37
Laguerre's and Newton's methods, 45
LR algorithm, 46
Muller's method, 44
QR algorithm, 51
for elliptic equations, 8, 103–107,
111
for linear equations, 21–23
minimization, 145, 146, 149,
153, 154
ordinary differential equations,
89–93
Courant condition, 123, 126
Crank-Nicolson method, 108
Cubic equation, rational solutions of,
159–162